T3-BSK-741

HEGEL'S PHILOSOPHY OF NATURE

HEGEL'S PHILOSOPHY OF NATURE

Volume One
Introduction, Foreword and Mechanics

Volume Two
Physics

Volume Three
Organics

HEGEL'S PHILOSOPHY OF NATURE

EDITED AND TRANSLATED
WITH AN INTRODUCTION AND EXPLANATORY NOTES BY

M. J. PETRY
M.A., D.Phil. (Oxon.)

VOLUME I

LONDON · GEORGE ALLEN AND UNWIN LTD
NEW YORK · HUMANITIES PRESS, INC

FIRST PUBLISHED IN 1970

SBN 04 100021 8

PRINTED IN GREAT BRITAIN
in 12 on 13 point Bembo type
BY UNWIN BROTHERS LIMITED
WOKING AND LONDON

PREFACE

Without the patience and linguistic help of my wife, this book could never have been written. Her family, and the German friends I made at Elsinore, have helped me to avoid many of the flaws generally incident to English translations from the German. I should like to express my very deep gratitude for all the help that they have given me.

Without the full co-operation of the Copenhagen Royal Natural Science Library and the University Library at Lund, I could never have undertaken the writing of the commentary. At one time it was, indeed, solely the cheerfulness, enthusiasm and efficiency with which their staffs helped me to trace references and acquire books, that encouraged me to believe that the work I had undertaken was completable.

I should like to acknowledge my indebtedness to Father F. C. Copleston S.J., whose perspicacity and tolerance made my work on Hegel at Oxford so rewarding and enjoyable, and to Sir Malcolm Knox and Professor W. B. Lockwood, who recommended my finished labours to the publishers.

M.J.P.

Reading
August 1968

CONTENTS

A*

The words in roman are those of Hegel's headings which appeared in the first edition of this work. The words in italics do not appear as headings in the text, but such identification of these passages was made on the contents page of the first edition of the work.

INTRODUCTION

a. ENCYCLOPAEDIAS

'Systems are useful not only in that one thinks about matters in an orderly manner, according to a certain plan, but in that one thinks about matters at all. The latter use is undoubtedly greater than the first.'—G. C. Lichtenberg.

If the Hegelian system is to be fully appreciated, it has to be grasped as a *whole*. Experience has shown that this is no easy matter, not only because the general principles involved in its structuralization have never been clearly presented and effectively criticized, but because, in the range of its subject matter, it is so bewilderingly comprehensive. Hegel's own teaching experience had made him aware of the difficulties involved in communicating satisfactorily however, and it was mainly in order that his system might be conveniently considered in its entirety that he produced his 'Encyclopaedia'. This work, which is therefore central to any understanding of his manner of thinking, was designed as a general guide to the courses of lectures he delivered at Heidelberg and Berlin between 1816 and 1831. As it was primarily a teaching book, he was constantly revising it, and during his lifetime three editions of it were prepared for the press (1817, 1827, 1830). The lectures were designed mainly for undergraduates, and it is therefore a consideration of Hegel as an encyclopaedist and a teacher which provides one of the readiest introductions to his philosophical system.

The problems facing encyclopaedists have changed very little since the beginning of the last century. Then, as now, most specialists were unwilling or unable to assess their disciplines in a satisfactory manner within any comprehensive or systematic exposition of knowledge as a whole. Aristotelianism had long since ceased to dominate the university teaching of Europe, and most philosophers, as philosophers, were as incapable as they are today of saying anything very helpful about the labours and problems of their academic colleagues and fellow citizens. Then, as now, the need for a synoptic view of knowledge was forced upon the notice of specialists as fresh discoveries gave indications of formerly unsuspected connections, especially in the natural sciences. Then, as now, various attempts were made to evolve such a view from inadequate premises and ephemeral interpretations, and then, as now, these attempts were over-valued and capably criticized.

The encyclopaedists of Hegel's day had already begun to assess this state of affairs in much the same way as their present-day counterparts. *Philosophical* encyclopaedias, such as Hegel's, were generally regarded as unsatisfactory in that they tended to impose a more or less arbitrary structuralization upon subject matter which was to be acquired in a much more trustworthy and intelligible manner from the specialists themselves. Étienne Chauvin (1640–1725), a French Huguenot pastor living in Berlin, had attempted to expound Cartesianism in an encyclopaedic form in his 'Lexicon rationale' (Rotterdam, 1692), Christian Wolff (1679–1754) had attempted to scholasticize Leibniz in a similar manner,[1] and J. J. Eschenburg produced the Kantian equivalent of their work in his 'Lehrbuch der Wissenschaftskunde' (Stettin and Leipzig, 1792). It was generally realized that writings of this kind merely emphasized the limitations and datedness of the philosophies on which they were based, and the irresponsible extravagances of Schellingianism finally brought the whole concept of philosophical encyclopaedias into disrepute. The effect of organizing knowledge in order to further *particular ends* had become evident in the success of Bayle's 'Dictionnaire historique et critique' (2 vols. Rotterdam, 1697) and Diderot's 'Encyclopédie, ou Dictionnaire raissoné des sciences, des arts et des métiers' (35 vols. Paris, 1751–1780) in creating and consolidating the intellectual atmosphere of the eighteenth century enlightenment. Although they are basically similar to the purely philosophical encyclopaedias, works of this kind have now proved their social effectiveness, and are therefore still compiled and countenanced by certain interests, regimes and churches. As they have never completely succeeded in integrating their subject matter into the ends for which they have been written however, they have generally been criticized for their lack of 'objectivity'.

Then, as now therefore, the most generally acceptable kind of encyclopaedia was arranged *alphabetically*, and like its modern counterpart, simply attempted to supply required information in a convenient manner. Compilations of this kind first made their appearance at the beginning of the eighteenth century, and enjoyed immediate popularity. In England, the 'Lexikon technicum' (London, 1704) by John Harris (1666?–1719) and the

[1] F. W. Kluge 'Christian von Wolff der Philosoph' (Breslau, 1831); W. Arnsperger 'Christian Wolff's Verhältniss zu Leibniz' (Heidelberg, 1897). See 'Die philosophischen Schriften von G. W. Leibniz' (ed. Gerhardt, Berlin, 1875–1890) vol. IV pp. 27–102, vol. VII pp. 43–247 for the possible germ of Wolff's encyclopaedic work.

'Cyclopaedia' (London, 1728) by Ephraim Chambers (c.1680?–1740) proved to be the most successful works of this kind. Their German counterparts were the 'Reales Staats- und Zeitungs- Lexikon' (Leipzig, 1704), edited by Johann Hubner (1668–1731) and the 'Allgemeines Lexicon der Künste und Wissenschaften' (Königsberg and Leipzig, 1721) by Johann Theodor Jablonski (1654–1731). In Germany however, this alphabetical arrangement tended to get out of hand as attempts were made to develop its comprehensiveness. The 'Grosses vollständiges Universal-Lexicon aller Wissenschaften und Künste' (64 vols. Halle and Leipzig, 1731–1754) was finally completed by K. G. Ludovici (1707–1778), but despite its many excellences, it proved to be an unwieldy work, and even before it had been completed, parts of it were, of course, out of date. A similar fate overtook the immense 'Allgemeine Encyclopädie der Wissenschaften und Künste' (Leipzig, 1818–1889), started by J. S. Ersch (1766–1826) and J. G. Gruber (c.1774–1851), which ran to 167 volumes before it was finally abandoned. Nevertheless, alphabetically arranged encyclopaedias of the modern kind and of modern dimensions were also beginning to make their appearance during Hegel's lifetime. Under the editorship of Archibald Constable (1774–1827), Macvey Napier (1776–1847) and Charles Maclaren (1782–1866), the fifth, sixth and seventh editions of the 'Encyclopaedia Britannica' showed a steadily improving standard of excellence with regard to lay-out and calibre of articles, and in Germany. D. A. F. Brockhaus (1772–1823), R. G. Löbel (1767–1799) and C. W. Franke (d.1831) improved the famous 'Konversations-Lexikon' in a similar manner.

Despite the well-tried success and convenience of the alphabetical encyclopaedia, it has certain rather obvious drawbacks and limitations. It is now outdated so rapidly by the precision and efficiency with which knowledge is acquired and made available, that its value as anything but a general reference book for the non-specialist is extremely questionable. Its main fault is however, that it fails to bring out the *natural interrelatedness* of its subject matter. Georg Simon Klügel (1739–1812), professor of mathematics and physics at Helmstedt, was one of the first to realize this, and in his 'Encyklopädie, oder Zusammenhängender Vortrag der gemeinnützigsten, insbesondere aus der Betrachtung der Natur und des Menschen gesammelten Kenntnisse' (3 vols. Berlin, 1782–1784), he made the first modern attempt at a non-philosophical *systematic* encyclopaedia. Charles Joseph Panckoucke (1736–1798) outlined a similar project in his 'Plan d'une Encyclopédie méthodique et par ordre des matières' (Paris, 1781), an essay which gave rise to a massive and uncompleted rearrangement of Diderot's work (196 vols. Paris, 1782–1832). It was Coleridge who originated the English equivalent of ventures of this kind, probably as the result of his having acquainted himself with the writings of Schelling, Oken and Hegel.[1] His introductory essay to the ill-starred 'Encyclopaedia metropolitana' (28 vols. London, 1817–1845) can hardly be expected to inspire confidence in the reliability of his method however, and has probably done more than any other single publication to bring 'systematic' encyclopaedias into discredit in the English-speaking world. All these attempts at systematization were in fact arbitrary arrangements of subject matter entirely devoid of any effective, efficient or well-founded guiding principle.[2] If the accomplished scientists and scholars of the day were persuaded to contribute to them, it was only on the understanding that although their articles might be situated in the works at the editor's discretion, the principles guiding the overall arrangement should not intrude upon their particular domains. Hegel may well have pondered over this kind of systematization as it was propounded in the early writings of Wilhelm Traugott Krug (1770–1842).[3]

The subject matter of Hegel's 'Encyclopaedia' is of course dated, and it is therefore somewhat curious that the commentary to this edition of his treatment of the natural sciences should be the only attempt to place any part of it fairly and squarely in its historical context. It is to be hoped that the rest will now be submitted to similar treatment, for despite the importance of the *structuralization* of knowledge worked out in the 'Encyclopaedia', it can hardly be maintained that an understanding of its subject matter is entirely irrelevant to any worthwhile criticism of it. It *is* the structuralization which constitutes the book's main importance however, and to some extent therefore, those who have hitherto attempted to develop or refute its expositions and arguments, may be excused for having concentrated so exclusively upon this feature of it. Hegel's criticism of the encyclopaedists of the day is implicit in the *structure* of this work, and it is only by exhibiting the relevance and validity of the structuralization he elicits from its subject matter, that the claim that he has managed to overcome the difficulties facing them and their modern counterparts can be substantiated.

The succeeding chapters of this introduction should make it evident

[1] See his annotated editions of their works listed in the British Museum Catalogue; cf. J. H. Muirhead 'Coleridge as a Philosopher' (London, 1930).

[2] See the criticism, by G. F. Pohl (1788–1849), of the alphabetical treatment of physics, in his review of the third volume of 'Gehler's Physikalisches Wörterbuch' (Leipzig, 1827): 'Jahrbücher für wissenschaftliche Kritik' July–Sept. 1829 (Stuttgart and Tübingen, 1829).

[3] 'Krug's Gesammelte Schriften' (12 vols. Brunswick, 1830–1841), vols VII and X.

that *levels* and *hierarchies*, the basic principles of the Hegelian structure, are as directly relevant to modern thinking as they were a century and a half ago. The current emphasis upon the importance of models and analogies in science might also provide a convenient *introduction* to Hegel's manner of thinking for many contemporary philosophers.[1] The central principle of the 'Encyclopaedia' is however the dialectic, and it is doubtful whether contemporary thinking is any more capable of employing it correctly than were Hegel's immediate followers. Despite the somewhat bizarre use of it made by the communists, Americans evidently feel obliged to deny that it is a principle at all,[2] and although it originated in Hegel's interpretation of the Trinity, Christian theologians, despite the present ferment of theological radicalism and re-orientation, have, in general, ignored it.[3] The failure of many professed Hegelians to distinguish clearly between the dialectic and the *categories* assessed in the first part of the 'Encyclopaedia', and even between dialectic and formal *logic*, has contributed to the fairly general confusion concerning the precise nature of this principle. Although the principle of a *sphere*, as it is formulated by Hegel, is intimately involved with the dialectic, it is also the immediate expression of levels and hierarchies, and contemporary thinkers will therefore have little difficulty in grasping at least one important aspect of its general significance. It can hardly be maintained however that contemporary thinking, of its own accord, has come to recognize the importance of the three basic distinctions in accordance with which the subject matter of the 'Encyclopaedia' is ranged within the spheres of 'Logic', 'Nature' and 'Spirit'. The wealth, variety and subtlety of *logical categories* as they are dealt with in most modern 'philosophies of science', would have delighted and fascinated Hegel, but there are no signs that contemporary thinkers are prepared to treat the investigation of their relative complexity as a separate discipline, essentially distinct from the natural and social sciences within which these categories make their appearance. '*Spirit*' (Geist) as a general term applied to psychology, law, politics, human history, art, religion and philosophy, to all the phenomena characteristic of consciousness, does not have the

[1] M. B. Hesse 'Models and Analogies in Science' (London, 1963); B. H. Kazemier 'The concept and the role of the model in mathematics and natural and social sciences' (Dordrecht, 1961).

[2] Walter Kaufmann for example, 'Hegel' (New York, 1965) p. 173.

[3] There have recently been signs that this situation is changing. Interest in Hegel's early theological writings and in the similarities between Christianity and Communism have contributed. See T. M. Knox and R. Kroner 'Hegel's Early Theological Writings' (Chicago, 1948); Henri Rondet S. J. 'Hegelianisme et Christianisme' (Paris, 1965); Jörg Splett 'Die Trinitätslehre G. W. F. Hegels' (Freiburg and Munich, 1965).

common currency in English that it has in German,[1] and although everyone is aware of the general features and problems of this sphere, Hegel's assessment and structuralization of it are very far from being generally discussed or recognized. The sphere of '*Nature*' however, in that it is regarded by Hegel as being distinct from purely logical considerations, and as being the immediate presupposition of consciousness, is distinguished in a manner that most modern scientists will probably find highly congenial. As his treatment of it is almost entirely free from epistemological quibbles, and consists of extremely detailed assessments of the whole range of the natural sciences, its subject matter, now that it has been placed in its historical context, provides an ideal starting point for a reappraisal of the whole Hegelian system. Faulty or irrelevant observations and erroneous or inaccurate thinking are more easily detected in the natural sciences than in either 'Logic' or 'Spirit', and it is to be hoped therefore that this critical edition of the 'Philosophy of Nature', by furthering an understanding of that part of the 'Encyclopaedia' in which the subject matter itself is least open to dispute, will help to bring about a clearer and fuller comprehension of the structural principles in which Hegelianism as a whole has its foundations. What is more, attempts to view the natural sciences as a *whole* are by no means alien to current habits of thought.[2] Collingwood's suggestion[3] that they might be given unity by being regarded as a 'form of thought' dependent upon history, a further 'form of thought', might be criticized by pointing out that despite the persistence of uncertainty in their details, many features of the natural world that were formerly unknown or misunderstood no longer have a history, in that they can be predicted, manipulated, and exploited with what amounts to an absolute precision and efficiency. The movements of Neptune for example, although they are like nearly all other natural phenomena in that they involve time, only have a *history* on account of the calculations and observations which led to their discovery. The spate of books on the philosophy of science published during the last decade or so[4] might, in general, be criticized from an Hegelian standpoint, by pointing out that

[1] A fairly accurate illustration of this is provided by 'Die Welt', one of the most popular of West German daily newspapers, which brings out a weekly supplement devoted to 'Die Geistige Welt', i.e. education, family life, fashions, history, theatre, music, art, literature etc., as opposed to science, commerce and politics.

[2] See for example Otto Neurath, Rudolf Carnap, Charles Morris 'International Encyclopaedia of Unified Science' (2 vols. Chicago, 1955).

[3] R. G. Collingwood 'The Idea of Nature' (Oxford, 1945).

[4] Mention might be made of the interesting *historical* approach to scientific method employed by E. H. Madden, 'Theories of Scientific Method' (Seattle, 1960), and the valuable attempts to clarify the problems involved in the conceptual foundations, methodology, theories, procedure, explanation etc.

there has been too much reluctance to admit the existence of consolidated and unproblematical scientific knowledge, too much emphasis upon the difficulties involved in verifying the correspondence between knowledge and fact, and a general failure to realize that although logical categories and psychological phenomena are involved in our *knowledge* of nature, they *also* constitute *distinct* levels of reality in so far as they are either simpler or more complex than the subject matter of the natural sciences.

From an Hegelian point of view, these approaches appear to emphasize the logical categories involved in the natural sciences and the human factors relevant to their development in an insufficiently hierarchical and somewhat incongruous manner. They are interesting and important to contemporary Hegelianism however, in that they tend to treat the sphere of 'Nature' as a whole, in that they generally recognize that understanding it implies the precise formulation of *thought* as well as the investigation of natural phenomena, and in that they implicitly acknowledge that this sphere cannot be assessed without reference to 'Spirit'. In this last respect they have much in common with the attempts that are made to humanize science by assessing it in the light of ethical, social or political objectives or by emphasizing the sociological factors in its historical development.[1] None of these attitudes is specifically and self-consciously Hegelian. Taken as a whole however they do seem to indicate that it is unwise to regard the 'Philosophy of Nature' as being entirely irrelevant to current problems and contemporary capabilities, and to the present widespread revival of interest in Hegel's writings.

The main difficulty encountered in interpreting the 'Encyclopaedia' has its origin in the fact that although it is helpful and even necessary to distinguish between its structure and its subject matter, these two aspects of it also have to be recognized as being ultimately identical. *Levels* of logical complexity are not the same as levels of complexity in the natural sciences or spirit, but the recognition of the principle of levels is essential to any precise definition of the subject matter of these spheres. *Hierarchies* of

---

of *modern* science to be found in A. Pap: 'An Introduction to the Philosophy of Science' (London, 1963); S. Körner 'Experience and Theory' (London, 1966); J. O. Wisdom 'Foundations of Inference in Natural Science (London, 1952); C. G. Hempel 'Aspects of Scientific Explanation' (New York, 1965).

[1] B. Glass 'Science and Ethical Values' (London, 1966): H. Margenau 'Ethics and Science' (Princeton, 1964); L. Hogben 'Science for the Citizen' (London, 1938): J. D. Bernal 'The Social Function of Science' (London, 1939); B. Barker 'Science and the Social Order' (London, 1953); H. Boyko 'Science and the future of Mankind' (The Hague, 1961); B. Barber and W. Hirsch 'The Sociology of Science' (New York, 1962); A. C. Benjamin 'Science, Technology and Human Values' (Columbia, 1965); G. Degré 'Science as a Social Institution' (New York, 1965); N. E. Fehl 'Science and Culture' (Hong Kong, 1965).

categories are not the same as hierarchies of natural phenomena, in physics and biology for example, or of groups in sociology, but the recognition of the principle of hierarchies is essential to any rational interpretation of the relationships between logical, physical, biological or sociological phenomena. The three moments of the Notion (universal, particular, singular) are not simply identical with the comprehensive unity of knowledge contained within the spheres of 'Logic', 'Nature' and 'Spirit', but the recognition of these *spheres*, of the differences which distinguish them, and of the identity which unites them, is essential to any exposition of the differentiated unity of their subject matters.

Hegelianism, if it is to be anything but an academic pastime, an exercise for historians of philosophy, demands an intimate and up-to-date knowledge of the subject matter of the 'Encyclopaedia'. Since it is the masterly manner in which it enables one to *assess* knowledge which constitutes its main originality and primary value however, there is always the danger that once the importance of its structure has been grasped, it will degenerate into scholasticism. It went out of favour because those who professed to expound it failed to clarify its structure and master its subject matter. If present trends continue, it will come into favour simply because it does not confine itself to word analysis and the particularity of knowledge. Word and sentence analysis is essential to clear and accurate thinking however,[1] and the emphasis upon the particularity of knowledge and research is basic to many of the most striking of modern accomplishments. It is interesting to observe therefore, that word and sentence analysis, as an explicitly philosophical discipline, developed as a reaction against the scholasticized Hegelianism of the late nineteenth century, and that the particularization of knowledge and research, as a fundamental habit of thought, first came into its own as a reaction against the scholasticized Aristotelianism of the late sixteenth century. Both developments were, in their way, justified, word analysis as a criticism of over-structuralized thought, Baconianism as a criticism of over-structuralized research. While both have, however, helped to cultivate a mental attitude capable of testing, investigating and experimenting intelligently and effectively, in a somewhat paradoxical and evidently inadvertent manner, they have also tended to further the general acceptance of the somewhat questionable assump-

[1] H. Glockner's 'Hegel-Lexikon' (improved ed. 2 vols. Stuttgart, 1957) laid the foundation of a systematic analysis of Hegel's vocabulary and use of language. Research of this kind is extremely effective in bringing out the radicalism and consistency of Hegel's thinking. For recent publications in this vein see W. var Dooren 'Het Totaliteitsbegrip bij Hegel en zijn Voorgangers' (Assen, 1965); Josef Simon 'Das Problem der Sprache bei Hegel' (Kohlhammer Verlag, Stuttgart, 1966).

tion that it is no longer within the power of man to assess, master and control the accomplishments of his genius.

This is apparent to a certain extent, if nineteenth century thought is compared with its twentieth century western counterpart. It is most noticeable however if post-Baconian *encyclopaedias* are compared with their mediaeval counterparts. Although the Aristotelian system lacks the comprehensive structuralization of the Hegelian, it was so effective in indicating the interrelatedness of various branches of enquiry and knowledge, that it was not until the early years of the seventeenth century that it became irrelevant to progressive encyclopaedic work. Through the writings of Aquinas, and in conjunction with the works of Pliny and St. Isidore, it came to exercise a profound influence upon mediaeval thought, and most of the great Latin encyclopaedias of the middle ages are to some extent reflections of it. The most popular of them, the 'De proprietatibus rerum' (c.1230) of Bartholomeus Anglicus, was republished in English as late as 1582, and the last of their kind, the 'Encyclopaedia, septem tomis distincta' of Johann Heinrich Alsted (1588–1638), appeared when Bacon and Descartes had already begun to regard knowledge from radically original points of view. In some important respects, the attitude of mind Aristotelianism helped to establish compares favourably with the state of affairs that might be expected to develop from the institutionalization of a mature Hegelianism. The 'unified sensibility' of the *art* which flourished when it was still the dominating intellectual influence in Europe has come to fascinate literary historians in that it contrasts so sharply with the 'divided sensibility' of the seventeenth century and the seemingly hopeless fragmentation of knowledge and outlook encountered today.[1] There is of course no reason why aesthetic considerations should not contribute to the current revival of Hegelianism. As it is, however, the extraordinary development of the *natural sciences* which distinguishes the present age from all others, it does at least seem likely that our tendency to lose ourselves in particularization has its origin in this development, and consequently, that too great an emphasis upon the *aesthetic* wholesomeness of Hegelianism might well reduce the outcome of the present revival of interest in it to nothing but the establishment of an esoteric cult. The most ardent of mediaevalists will have to admit moreover, that even the famous 'trivium' and 'quadrivium' of the mediaeval educational system are very largely irrelevant to our present needs, and that today, mediaeval

[1] E. M. W. Tillyard 'The Elizabethan World Picture' (London, 1943); P. H. Kocher 'Science and Religion in Elizabethan England' (Huntingdon Library, 1953); R. S. Westfall 'Science and Religion in Seventeenth Century England' (Yale Univ. Press, 1958).

encyclopaedias, since the arrangements they provide are clearly arbitrary and their subject matter is hopelessly dated, can hardly be regarded as having anything but an historical value. It is indeed to be doubted whether Petrarch's friend Domenico Bandini (c. 1335–1418), when he began his gigantic 'Fons memorabilium universi' with a consideration of God, and divided it into five parts in honour of Christ's wounds, was any closer to formulating a truly balanced assessment of knowledge than the most specialized of modern research students.[1] It is often asserted that it was Bacon who initiated the wholesale rejection of compilations of this kind. It is certainly true that his writings appeared at the beginning of an age in which emphasis has been laid, to an ever increasing extent, upon the particularity of knowledge and research. It is not often realized however, that the failure of most post-Baconian attempts to synthesize the multifarious and often startlingly successful results which such an emphasis has brought about, is due not only or even mainly to the immense range of knowledge now to be assimilated, but to the inadequate or unsatisfactory nature of the premises and principles on which they have been founded. It is, moreover, frequently forgotten, that although we are justified in regarding Bacon as the champion of induction, he never regarded his method as being incompatible with the attempt to view knowledge as a whole.[2] In the introduction to 'The Great Instauration' (1620) for example, he makes it known that he had planned to structuralize research in a manner not so very different from that of his mediaeval predecessors, and the words in which he characterizes the social potential and significance of such an endeavour might well be taken as summing up the best that is to be hoped for from any widespread understanding of a truly encyclopaedic 'philosophy of nature'. He writes as follows of his general plan: 'But to perfect (it) is a thing both above my strength and beyond my expectation. What I have been able to do is to give it, as I hope, a not contemptible start. The destiny of the human race will supply the issue, and that issue will perhaps be such as men in the present state of their fortunes and of their understandings cannot easily grasp or measure. For what is at stake is not merely a mental satisfaction but the very reality of man's wellbeing, and all his power of action. Man is the helper and interpreter of Nature. He can only act and understand in so far as by working upon her or observing her he has come to perceive her order. Beyond this he hath neither knowledge nor power. For there is no strength that can break

[1] Robert Collison 'Encyclopaedias: their history throughout the ages' (New York and London, 1964) pp. 70–72.

[2] B. Farrington 'Francis Bacon, philosopher of industrial science' (London, 1951).

the causal chain. Nature cannot be conquered but by obeying her. Accordingly these twin goals, human science and human power, come in the end to one. To be ignorant of causes is to be frustrated in action.'

The Hegelian system is truly encyclopaedic. If it is to be fully appreciated therefore, it has to be grasped as a whole, and we have Hegel's own authority for regarding the 'Encyclopaedia' as the most convenient foundation on which to base the *study* which this entails. For the purposes of criticizing and assessing this work, it will probably be helpful to draw a distinction between its structure and its subject matter, although it should always be remembered that these two aspects of it, though they may not be identical, are very closely interdependent. The 'Philosophy of Nature', despite its having been widely ignored by Hegelians and non-Hegelians alike, constitutes an integral part of the whole. In that its subject matter is less open to dispute than that of the other 'spheres', and in that it is directly relevant to many contemporary attitudes and problems, it may be regarded as one of the best introductions to Hegel's manner of thinking. In its structuralization of the natural sciences it has much in common with mediaeval scholasticism, and will therefore present a challenge to modern thinkers. Many scientists and historians of science will find much in its subject matter that is interesting and familiar however, and it is to be hoped that their recognition of Hegel's mastery in assessing the *particularities* of natural science, will encourage others to look in a new way at his 'Logic' and his 'Philosophy of Spirit'.

b. LEVELS, HIERARCHIES AND SPHERES

'The universe is a system, whose very essence consists in subordination; a scale of beings descending, by insensible degrees, from infinite perfection to absolute nothing.'—Soame Jenyns.

Dr. Johnson's slashing review of 'A Free Enquiry into the Nature and Origin of Evil' (London, 1757) by Soame Jenyns (1704–1787), demonstrates in a strikingly lucid manner the philosophical problems that faced a mid-eighteenth century writer attempting to make use of hierarchical thinking in dealing with moral or philosophical issues.[1] It shows very clearly, that although such thinking was then widespread among poets, theologians and philosophers, it was very far from bridging the gap between them and the natural scientists, and that those who still used it in

[1] 'The Literary Magazine' 1757: 'The Works of Samuel Johnson' (9 vols. London, 1825) vol. VI, pp. 47–76.

the grandiose manner of classical antiquity and the middle ages were almost entirely ignorant of its practical application. Jenyns however, who was a gentleman by birth and profession, a politician by occupation, and a philosopher only out of interest, had defined evil in a manner which might well have pleased Hegel had he read him.[1] 'These real evils,' he says, 'proceed from . . . subordination, without which no created system can subsist; all subordination implying imperfection, all imperfection evil, and all evil some kind of inconvenience or suffering'. Johnson attacks this basic concept in a remarkably acute manner by pointing out the futility of attempting to define the extremes of infinity and nullity, the evident impossibility of indicating the relationship between that which is infinite and that which is finite, and the lack of any reliable method by which the gradations linking infinity with nullity might be enumerated. His criticism reads like a summary of the programme Hegel must have set himself when the outlines of his system first became apparent about the turn of the century, and he began to concern himself with the significance of spheres, hierarchies and levels. Johnson rounds it off by drawing the following general conclusions, all of which were to be revised by his German contemporary. 'This scale of being I have demonstrated to be raised by presumptuous imagination, to rest on nothing at the bottom, to lean on nothing at the top, and to have vacuities from step to step, through which any order of being may sink into nihility without inconvenience, so far as we can judge, to the next rank above or below it.'

Had Johnson been more intimately acquainted with the natural sciences, he might not have been quite so outspoken in his rejection of a concept which, although it was often used in a clumsy and incongruous manner, was by no means irrelevant to the intellectual problems of his day. Taking the 'great chain of being' only as it was expounded by contemporary poets and philosophers, he may well have been justified in demolishing it as he did. He seems however to have been ignorant of its origins, since he refers to it as the 'Arabian scale of existence', and he would probably have treated it with more respect had he known that it had in fact been inherited from the Greeks. Professor Lovejoy has shown that its ultimate origin lies in Platonic dualism, in Plato's contrasting the visible universe with the ideal world of the demiurge and the eternal forms in the 'Timaeus', and in his judging politics in the light of absolute justice in the 'Republic'.[2] Both these undertakings involved the formulation of a *graded*

[1] See the note III p. 330. Hegel took evil to be, 'nothing but the inadequacy of that which *is* to that which *should* be.' ('Encyclopaedia' § 472, cf. § 23, § 35).

[2] A. O. Lovejoy 'The Great Chain of Being' (Cambridge, Mass., 1936).

approximation to an ideal. In Aristotle this concept reappeared in a more sophisticated manner as the distinction between matter and form, and it was mainly through *his* writings that Platonic dualism and the great chain of being came to dominate the intellectual life of Europe in the later middle ages.[1] During this period it provided the generally recognized framework for the assessment of all knowledge, and remnants of its influence upon education may still be found in the seniority accorded to the various faculties in the older universities of Europe. Theology, concerned as it is with human knowledge of the being and attributes of God, was recognized as of necessity the most comprehensive of all disciplines, and professors of it therefore took precedence over all others in university functions. Law, Medicine, Literature etc. found their positions beneath it in accordance with the *relative comprehensiveness* of their subject matters.[2] As Hegel notes,[3] the basic question the system posed for philosophers and theologians was that of the creation of the world, and of the relationship between God and what is created. Between about 1300 and about 1600, and largely on account of the use made of Aristotelianism by the Thomists, the being and attributes of God and the particularity of knowledge were not regarded as presenting theologians and natural scientists with anything resembling an irreconcilable conflict. The potential contradiction implicit in any comparing of scientific with religious truth, like the actual contradiction discovered through the conflict between positive and natural law, was overcome by postulating a hierarchy in which one took precedence over the other on account of its greater comprehensiveness or wider applicability, and in which separate disciplines could therefore be regarded as complementary. As has been noticed, the intellectual harmony resulting from this is echoed in the encylopaedias of the time, and is apparent in mediaeval humanism and in the 'unified sensibility' of Elizabethan literature.

In that 'the great chain of being' was used to consolidate a world picture based to a very great extent upon Ptolemy and Aristotle, it might have been expected to have been fairly conclusively discredited by the Copernican and Baconian revolutions. Professor Lovejoy, who emphasizes the otherworldliness of the middle ages, and tends to overlook its humanism, naturally regards the fact that hierarchical thinking was most vociferously

[1] W. Jaeger 'Aristotle' (tr. Robinson, Oxford, 1934) points out the persistence of Platonic dualism in the Aristotelian system. G. R. G. Mure 'An Introduction to Hegel' (Oxford, 1940) illustrates the relevance of Aristotle to an understanding of Hegel; cf. Nicolai Hartmann 'Aristoteles und Hegel' (2nd ed. Erfurt, 1933).

[2] H. Rashdall 'Universities of Europe in the Middle Ages' (3 vols. Oxford, 1895 ed. Powicke and Emden, 1936).

[3] §§ 246, 247.

advocated in the seventeenth and eighteenth centuries, as being somewhat paradoxical.[1] He is evidently unaware, that as the sources on which he bases his history of the subject are predominantly literary and philosophical, his view is somewhat unbalanced, and he certainly fails to note that metaphysically unpretentious hierarchical arrangements of the various sciences have *never* gone out of fashion. In the period which puzzles him, the great chain of being was being propounded by men who were very largely ignorant of its precise relevance to the natural sciences, and scientists who employed it as a matter of convenience within their particular disciplines were no longer prepared or able, as they had been in the middle ages, to acknowledge its more general significance.[2]

A chasm, as Johnson calls it, had opened between men's conceptions of the 'highest being' and of 'positive existence', and as it widened it became increasingly obvious that the *religious* culture of the time was unable to bridge it. Attempts were made to tinsel science with a veneer of religiosity, but they merely tended to confirm the opinions of those convinced of the hopelessness or perversity of all such undertakings. 'The Religious Philosopher . . . designed for the conviction of atheists and infidels' (3 vols, tr. Chamberlayne, 4th ed. London, 1730), by Bernard Nieuwentjdt (1654–1718), which was still popular in Hegel's day, enlisted considerable scientific knowledge in the service of its arguments, but its arrangement was chaotic, and the doubt it attempted to cast upon the reality of the heliocentric orbit of the earth can hardly have recommended it to the scientifically enlightened. 'Physico and Astro Theology; or, a demonstration of the Being and Attributes of God', by William Derham (1657–1735), had reached fifteen editions by 1798, and was scarcely less popular in Germany (tr. J. A. Fabricio, Hamburg, 1750), but it was inferior even to Nieuwentjdt's work as a responsible and systematic survey of the natural sciences, as were the pious 'Lectures on Natural and Experimental Philosophy' (5 vols. London, 1794) by George Adams (1750–1795) instrument-maker to George III. Jenyns contributed in a light and elegant manner with his 'A View of the internal Evidence of the Christian Religion' (London, 1776), which gained the distinction of being translated into French, and William Paley (1743–1805) produced his by no means entirely contemptible 'Natural Theology; or, evidence of the existence and attributes of the Deity; collected from the appearances of nature' (London, 1802), in which an attempt is made to prove the existence of the Deity

[1] op. cit. p. 142.

[2] A possible exception to this is Heinrich Friedrich Link (1767–1851): see 'Ueber die Leiter der Natur' (Rostock and Leipzig, 1794): cf. note III p. 263.

from the *design* traceable in natural phenomena. Paley's work is interesting in that, like Hegel's,[1] it contains an unusual rejection of astronomy as the best medium 'through which to prove the agency of an intelligent Creator' (ch. XXII), and a concentration upon the human anatomy on account of its *complexity*. 'For my part,' says Paley, 'I take my stand in human anatomy.' (ch. XXVII).[2]

The natural sciences themselves occasionally showed a certain reluctance to discard theologically tinged terminology. C. G. Gillipsie has shown for example, how the providentialist view lingered on in British geology between 1790 and 1850.[3] On the whole however, it was becoming increasingly apparent, during Hegel's lifetime, that science and religion were employing ostensibly incompatible means of expression. What is more, specialization of interest and the fragmentation of knowledge were already well advanced within the natural sciences themselves, and most of the great works of scientific synthesis, although by modern standards their range is impressive, were already confined to fairly limited fields of knowledge. Towards the close of the eighteenth century, the great chain of being was reinterpreted, in the organic sciences, as a *temporal* progression, and may therefore be regarded as having contributed to the development of evolutionary theories.[4] As attempts have been made, notably by David George Ritchie (1853–1903) in his 'Darwin and Hegel, with other philosophical studies' (London, 1893), to present Hegel as the philosopher of evolution, the strictly qualified way in which evolution is compatible with Hegelianism should perhaps be indicated. In that the evolution of one species out of another is regarded as taking place in a period of time, it is clear that the temporal sequence of the complex factors involved in this development, if it can be relevantly and satisfactorily reconstructed and explained, can do nothing but deepen our knowledge of the organic phenomena with which we are concerned as practising geologists, botanists and zoologists. The main principle behind the organization of the subject matter of the 'Encyclopaedia' is however that of a progression from what is more *simple* to what is more *complex*. It may well be the case that what evolves in a temporal sequence also exhibits a progression of this sort, but this is by no means necessarily so, and a temporal sequence of the kind

[1] § 268 Addition.

[2] 'There is but one temple in the world and that is the human body. There is nothing holier than this noble shape. To bow before men is to render a homage to this revelation in the flesh.' G. F. P. von Hardenberg (1772–1801): 'Novalis Gesammelte Werke' (ed. C. Seelig, 4 vols. Zürich, 1945–6) vol. IV, p. 222.

[3] C. G. Gillipsie 'Genesis and Geology' (Cambridge, Mass., 1951).

[4] Lovejoy op. cit. ch. IX.

significant in a biological context is in any case almost entirely irrelevant to an understanding of 'Mechanics' or 'Physics'. Although Hegel's rejection of the *philosophical* pretentiousness of the evolutionary ideas current in the opening decades of the last century is therefore decided and forthright, it is cautious and qualified in matters of detail relating to the state of knowledge in the various *organic sciences*.[1]

In their immediate *application* to the natural sciences, Hegel's levels, hierarchies and spheres were designed to meet the criticism that the great chain of being provided no reliable method by which the gradations linking its extremities might be enumerated and ranged in a rational sequence. The *origin* of these principles is to be found in the natural science of the time, and before proceeding to analyze them and indicate their relevance to modern thinking, it may therefore be of interest to illustrate the variety of contexts in which they occurred a century and a half ago. Orderly expositions, in which the subject matter was presented by beginning with its basic principles and progressing to more and more complex considerations, are to be found in many eighteenth and early nineteenth century scientific publications. Most of them were quite devoid of philosophical pretentions, and seem simply to have arisen out of the practical needs of those who worked them out. Newton's 'Mathematical Principles' (1687, ed. Cajori, Berkeley, 1947) provides one of the best examples of this in the sphere of mechanics. The book begins with definitions and laws of motion, proceeds to the motion of bodies and the same in resisting mediums, and concludes with a 'system of the world', involving the consideration of concrete problems concerning the planets, the moon, comets, etc. The fundamentally hierarchical thinking motivating this arrangement is explained in the scholium to book I section IX, 'In mathematics we are to investigate the quantities of forces with their proportions consequent upon any conditions supposed; then, when we enter upon physics, we compare those proportions with the phenomena of Nature, that we may know what conditions of those forces answer to the several kinds of attractive bodies. And this preparation being made, we argue more safely concerning the physical species, causes and proportions of the forces.' Although Hegel criticizes Newton severely for what he considers to be an unwarranted scientific use of the intellectual convenience of hierarchical thinking, he

[1] See § 249 Remark. 'The granitic primitive rocks which constitute the deepest strata, and which were formed one after the other, are said to be the first, and to be followed by regenerated granite, which has disintegrated and been deposited . . . Nothing whatever is made comprehensible by the succession of stratifications . . . This whole style of explanation is nothing but a transformation of spatial juxtaposition into temporal succession.' (§ 339 Add.). For a survey of the *zoological* literature forming the basis of the exposition in § 370, see the note III p. 366.

evidently found much that was acceptable in this general method, since he praises a similar publication, 'Traité de mécanique élémentaire' (Paris, 1801), by L. B. Francoeur (1773–1849), which treats mechanics by progressing from statics to dynamics and hydrostatics, and concluding with an exposition of the complex phenomena of hydrodynamics.

This kind of exposition is also found in many of the most popular schoolbooks of the time devoted to the general subject matter of mechanics and physics. It is basic, for example, to the lay-out of the 'Institutes of Natural Philosophy' (London, 1785, 3rd ed. 1802) by William Enfield (1741–1707), to the 'Introduction to Natural Philosophy' (London, 1781, 5th ed. 1805)[1] by William Nicholson (1753–1815), and to their German equivalent, a work quoted by Hegel on several occasions, 'Grundriss der Naturlehre' (Halle, 1787, 6th ed. 1820) by F. A. C. Gren (1760–1798). Nor was it confined solely to general works of this kind, although it did of course tend to be less in evidence as specialization increased. The famous lectures delivered at the Royal Institute in 1802–1803 by Thomas Young (1773–1829),[2] proceed in the same manner, beginning with mechanics and ending with vegetable and animal life, as does the highly accomplished and immensely influential 'Système des Connaissances chimiques' (11 vols. Paris, 1801) by A. F. Fourcroy (1755–1809). It was in fact in the chemistry textbooks of the time that the method came into its own. Nearly all of them begin with a consideration of first principles, and then proceed to consider simple and compound bodies, acids, salts, metals, vegetable and animal substances, in that order. 'A System of Chemistry' (4 vols. Edinburgh, 1802, 4th ed. 1817) by Thomas Thomson (1773–1852), translated into German by F. B. Wolff (1766–1845),[3] provides a good Anglo-German example of this.

Richard Kirwan (1733–1812), in his 'Elements of Mineralogy' (1784, 3rd ed. 2 vols., London, 1810), vol. I ch. IV, explains the value of this kind of hierarchical thinking in the classification of minerals, 'On the most general view of an indiscriminate heap of earths and stones, we may readily perceive that some have an *homogeneous* aspect; none of the parts of which their volume consists bearing the appearance of being composed differently from one another. Others on the contrary visibly involve two or more heterogeneous substances, either adhering to, or inhering one in the other; these are called *aggregates*. Lastly, others seem to participate of the nature of two (or perhaps more) heterogeneous fossils, without however

[1] Germ. tr. A. F. Ludike 'Einleitung in die Naturlehre' (2 vols. Leipzig, 1787).
[2] 'A Course of Lectures on Natural Philosophy' (2 vols., London, 1807).
[3] 'System der Chemie' (5 vols., Berlin, 1805–1811).

any visible separation of one from the other: these I call *derivatives*. Thus we have three primary divisions of earths or stones.' It was however in the mineral, vegetable and animal kingdoms that the hierarchical thinking of the early nineteenth century found itself most deeply involved in seemingly unresolvable scientific controversies. Abraham Gottlob Werner (1749–1817), by means of his 'Classification der Gebirgsarten' (Dresden, 1787), had popularized an arrangement of rocks in which a progression was made from 'primitives' such as granite, gneiss and mica, to 'transitions' such as slate, chalk and trapp, 'fletz' such as sandstone, basalt and coal, 'alluviums' such as sand and brown coal, and volcanic formations.[1] The emphasis he laid upon the part played by water in the formation of geological phenomena involved his followers in a protracted controversy with the disciples of James Hutton (1726–1797) of Edinburgh however.[2] Hutton had emphasized the importance of heat, and when Hegel was lecturing at Berlin, the rival geological theories were only just beginning to be regarded as either compatible or obsolete. In botanical studies, the avowedly artificial classification of Linné was challenged, on the continent, by A. L. de Jussieu (1748–1836), in his 'Genera plantarum' (Paris, 1789). This attempt to formulate a natural system did not meet with immediate general acceptance however, so that Goethe's attempt at a hierarchical interpretation of the plant world[3] was regarded as a somewhat hazardous undertaking, and in England, purely Linnaean works such as the 'Introduction to Physiological and Systematic Botany' (London, 1807, Germ. tr. J. A. Schulter, Vienna, 1819) by Sir James Edward Smith (1759–1828), and the 'Botanical Arrangement of all the Vegetables naturally growing in Great Britain' (2 vols., London, 1776), by William Withering (1741–1799), were still being re-edited in the 1830's. A similar situation prevailed in the spheres of comparative anatomy and zoology. As data accumulated and new affinities became evident, attempts were made to abandon the artificial classification of Linnés 'Systema naturae'. The hierarchical conceptions of Lamarck and Cuvier were by no means fully satisfactory however, and their involving development in time, as Hegel notes, tended to introduce irrelevant considerations into the uses or assessments that were made of them.[4]

Nevertheless, with such a wealth of hierarchical thinking in evidence

[1] For contemporary British adaptations, see Robert Jameson 'System of Mineralogy' (3 vols. Edinburgh, 1816); T. Weaver 'Treatise on . . . Fossils' (Dublin, 1805).

[2] John Playfair (1748–1819) 'Illustrations of the Huttonian Theory' (Edinburgh, 1802, ed. White, New York, 1964).

[3] 'Die Metamorphose der Pflanzen' (Gotha, 1790).

[4] Note III p. 366.

in the various natural sciences of his day, it is not perhaps surprising that Hegel should have realized the general value of it when he came to consider the possibility of structuralizing knowledge in an encyclopaedic manner. His acumen appears in the carefully qualified way in which he employed the basic concept however, and it is primarily the critical analysis to which he submitted it that constitutes the relevance of his work to modern thinking.

Johnson's criticism that the scale of being had, 'vacuities from step to step, through which any order of being may sink into nihility without inconvenience . . . to the next above or below it', though it may have been difficult to answer with reference to 'Logic' or 'Spirit', was refuted in superabundance by the natural sciences of the day. Wherever scientists examined natural phenomena, the data they collected forced them to recognize evidently *stable* qualitative differences, in the interpretation and exposition of which they frequently found it not only convenient, but necessary to postulate a scale or hierarchy involving degrees of complexity. It is evident from his first full-scale attempt to work out a systematic encyclopaedia, that Hegel had grasped the general importance of this procedure at a very early stage. It seems moreover to have been an examination of the natural sciences and the 'logical' and 'metaphysical' categories they involved which had impressed the importance of it upon him, for whereas this attempt includes a careful and ample exposition of an extensive range of categories and natural phenomena, it lacks a section on 'Spirit'.[1]

Once the importance of distinguishing degrees of complexity has become apparent however, two kinds of problem present themselves. The scientist who is actually investigating natural phenomena finds that although the general structure of his work may not need constant revision, the details of it usually do, and that on occasions certain discoveries or interpretations are liable to change even the general structure in a quite radical manner. Kirwan was an accomplished and respected mineralogist for example, but it is doubtful whether many of his twentieth century counterparts would find his 'primary divisions of earths or stones' very helpful in throwing light upon current research. The complexity relationships

[1] This could simply be due to Hegel's having stopped writing it out however, for it also lacks an 'Organics'. The manuscript, which is in any case incomplete, shows signs of careful revision, and the work may originally have been designed for publication. It dates from 1801–2. See 'Jenenser Logik, Metaphysik und Naturphilosophie' (ed. G. Lasson, Leipzig, 1923); 'Philosophische Bibliothek' (Felix Meiner Verlag, Hamburg, 1967). A critical German edition is in course of preparation (Dr. Kimmerle). Hermann Schmitz, 'Hegel als Denker der Individualität' (Meisenheim, 1957) pp. 122–126 discusses the evidence of the syllogistic origins of the dialectic to be found in this work.

indicated by the natural sciences are, in fact, changing continuously. They were revised fairly extensively during Hegel's lifetime, and any modern scientist, picking up this book, will have no difficulty in seeing the further revision that has taken place since the 1820's. It is essential therefore that a distinction should be made between the subject matter and the principles of hierarchical thinking. Many eighteenth century writers, to whom the great chain of being was simply a convenient and imaginatively satisfying dogma failed to realize this, and applied the doctrine to contemporary knowledge as if it were already to be grasped as complete in all its details.[1] It was this static and metaphysically irresponsible interpretation of it, which would certainly have been less widespread had the chasm dividing the natural sciences from theology and philosophy been less deep, which eventually brought the whole method of hierarchical thinking into general discredit.[2] When Schelling and his followers made their attempt at bridging this chasm, they also made the mistake of failing to formulate the principles of their thought as distinct from the subject matter with which they were dealing, and were therefore led into interpreting natural phenomena by postulating sequences and connections which outraged those engaged in the normal routine of sober and painstaking research. Hegel is justified in disassociating himself from the Schellingians in that while the subject matter of the 'Encylopaedia' is assessed solely on its own merits, it is also referred back to a set of clearly definable and consistently employed principles. If the natural science of the day is questioned, this is usually because Hegel thinks that it is overlooking qualitative differences. He never quarrels with it simply in order to make striking observations or indicate novel connections.[3]

Having grasped the general significance of distinguishing degrees of complexity, and acknowledged the state of continuous change in the natural sciences, it is therefore the investigation of the *principles* involved in Hegel's structuralization of knowledge, which presents us with the second kind of problem. Hegel had realized, at the latest by the autumn of

[1] Mainly poets, theologians and philosophers of course. A good example of the doctrines being used in this form in a *theological* context is to be found in the well-known 'De Origine Mali' (Dublin and London, 1702, tr. E. Law, 2nd ed. 2 vols. London, 1732) by William King (1650–1729), archbishop of Dublin. 'From the supposition of a Scale of Beings, gradually descending from perfection to nonentity, and complete in every intermediate rank and degree, we shall soon see the absurdity of such questions as these, Why was not man made more perfect? Why are not his faculties equal to those of angels? Since this is only asking why he was not placed in a different class of beings, when at the same time all other classes are supposed to be full.' (vol. I p. 131).

[2] Lovejoy op. cit. pp. 328–329; cf. Josiah Royce (1855–1916) 'The Religious Aspect of Philosophy' (Boston, Mass., 1885) pp. 248–249.

[3] This should be made abundantly clear by the commentary: see, for example §§ 270, 274–278, 317–320, 330, 371.

1801, that the natural sciences could not be satisfactorily treated merely by distinguishing levels of subject matter and ranging them in hierarchies. It became apparent to him, that the sequence of levels formulated on these principles did not exhibit a simple and uniform progression. Goethe's 'Die Metamorphose der Pflanzen' (Gotha, 1790) might be used in order to expound botanical phenomena in a rational sequence, and Johann Hermann's 'Affinitatum Animalium Tabulam' (Argentorati, 1777) might be used to the same purpose in animal physiology and zoology. Botany and animal physiology had to be juxtaposed in the overall sequence however (§ 349),[1] and it was clear that the levels formulated *within* the botanical hierarchy, like those *within* the zoological hierarchy, had factors in common which differed from those justifying the juxtaposing of the most complex botanical level and the simplest level of animal physiology. Hegel had noticed in fact, that although the formulation and juxtaposing of levels might be motivated solely by the principle of increasing degrees of *complexity*, the *qualitative* differences initiated by the transitions from one level to the next varied very widely in their degree of *comprehensiveness*. This was often most apparent in closely related levels. The transition from 'Logic' to space for example (§ 254), and that from the point to the line (§ 256), both involved a straightforward and evidently valid juxtaposing of subject matters, but they differed very widely indeed in the comprehensiveness of the qualitative differences they initiated. It was evidently a consideration of this which led Hegel to formulate the principle of *spheres*. As a principle, it is as revisable and as intimately involved with the subject matter of the 'Encyclopaedia' as are levels and hierarchies, and once its significance is grasped, the understanding of the general structure of this work and of the 'Philosophy of Nature' is by no means difficult. Spheres consist of levels and hierarchies. They also contribute to the formation of more comprehensive spheres however, within which they are themselves simply levels ranged in hierarchies. Botany is a fairly comprehensive sphere of scientific enquiry for example; within the more comprehensive sphere of organics however, it constitutes a level in a hierarchy also involving geology and zoology. Organics, in its turn, constitutes a level, together with mechanics and physics, within the still more comprehensive sphere of 'Nature'. The most comprehensive or complex sphere of all is that of the 'Encyclopaedia' as a whole, within which the three major spheres of 'Logic', 'Nature' and 'Spirit' constitute the final hierarchy of complexity relationships.

[1] Note III p. 298.

It is in the structure of the 'Encyclopaedia' as a *whole*, and, consequently, in the structure of the sphere, that the *dialectic* had its origin and finds its fulfillment. As the theological problems which preoccupied him during the 1790's gave way to the encyclopaedic problems which preoccupied him at Jena (1800–1806), Hegel came to regard the Three Persons of the Christian Trinity as a theological prefiguration of the three major spheres of the 'Encyclopaedia'.[1] Both the dogma and the structure were interpreted by him as exhibiting, in their unity, the syllogistic interdependence of the universal, the particular and the singular.[2] Within each sphere therefore, he attempts to exhibit the levels as progressing from what is general to the sphere as a whole, to what is more isolated and particular, and finally to what holds within itself both generalities and particularities. This triadic pattern or structure, severely regulated as it is by levels, hierarchies and spheres, and involving as it does an immense wealth of observation and erudition, constitutes the central and all-pervading principle of the 'Encyclopaedia'. Hegel refers to it, in the course of his expositions, as the '*Notion*', and in these lectures, often invokes it in order to indicate the 'imperfection' of the natural sciences, 'This idealism, which recognizes the Idea throughout the whole of nature, is at the same time realism, for the Notion of living existence is the Idea as reality, even though in other respects the individuals only correspond to one moment of the Notion. In real, sensuous being, philosophy recognizes the Notion in general. One must start from the Notion, and even if it should as yet be unable to exhaust what is called the 'abundant variety' of nature, and there is still a great deal of particularity to be explained, it must be trusted nevertheless. The demand that there should be an explanation of this particularity is generally vague, and it is no reflection on the Notion that it is not fulfilled. With the theories of the empirical physicists the position is quite the reverse however, for as their validity depends solely upon singular instances, they are obliged to explain everything. The Notion holds good of its own accord however, and singularity will therefore yield itself in due course.' (§ 353 Add.). It is indeed impossible to overestimate the importance of this principle in the expositions of the 'Encyclopaedia', 'Philosophy has to proceed on the basis of the Notion, and even if it demonstrates very little, one has to be satisfied. It is an error on the part of the philosophy of nature to attempt to assess all phenomena; this is done in the finite sciences, where everything has to be reduced to general

[1] For a recent discussion of this see Claude Bruaire 'Logique et religion chrétienne dans la philosophie de Hegel' (Paris, 1964) pt. II ch. ii.

[2] Hermann Schmitz 'Hegel als Denker der Individualität' (Meisenheim, 1957) pp. 90–163.

conceptions (hypotheses). In these sciences the empirical element is the sole confirmation of the hypothesis, so that everything has to be explained. Whatever is known through the Notion is its own explanation and stands firm however, so that philosophy need not be disturbed if the explanation of each and every phenomenon has not yet been completed.' (§ 270 Add.).

The 'Encyclopaedia' has two aspects therefore, which, while they have to be recognized as being distinct, also have to be recognized as involving one another and as being ultimately or ideally identical. It is essential that its *subject matter* should be regarded as being open to constant revision in the light of the changing state of knowledge. It is no less essential however that this subject matter should be structuralized with reference to the *principles* through which it becomes most fully intelligible, and that these principles should be recognized as *absolute* and changeless. Unless the work is regarded in this manner, each of the three main points in Johnson's attack will be fully justified; there *will* be no way of defining the extremes of infinity and nullity, it *will* be impossible to indicate the relationship between what is infinite and what is finite, and there *will* be no reliable method by which the levels linking infinity with nullity might be enumerated.

When he searched the thought of his time for principles that might be used in a systematic exposition of knowledge as a whole, Hegel discovered, therefore, an ancient and scholasticized metaphysical system needing radical revision in order to make it relevant to current intellectual insights, a Christianity which had failed to cope with the rapid changes brought about by Copernicanism, Baconianism, Rousseauism, and an extensively fragmented treatment of the natural sciences. The intellectual climate at *present* is in many respects more favourable to the understanding and acceptance of his 'Encyclopaedia' than that at the beginning of the last century, and it may therefore not be entirely out of place to indicate some features of contemporary thinking in the natural sciences which have a direct bearing upon it.

It has already been noticed that the present readiness to regard the problems presented by the natural sciences as a *whole*,[1] to recognize the relevance to natural science of exact formulations of *thought* as well as orderly

[1] 'The large and panoramic systems of idealistic philosophy are, as it were, late branches of a deformed scholasticism. Hegelianism is a typical metaphysical system of our age; Thomism is a typical scholastic system which is still living in the Catholic church and also attracting some persons outside the Catholic church. Both these systems have not so far shown any disposition to logicalize empirical science, to form a quasi-addition to their philosophico-religious structures.' Otto Neurath, Rudolf Carnap, Charles Morris 'International Encyclopaedia of Unified Science' (2 vols. Chicago, 1955) vol. I p. 7.

arrangements of subject matter, and to acknowledge that an awareness of the importance of psychological, social, political, historical factors[1] is essential to any balanced assessment of this *sphere*, all provide ground which many modern thinkers have come to share with Hegel. This ground has to be regarded as particularly valuable, fertile and interesting, precisely because those who have chosen to till it have been very largely unaware of Hegel's having acknowledged the potentiality of their labours.

The most stimulating and encouraging feature of the link-up between the 'Philosophy of Nature' and modern thinking about natural science, is undoubtedly this general agreement on the broad outlines of the approach required for any balanced assessment of the problems presented by natural phenomena. The most fascinating features of it are however the similarities in detail which have become apparent of recent years. As might be expected, two main attitudes have developed in the current treatment of *levels*. R. O. Kapp has emphasized the importance of resolving observations of complex phenomena into generalizations,[2] and J. G. Kemeny, after indicating the significance of reducing complex fields of natural science to a few fundamental entities has even gone so far as to conclude that, 'We could thus picture the scientist as striving to the goal of finding the law of nature which would enable him to explain all facts with perfect accuracy.'[3] The same manner of thinking, although it is carefully qualified, appears in an article by P. Oppenheim and H. Putnam, in which it is suggested that our view of nature might be given unity by a process of 'micro-reduction', out of which levels of elementary particles, atoms, molecules, cells, multicellular living things and social groups would eventually emerge.[4] However, J. H. Woodger's work at the Middlesex Hospital Medical School in applying the method of the 'Principia Mathematica' to cytological problems,[5] has had the interesting philosophical result of forcing him to suggest an amplification of Whitehead and Russell's work on the theory of relations, in the interest of distinguishing

[1] i.e. the sphere of 'Spirit'.

[2] 'I wish to make the bold claim here that, in physics, the rule of economy of hypotheses can be so expressed and defined that it acquires a status far higher than the one usually accorded to it; I wish to raise it from a mere rule of procedure to one of the great universal principles to which the whole of the physical world conforms. At this level it would be worded as follows: *In physics the minimum assumption always constitutes the true generalisation.*' 'Ockam's Razor and the unification of Physical Science' ('British Journal for the Philosophy of Science' vol. VIII, Feb. 1958, no. 32, pp. 265–280: cf. vol. XI pp. 55–62, May 1960).

[3] 'A Philosopher Looks at Science' (Princeton, 1959) pp. 167–173.

[4] H. Feigl and G. Maxwell 'Minnesota Studies in the Philosophy of Science' (3 vols., Minneapolis, 1962) vol. II pp. 3–36, 'Unity of Science as a working hypothesis.'

[5] 'The Axiomatic Method in Biology' (Cambridge, 1937).

between progressions and levels involved in hierarchies.[1] Karl Menger has also indicated the need for a revision of pure and applied mathematics in order to facilitate the treatment of the relationships between quantitative *and qualitative* factors which so frequently become apparent in scientific work of all kinds. He suggests that Ockam's razor should be qualified by the proposition that, 'Entities must not be reduced to the point of inadequacy, i.e. it is vain to try to do with fewer what requires more', and that what modern mathematics needs is not a razor but a separator or prism for resolving conceptual mixtures with the spectra of their meanings.[2] M. Bunge[3] and R. B. Braithwaite have both attempted to indicate the wider philosophical significance of postulating levels in order to allow validity to apparently contradictory or complementary hypotheses concerned with various degrees of complexity or comprehensiveness. 'In order that the propositions should form an ascending hierarchy they must, of course, cover a wider and wider range of possible experience, so that a higher-level hypothesis could be refuted by observations which would not refute a hypothesis standing at a lower level. But, provided that there is no evidence refuting the highest-level hypothesis, the evidence establishing it need be no more than that establishing a lower-level hypothesis for it to be regarded as providing an explanation for the latter and as thereby raising the latter's intellectual status in relation to comparable hypotheses for which we can provide no such explanation.'[4] Bunge has also attempted to define a level as, 'a section of reality characterized by a set of interlocked properties and laws, some of which are peculiar to the given domain', and to indicate the stability of the *ontic* levels to which the evident fluidity of our *knowledge* corresponds. This distinction between being and knowledge raises an issue which Hegel resolutely refuses to regard as a problem. One might of course ask on what grounds one postulates stable ontic levels if they are not those of our knowledge of them. Bunge gives a theoretical answer to this by pointing out that if these levels

[1] 'And by a hierarchy I mean any relation which is one-many and such that its converse domain is identical with the whole set of terms to which the beginning of the relation stands in some power of the relation. This is a purely abstract definition because the notion of heirarchy as used here is not one belonging to any particular empirical science. It is a purely set-theoretical notion. At the same time it does not occur in those sections of Whitehead and Russell's "Principia Mathematica" which are devoted to the theory of relations.' 'Biology and Physics' ('British Journal for the Philosophy of Science' vol. XI, Aug. 1960, no. 42 pp. 89–100).

[2] 'A Counterpart of Occam's razor in the ontological uses of pure and applied mathematics' ('Synthèse' vol. XII, no. 4, pp. 415–428, Dec. 1960). Cf. W. V. O. Quine 'Mathematical Logic' (Harvard, 1951) §§ 28–29.

[3] 'The Myth of Simplicity: problems of scientific philosophy' (Englewood, 1963).

[4] R. B. Braithwaite 'Scientific Explanation' (Cambridge, 1953) pp. 345–347. Cf. D. Bohm 'Causality and Chance in Modern Physics' (London, 1957) pp. 164–170.

were not comparatively stable, nothing would be irrelevant to anything else and the various sciences would be impossible. Hegel, whose 'Logic' and 'Psychology' are directly relevant here, would probably have added to this that the difference between being and knowledge assumed by the distinction is only partially valid: the subject matter of the natural sciences, in that it involves time and constitutes knowledge is, of course, continually changing; in that it is also to be assessed in its graded, hierarchical and spherical aspect however, a rational interpretation of it will also have to recognize its structural stability.

The principle of *hierarchies* also occurs widely in modern thinking, although it is frequently employed only in its rather primitive eighteenth century form, as a vague progression from what is more simple to what is more complex.[1] As it has been formulated by Woodger however, it has helped to clarify extremely intricate cytological problems, and, through its more recent use in embryology, given rise to the postulation of a three-dimensional co-ordinate system, the axes of which are related to the idealized planes of morphological symmetry in a developing embryo—an emergence of the triadic structure in rationalized embryology which would most certainly have fascinated Hegel.[2] J. W. Addison's suggestion[3] that the theories of particular hierarchies that have arisen more or less independently in analysis, recursive function theory and pure logic might be used to realize Hilbert's concept of a unified science of mathematics,[4] could be regarded as providing the counterpart to Woodger's work in the sphere of pure mathematics. R. Harré has pointed out that in a true hierarchy the retrogression is asymmetrical. If, for example, (a) a chemical explanation is given of a reaction; (b) a valency explanation is given of chemistry; and (c) an electronic explanation is given of valency;

[1] See, for example, the lay-out in the anthology of articles collected by H. Feigl and W. Sellars. 'Readings in Philosophical Analysis' (New York, 1943), where a beginning is made with 'Is Existence a predicate?' and a conclusion is reached with 'The Freedom of the Will'.

[2] Note III p. 355. See J. R. Gregg and F. T. C. Harris 'Form and Strategy in Science' (Dordrecht 1964) pp. 234–250.

[3] 'The Theory of Hierarchies' in E. Nagel, P. Suppes, A. Tarski 'Logic, Methodology and Philosophy of Science' (Stanford, 1962) pp. 26–37. Cf. S. C. Kleene 'Introduction to Metamathematics' (New York and Amsterdam, 1952); G. Asser 'Das Repräsentantenproblem' ('Zeitschrift für mathematische Logik und Grundlagen der Mathematik' vol. I pp. 252–263, 1955); J. W. Addison 'Separation principles in the hierarchies of classical and effective descriptive set theory' ('Fundamenta Mathematicae' vol. 46 pp. 123–135, 1959); E. W. Beth 'The Foundations of Mathematics' (Amsterdam, 1965) pp. 194–201.

[4] David Hilbert (1862–1943) 'Mathematical Problems' (tr. Newson 'Bulletin of the American Mathematical Society' vol. 8 pp. 437–479, 1901–2), 'The question is urged upon us whether mathematics is doomed to the fate of those other sciences that have split up into separate branches, whose representatives scarcely understand one another, and whose connection becomes ever more loose. I do not believe this nor wish it, . . . with the extension of mathematics, its organic character is not lost but only manifests itself more clearly.'

although (b) is necessarily involved in a full explanation of (a), the converse is not the case. Similarly, although (c) is necessarily involved in a full explanation of (b), the converse is not the case. Harré presents this very lucidly, and if his exposition is borne in mind, a lot of light will be thrown upon the practical and purely scientific value of Hegel's arrangement of the *subject matter* of the 'Philosophy of Nature'.[1] Theodor Litt has even suggested that the whole 'Encyclopaedia' is to be more readily appreciated if its levels are considered in the converse order to that in which Hegel lectured upon them.[2] One of the most ambitious and brilliant attempts to demonstrate the relevance of hierarchical thinking to contemporary physics has been made by Laszlo Tisza.[3] He points out that the great triumphs of nineteenth century physics lay in the reduction of mechanics, electrodynamics, thermodynamics to classical mechanics, and that they are still relevant to our thinking in that they exhibit the simplifying and unifying power of certain high-level abstractions. Twentieth century developments have shown however that basic disciplines such as classical mechanics, thermodynamics and quantum mechanics are too complex and diverse to be compressed within the confines of a single rigorously built deductive system. Tisza proposes therefore that this sphere should be regarded as a 'cluster' of deductive systems, and that the procedure of logical differentiation which grasping it will therefore entail should be held in check through what he calls 'the logical integration of deductive systems'. This involves an investigation of the interrelationships sustaining the compatibility or mutual consistency of the various systems recognized. By bearing in mind compatibility, controlled inconsistency, supplementary relations and the fact that many relationships are, as yet, incompletely understood, he manages to work out a tentative grading of gravitational theories, mechanics, dynamics, and thermodynamics.

Now that the uncertainty principle in quantum mechanics seems to have been effectively questioned by Alfred Landé,[4] there would appear to be

[1] R. Harré 'Matter and Method' (London, 1964) pp. 24–31.

[2] 'Hegel, Versuch einer kritischen Erneuerung' (Heidelberg, 1953).

[3] 'The Conceptual Structure of Physics' ('Reviews of Modern Physics' vol. 35, no. 1, pp. 151–185, Jan. 1963); R. S. Cohen and W. Wartofsky 'Boston Studies in the Philosophy of Science' (2 vols. Dordrecht and New York, 1963–1965) vol. I pp. 55–76.

[4] 'Why do quantum theorists ignore quantum theory?' ('British Journal for the Philosophy of Science' vol. XV pp. 307–313, 1965); 'New Foundations of Quantum Mechanics' (Cambridge, 1965), 'The innovation of this book is to point out that there are serious faults in the purely *physical* arguments which have led to the current dualistic doctrines according to which diffraction and other wavelike phenomena of matter force us to accept two contradictory pictures, together with an elaborate subjectivist interpretation of atomic events, instead of one unitary reality. The faulty physics consists in ignoring an important element of the quantum mechanics of particles, namely the rule for the quantized exchange of linear momentum (Duane's third quantum rule, 1923) established in perfect

little point in dealing in detail with the purely scientific origins of the idea of complementarity, or with the religious capital which the modern counterparts of Nieuwentjdt, Derham, Adams and Paley have attempted to extract from it. Although this concept is certainly consistent with hierarchical thinking, its valid applicability is one-way, and very largely self-evident. It may be said for example, that a physicist's analysis of a stone complements a chemist's *for a geologist,* or that a biologist's account of a person complements a psychologist's *for a judge*, but Mr. Alexander[1] was perfectly justified in feeling uneasy when he surmised that Messrs. MacKay and Coulson[2] might be inclined to use the concept in an attempt to make *him* admit the reasonableness of being religious. A true hierarchy is asymmetrical, so that whereas an exclusively scientific attitude of mind is at least potentially intelligible to predominantly religious thinking, the converse is by no means the case.

The *spheres* of subject matter recognized by Hegel in the 'Philosophy of Nature' simply reflect the natural science of his day, and many of them, in their general outlines, might still be regarded as valid. Contemporary science finds no difficulty in recognizing distinct disciplines. Research is continually bringing to light hitherto unrecognized affinities and connections however, and attempts are therefore made to postulate metaphysical principles capable of making various disciplines more generally intelligible. Very few modern physicists, once they have begun to consider the general significance of inter-discipline relationships, have been able to keep to the kind of positivism employed so effectively by Tisza, and as most of them are not trained metaphysicians, the principles they have formulated have, on the whole, been unsatisfactory. Harré tends to accept Collingwood's relativistic historicism, 'In every hierarchy of explanatory mechanisms there is, at any given historical period, an ultimate or final mechanism which, in that period, does not call for an explanation. The characteristics of this mechanism, or the concepts of what counts for the time being as the ultimate explanation, can be expressed in what I shall call the *General Conceptual System* of the period.'[3] Ernest Nagel, evidently influenced by the success of evolutionary theories in organics, formulates the principle of

---

analogy to the quantum rule for the energy (Planck) and for the angular momentum (Sommerfeld-Wilson). The third quantum rule yields indeed a complete explanation of all the wavelike phenomena of matter.'

[1] Peter Alexander 'Complementary Descriptions' ('Mind' vol. 65 pp. 145–165, 1956).

[2] D. M. MacKay 'Science and Faith' ('The Listener' Sept. 11, 1952); C. A. Coulson 'Christianity in an Age of Science' ('Riddell Memorial Lectures' 1953).

[3] 'Matter and Method' (London, 1964) p. 27.

'emergence' in order to make the relationships between various spheres of physics intelligible.[1] D. Bohm has made much of a similar principle, which he calls 'becoming'.[2] It is of course the biologists who are best qualified, on account of the nature of the subject matter with which they are concerned, to appreciate the metaphysical structure of a sphere.[3] Bertalanffy has, for example, criticized Russell's noble but only partly justifiable championing of the tenet that the understanding of a part does not necessarily involve a consideration of the whole,[4] 'If you take any realm of biological phenomena, whether embryonic development, metabolism, activity of the nervous system, biocoenoses etc., it is always so that a behaviour of an element is different within the system from what it is in isolation. You cannot sum up the behaviour of the whole from the individual parts.'[5] It seems likely moreover, that thinking in terms of levels, hierarchies and spheres, rather than in terms which necessarily involve simple progressions in time, might throw a lot of light upon the value of certain attempts to justify the concept of teleology as it is taken to apply to biological development.[6]

The uses made of the principles of levels, hierarchies and spheres by contemporary thinkers have not, as yet, been used to throw any light upon the origin and significance of Hegel's dialectic. To a very large extent therefore, the contemporary views noticed in this chapter have to be regarded as revisable and ephemeral, and it is indeed doubtful whether any of their proponents would wish to claim that they should be regarded as in any way absolute or permanent. Taken as a whole however, they do constitute a great advance upon the scientific thinking of the early nineteenth century. In that they have not drawn their inspiration from any consciously preformulated metaphysic, but have arisen spontaneously out of attempts to grasp widely diverse and intricate phenomena, they are of great interest to contemporary Hegelianism, not only because they bear out the validity of Hegel's criticism of the 'physics' and metaphysics of

[1] 'The Structure of Science' (London, 1961) ch. 11 pp. 336–398.

[2] 'Causality and Chance in Modern Physics' (London, 1957).

[3] A. B. Novikoff 'The Concept of Integrative Levels and Biology' ('Science' new series volume 101 pp. 209–215, 1945).

[4] In, for example, 'Human knowledge, its scope and limits' (London, 1948).

[5] Ludwig von Bertalanffy 'An outline of general system theory' ('The British Journal for the Philsophy of Science' vol. I pp. 134–165, 1950).

[6] R. B. Braithwaite 'Scientific Explanation' (Cambridge, 1953) ch. X. Cf. J. H. Woodger op. cit. 1960, 'In conclusion we may say that biology is concerned with objects whose parts (or some of them) exhibit hierarchical order in space and are themselves ordered by hierarchies whose fields are extended in time; this type of order being connected with the occurrence in these biological objects of parts which are existentially dependent upon one another.'

his own day, but because they give such an unmistakable indication of the relevance of his 'Encyclopaedia' to present problems.

c. LOGIC, NATURE, SPIRIT

'Perception would, of course, be held by Hegel to be more or less erroneous. Nothing really exists, according to his system, but Spirits. Bodies only appear to exist.'—J. M. E. McTaggart.

The categories of Hegel's 'Logic' have yet to be traced to their origins in the history of philosophy and the natural sciences in the way that the subject matter of the 'Philosophy of Nature' has now been related to its sources. As the general principles of the 'Encyclopaedia' have moreover never been enunciated in a lucid, succinct and usable form, and the English translations of the 'Logic' leave much to be desired,[1] the general results produced by the impact of the 'Logic' upon British thinkers have been somewhat lacking in clarity and coherence, and have therefore had the deplorable effect of simply mystifying, irritating and bewildering the supposedly uninitiated. This is particularly noticeable in respect of those writers who, after reading the 'Logic', have gone on to expound the relationship in which they think it stands to 'Nature'. McTaggart's remark is by no means the choicest of their utterances.[2] S. Alexander invokes the condensation of points from the 'complete law of the universe' in order to clarify the matter.[3] H. S. Macran's investigations into the categories immediately preceding 'Nature' led him to regard it as, 'the mere lump that the idea is gradually to leaven, the *vile corpus* on which the idea is to demonstrate its truth'. He then proceeds to illustrate his point, 'The oak,

[1] Hegel's first logic (1801/2), and the simplified versions of the subject he prepared for his students at Nuremberg (1808/16), have never been translated: see 'Jenenser Logik' (ed. Lasson, Leipzig, 1923), 'Philosophische Propädeutik' (ed. Rosenkranz, Stuttgart, 1961). His main work on the subject 'Wissenschaft der Logik' (3 pts. Nuremberg, 1812/16) has been translated in its entirety by W. H. Johnston and L. G. Struthers, 'Hegel's Science of Logic' (2 vols. London, 1929). Parts of it were translated by J. H. Stirling (1865) and H. S. Macran (1912/29). W. Wallace brought out an English version of that part of the 'Encyclopaedia' devoted to the subject, 'The Logic of Hegel' (Oxford, 1873). H. Glockner's 'Hegel-Lexikon' (improved ed. 2 vols. Stuttgart, 1957), which appeared in conjunction with the 'Sämtliche Werke' (22 vols. Stuttgart, 1957), by bringing out the *consistency* in Hegel's use of language, has initiated a new approach in Hegel scholarship. If Anglo-Saxon linguistic analysis had given rise, as it should have done, to an English equivalent of Rudolf Eisler's 'Wörterbuch der philosophischen Begriffe' (1899, 4th ed. 3 vols. Berlin, 1927–1929) or J. Hoffmeister's 'Wörterbuch der philosophischen Begriffe' (Hamburg, 1955), there might have been a chance of revising these translations in a worthwhile manner.

[2] 'A Commentary on Hegel's Logic' (Cambridge, 1910), p. 9.

[3] 'Hegel's Conception of Nature' ('Mind' vol. XI pp. 495–523, 1886) pp. 499–500.

for example, with its coherence of parts, differentiation of functions, and general unity of aim, as compared, say, with the indifference and coherence of clay, is on the way to the absolute identity of the idea, but no more'.[1] William Wallace would even have us believe that 'endless times and spaces', writings in organisms, silent images, Lethe, the 'Divine Comedy' (in Italian) and Condillac are all relevant to an understanding of the transition from 'Logic' to Nature.[2]

Nonsense such as this is of course inexcusable. It cannot be denied however that certain problems are presented by the 'Logic' and by the relationship in which it stands to 'Nature' and 'Spirit', and before proceeding to look in detail at some of the main features of the 'Philosophy of Nature', they should perhaps be noticed.

As the subject matter of the 'Encyclopaedia' is ranged in order of complexity, we are safe in assuming that the fact that the 'Logic' precedes 'Nature' in the general lay-out of the work implies that Hegel regarded its subject matter as being less complex than that of the natural sciences. He thought therefore, that whereas the complexity relationships of categories might be investigated and fully understood without reference to natural phenomena, nature and spirit presuppose categories in the same way that geology presupposes chemistry and physics, and the law psychology and biology etc. The 'Logic' is in fact an attempt to establish the investigation of the relative complexity of categories, and the ordering of the resultant subject matter by means of the principles of levels, hierarchies and spheres, as a distinct discipline.

This point has been grasped in a fairly lucid manner by a number of commentators, who have then proceeded to criticize Hegel for illustrating the expositions of the 'Logic' by making copious references to the subject matters of 'Nature' and 'Spirit'.[3] This criticism has its origin in their failure to understand the nature of the categories and to distinguish between the subject matter and the structuralization of the 'Logic'. In attempting to reconstruct the first sphere of the 'Encyclopaedia' without reference to the 'Nature' and 'Spirit' of Hegel's day and to the developments that have taken place since, these commentators have indeed shown as complete a miscomprehension of the discipline Hegel was attempting to establish as those critics who have claimed that the categories are

[1] 'Hegel's Doctrine of Formal Logic' (Oxford, 1912) pp. 88–89; cf. his 'Hegel's Logic of World and Idea' (Oxford, 1929).

[2] W. Wallace 'Prolegomena to the study of Hegel's Philosophy' (Oxford, 1894) pp. 476–477.

[3] J. M. E. McTaggart 'A Commentary on Hegel's Logic' (Cambridge, 1910); W. T. Stace 'The Philosophy of Hegel' (Dover Publications, 1955).

nothing but the natural or spiritual phenomena from which they are supposed to be distinct.[1]

The categories of the 'Logic' stand in relation to natural and spiritual phenomena in something like the same way as do the principles of the dialectic noticed in the previous chapter. They are an integral part of these phenomena, and yet, on account of their greater simplicity, universality or generality, and on account of the complexity relationships in which they stand to one another as categories, they have also to be regarded as constituting a distinct sphere and as demanding treatment in a distinct discipline.[2] It may not be amiss to establish this point with reference to *measure*, which is fairly typical of the general range of categories assessed in the 'Logic'.[3] Hegel illustrates its significance by pointing out that water and minerals, when they are chemically analyzed, are found to be qualities conditioned by the measures of the quantitative ratios between the matters they contain; that the various kinds of plants and animals have certain fairly standard measurements which become less important as distinguishing features in less complex organisms, ammonites for example being both microscopic and as large as cart-wheels; that in Greek social ethics all human things, riches, honour and power, as well as joy and pain, had their definite measure, the transgression of which was regarded as leading to ruin and destruction; and that the category is used theologically when, as in the Psalms, God is said to have established the *bounds* of the sea and the land, the rivers and the hills, or when it is said that He is the measure of all things. In the slightly more complex category of *rule* or *standard*, an increase or diminution on a scale of degrees proceeds by arithmetical progression, and is only limited by abrupt transitions of a qualitative character. Hegel illustrates this category by pointing out that an arithmetical progression in numbers of vibrations constitutes a musical

[1] Friedrich Adolf Trendelenburg (1802–1872) 'Geschichte der Kategorienlehre' (Berlin, 1846); cf. his 'Logische Untersuchungen' (2 vols. Leipzig, 1862) pp. 38–42. A fairly balanced view of the matter is however to be found in Andrew *Seth* (Pringle-Pattison) (1856–1931), 'Hegelianism and Personality' (Edinburgh and London, 1887) Lecture III, and in an article by George Kent (1842–1892), a Norwegian clergyman of English descent; see 'Die Lehre Hegels vom Wesen der Erfahrung und ihre Bedeutung für das Erkennen' ('Christiania Videnskabs-Selskabs Forhandlinger' 1891 no. 5).

[2] The *dual* nature of all valid universals is brought out extremely well by R. I. Aaron in 'The Theory of Universals' (Oxford, 1967); see p. 240, 'We cannot then simply say that a universal is a natural recurrence. Any principle of grouping is a universal and we cannot identify principle of grouping with natural recurrence. This is an avowal that the question "What is a universal?" cannot be answered in one sentence, but needs two. *Universals are natural recurrences*; *universals are principles of grouping or classifying*.'

[3] §§ 107–111 of the 'Encyclopaedia'; see 'The Logic of Hegel' (tr. Wallace, Oxford, 1963) pp. 201–206, cf. 'Hegel's Science of Logic' (tr. Johnston and Struthers, 2 vols. London, 1961) vol. I pp. 345–393. McTaggart op. cit. ch. IV regards Hegel's treatment of the category as being invalid.

scale consisting of distinct notes; that degrees of oxidation distinguish the oxides of certain metals; that although the plucking out of a single hair will not make a horse tailless, the continuation of this operation will; that, 'in the matter of expenditure, there is a certain latitude within which a more or less does not matter; but when measure . . . is exceeded on one side or the other . . . good economy turns into avarice or prodigality'; and that, with regard to the territory and population of a state, 'we must not forget, that by continual increase or diminution . . . we finally get to a point where, apart from all other circumstances, this quantitative alteration alone necessarily draws with it an alteration in the quality of the constitution.'[1]

It will be apparent from this that Hegel regards measure and rule as *categories* simply because a comprehension of any one of the various natural and spiritual phenomena of which they constitute an integral part, does not provide a complete understanding of the part they play in comprehension as a whole; because they are, in fact, more general or universal than any of the particular instances in which they may be noticed. It will also be apparent that measure presupposes, for example, the categories of quality and quantity, and is itself the presupposition of rule, that it is in fact involved in complexity relationships with other categories. Consequently, it also constitutes a level in the *hierarchy* of categories expounded within the *sphere* of 'Logic', and, as Hegel shows, is itself a sphere containing levels and a hierarchy. Since the overall *structure* of the 'Logic' is identical with the overall structures of 'Nature' and 'Spirit', there is a somewhat loose and vague correspondence between the simplest categories of the 'Logic', the basic levels of 'Nature', and the most primitive stages of 'Spirit' etc., and Hegel occasionally calls attention to this in the course of these lectures.[2]

The subject matter of the 'Logic' is, therefore, as revisable as the subject matters of 'Nature' and 'Spirit', and must be as completely incomprehensible as the natural science and the spiritual activity assessed in the 'Encyclopaedia' to those who are unaware of its origins. Many of the categories recognized by Hegel are still in use, some are obsolete however, and not a few of the complexity relationships he formulates need revision in the light of the developments that have taken place since the work was published.[3]

[1] For a *recent* treatment of this category and a useful bibliographical note on the literature relating to it, see A. Pap 'An Introduction to the Philosophy of Science' (London 1963) ch. 8; cf. J. G. Kemeny 'A Philosopher looks at Science' (New York, 1964) ch. 8.

[2] § 254 Remark, § 274 Addition, § 337.

[3] Hegel wrote out three main versions of it, which are by no means identical: see 'Jenenser Logik Metaphysik und Naturphilosophie' (ed. G. Lasson, Leipzig, 1923), which dates from 1801–1802, 'The

Schelling, in the lectures he delivered at the University of Munich in 1827, was the first to point out that the formulation of the subject matter of the Hegel's 'Logic' presupposes the use of *intuition*, 'Hegel has attempted to erect his abstract logic *over* the philosophy of nature. He has imported into it the method of the philosophy of nature however; it is not difficult to imagine what had to be perpetrated in order that a method having nothing but nature as its content and the perception of nature as its guide might be raised into something *simply* logical; he was forced to reject and violate these forms of intuition and yet to proceed on the basis of them, and it is therefore by no means difficult to make the perfectly correct observation, that even in the first step of his logic Hegel presupposes intuition, and that without relying upon it, he could make no progress at all.'[1] The point of the initial categories of the 'Logic' is that they should constitute the simplest levels of their sphere however, not that they should be without presupposition. Within the 'Encyclopaedia' as a whole, the 'Logic' has the sphere of 'Spirit' as its antecedent, which implies that certain levels of general culture, spiritual insight and philosophical competence are necessary precondition for any precise formulation of logical categories.[2] What is more, Hegel never denies that it is intuition that provides the *subject matter* of the 'Encyclopaedia'. He parted ways with Schelling in that he realized that a distinction had to be drawn between intuition and rational thought, i.e. between subject matter and structuralization, 'We can assemble all the separate constituents of the flower, but this will not make the flower. Intuition has therefore been reinstated in the philosophy of nature, and set above reflection, but this gets us nowhere, because one cannot philosophize on the basis of intuition. Intuition has to be submitted to thought, so that what has been dismembered may be restored to simple universality through thought. This contemplated unity is the Notion, which contains the determinate differences simply as an immanent and self-moving unity. Philosophic universality is not indifferent to the determinations; it is the self-fulfilling universality, the diamantine identity, which at the same time holds difference within itself.'[3]

Formal logic constitutes two main levels within the third major hier-

Science of Logic' op. cit. which dates from 1812–1816, and the 'Encyclopaedia' 'Logic' (tr. Wallace) op. cit., which was first published in 1817 and revised in 1827 and 1830. Cf. J. B. Baillie 'The Origin and Significance of Hegel's Logic' (London, 1901).

[1] 'Werke' (ed. Schröter, 12 cols., Munich, 1927–1954) vol. 5 p. 208; cf. his 'Abhandlung über die Quelle der ewigen Wahrheiten' ('Akademie der Wissenschaften zu Berlin' 17th Jan. 1850), 'Werke' vol. 5 p. 765.

[2] See Hegel's 'Phenomenology of Mind' (1807, tr. Baillie, London, 1931); Jean Hyppolite 'Genèse et Structure de la Phénoménologie de l'Esprit de Hegel' (Paris, 1946). There is a competent survey of the main arguments of this work in G. R. G. Mure 'The Philosophy of Hegel' (London, 1965).

[3] § 246 Addition.

archy of the logical sphere,[1] and is therefore part of the *subject matter* of the 'Encyclopaedia'. The *principles* on which the 'Logic' is structuralized should therefore be very carefully distinguished from both categories and formal logic, and it is the failure to do this which accounts for most of the confusion in the attempts that have been made to assess and expound the significance of this part of the 'Encyclopaedia'.[2] The principles of levels, heirarchies and spheres are in fact employed consistently throughout the 'Logic' in precisely the same way as they are in the spheres of 'Nature' and 'Spirit', and with roughly the same amount of success and failure. Vilhelm Sjögren (1866–1929), so far as I am aware, was the first to recognize this, 'The method is so modified therefore, that the object's teleological determinateness becomes a basis for exposition, or, to use Kant's terminology, a foundation for the synthesis. As a result of the method as such therefore, the form is conceived rationalistically, but as a result of the object of this method, empirically. The state of correspondence between these concepts is to be recovered by the graded' (i.e. hierarchical) 'sublation of the state of opposition in which they stand to one another as the result of the object's form. The form of the object is determined by the concept of a level, but this concept does not actually determine the form of the subordinate stratum.'[3]

The transition from 'Logic' to 'Nature' is therefore no different from any other transition in the 'Encyclopaedia'. Hegel concludes the 'Logic' with the Idea, simply because it was the most complex level he was able to formulate in this sphere, the *category* which coincided most fully with the *principles* of the *Notion*, the fulfillment of the *dialect*. 'The Idea may be described in many ways. It may be called *reason* (and this is the proper philosophical signification of *reason*); *subject-object*; the *unity of that which is of an ideal nature* and *that which is of a real nature, of the finite and the infinite, of soul and body*; the *possibility which has its actuality in itself*; that, the *nature* of which can *only* be *grasped* as *existent* etc. All these descriptions apply,

[1] 'Encyclopaedia' §§ 160–192. Cf. H. S. Macran 'Hegel's Doctrine of Formal Logic' (Oxford, 1912).

[2] Of English commentators on the 'Logic', A. S. Pringle-Pattison (1856–1931) has come the closest to making these essential distinctions; see his 'Hegelianism and Personality' (Edinburgh and London, 1887) lectures III and IV. 'He (Hegel) presents everything synthetically, though it must first have been got analytically by an ordinary process of reflection upon the facts which are the common property of every thinker. Thus the notions with which the Logic deals admittedly form part and parcel of the apparatus of everyday thought, and the development which Hegel gives them is simply their systematic placing.'

[3] 'Om den dialektiska metodens ställning i Hegels logik' (Uppsala, 1887) p. 23, cf. p. 34. A similar but less succinct exposition of the basic principles of the 'Logic' is to be found in Betty Heimann's 'System und Methode in Hegels Philosophie' (Leipzig, 1927), 'Jede Philosophie ein Versuch ist näher an die funktionale Struktur der Vernunft heranzukommen.' (p. 474).

since the Idea contains all the relationships of the understanding, but contains them in their *infinite* self-return and self-identity.'[1] He begins 'Nature' with space,[2] simply because it was the least complex level recognized in the natural science of his day. The characterization of space as 'sensuous insensibility', i.e. as having a predominantly *logical* aspect, and as 'non-sensuous sensibility', i.e. as also having a predominantly *natural* aspect,[3] is by no means entirely irrelevant to the consideration of the logical antecedent of the three dimensions of classical geometry.[4] The *main* importance of the transition from 'Logic' to 'Nature' is however the major qualitative difference it initiates. According to Hegel, the distinguishing feature of the sphere concluded by means of the Idea is its *universality*, the categories being involved in but not confined to natural and spiritual phenomena, whereas the distinguishing feature of the sphere initiated by space is its *particularity*, the levels of nature consisting as they do of more or less tangible objects. Like all other transitions throughout the 'Encyclopaedia' this one is undoubtedly revisable, but it presents no particular difficulties once the basic principles of Hegel's system are understood.

Schelling was the first to concentrate upon the transition from 'Logic' to 'Nature' after having, perhaps wilfully, misrepresented the general significance of Hegel's work, and so far as I am aware, no one has tackled him fairly and squarely on the point, apart from Michelet.[5] Like most of those who have accepted his misrepresentation and reiterated his criticism, he concentrates upon the actual *wording* of § 244, 'There is nothing in the Logic that might change the world. Hegel *has* to reach actuality. In the Idea itself however, there is absolutely no necessity for further movement or for becoming anything else . . . This expression "let forth"—the Idea lets nature forth—is one of the strangest, most ambiguous and also therefore one of the least pinnable expressions behind which this philosophy withdraws at difficult junctures. Jakob Boehme says: the divine freedom vomits itself forth into nature. Hegel says: the divine Idea lets nature forth. What are we to understand by this letting forth?'[6] This implied in effect

[1] 'Encyclopaedia' § 214.
[2] op. cit. § 254.
[3] op. cit. § 254 Addition.
[4] Note I p. 307.
[5] See his foreword to these lectures.
[6] Munich lectures, 1827 op.cit. p. 223. When Schelling's disciple Herbert Beckers (1806–1889) published a translation of Victor Cousin's 'Fragments philosophiques' (Paris, 1833), Schelling wrote an introduction to it in which he repeated this criticism of Hegel. See 'Victor Cousin über französische und deutsche Philosophie' (Stuttgart and Tübingen, 1834); Schelling's 'Werke' op. cit. suppl. vol. 4 pp. 445–468. Cf. ch. e.

'Mit Worten lässt sich trefflich streiten.'

that the Hegelian system was panlogistic in intention, and that the philosophies of nature and spirit constituted attempts to *force* subject matter that was clearly open to valid non-logical interpretations into a preconceived and somewhat dubiously formulated series of logical categories. The sensitive and revisable relationships indicated and elicited by means of the principles of the dialectic, were therefore interpreted by those who were often as ignorant of the subject matter as they were of the structure of the 'Encyclopaedia', as constituting a rigid *deductive* system bent on laying down the law in domains of knowledge where even specialists laboured with humility and formulated theories with diffidence. Enthusiasts such as Hauptmann,[1] Hoffmann,[2] Jahn[3] and Marx, encouraged by the chorus of critics which the general acceptance of such an intepretation called forth, set about 'revising' Hegelianism by discarding its metaphysical presuppositions as irrelevancies, and applying their own conceptions of its general significance to those spheres or disciplines of which they happened to know something. Although the results of this were often ludicrous, they were, on occasions, effective and interesting. They could never be regarded as specifically Hegelian however.

The most deplorable outcome of these bars sinister in Hegelian pedigrees has undoubtedly been the aura of *finality* in which Marxists have been encouraged to invest their views on economics, sociology, politics and history, as a result of their supposedly Hegelian ancestry. It would be idle and ignoble to question the idealism and compassion of Marx, or to deny the psychological and political *effectiveness* of his version of dialectic. It is however doubtful whether his writings would have been entirely ineffective had he never heard of Hegel. Their intellectual influence must moreover be criticized from an Hegelian standpoint by pointing out that they are relevant to an important but limited sphere of knowledge and activity, within which their validity is probably only relative, and that

[1] Moritz Hauptmann (1792–1868), in 'Die Natur der Harmonik und Metrik' (Leipzig, 1853), Eng. tr. W. E. Heathcote 'The Nature of Harmony and Metre' (London, 1888), attempted to reconstruct musical harmony dialectically from 'the three directly intelligible intervals' of the octave, the fifth and the major third.

[2] Karl Richard Hoffmann (1797–1877) studied at Erlangen and Berlin, and in 1819 began to teach medicine in the Prussian capital. He was subsequently professor of pathology, materia medica and hygiene at Landshut and Würzburg. In his 'Vergleichende Idealpathologie, Ein Versuch, die Krankheiten als Rückfälle der Idee des Lebens auf tiefere normale Lebensstufen darzustellen' (Stuttgart 1834, 2nd ed. 1839), he suggested that certain human diseases might be regarded as relapses from the human to certain animal *levels*. Thus, *scrofula* is interpreted as a sinking to the insect level, *rickets* as a sinking to the level of mollusca, and *epilepsy* as a relapse to the level of oscillatoria.

[3] Ferdinand Jahn (1804–1859) of Meiningen put forward views resembling Hoffmann's in his, 'Die abnormen Zustände des menschlichen Lebens als Nachbildungen und Wiederholungen normaler Zustände des Thierlebens' (Eisenach, 1842).

they in no way qualify those who read or act on them for making pronouncements upon knowledge or activity as a whole. Communism has, however, often attempted to influence activity and research at levels to which the effectiveness or desirability of its economic, social or political doctrines is very largely irrelevant. A professing communist is not, of course, confined to having valid views only on economic, social or political matters, and he may well be justified in bearing in mind such things as biological, aesthetic or religious factors when attempting to further his economic, social or political ends. Pursuing these ends does not in itself provide any *final* confirmation of his opinions on anything however, and he would in fact be better advised to admit that the validity of his views on most subjects is probably as uncertain, limited and fragmentary as those of anyone else. Communists are not of course the only politically-minded people who would do well to bear this in mind.

Tracing the effect of Schelling's interpretation of Hegel upon the intellectual history of the last century and a quarter would therefore be an extremely worthwhile undertaking. An analysis of the misrepresentations it has involved, the critics it has inspired[1] and the errors it has perpetuated is, for instance, an essential pre-condition for any constructive outcome in the present dialogue between Christians and Marxists.

The 'Philosophy of Nature', like the rest of the 'Encyclopaedia', is therefore in a sense dualistic, since a distinction has to be drawn between its subject matter and its structure. The principles of this structure having been indicated and established, and the relationship in which 'Nature' stands to the sphere of 'Logic' clarified, it remains for us to take note of some of the main features of Hegel's treatment of the subject matter in this part of the 'Encyclopaedia'. The sources from which Hegel drew his information on the natural sciences have been indicated in the commentary, and are in no way remarkable. He often refers to the standard works and textbooks of his day, and he evidently read the main scientific periodicals in German, French and English. There is some evidence that the bulk

[1] Christian Hermann Weisse (1801–1886) was evidently the first to develop a valid line of criticism for himself by presenting Hegelianism as being panlogistic rather than dialectical: see 'Ueber den gegenwärtigen Standpunkt der philosophischen Wissenschaft' (Leipzig, 1829); 'Grundzüge der Metaphysik' (Hamburg, 1835); 'Hegel und das Newtonische Gesetz der Kraftwirkung' ('Zeitschrift für Philosophie und spekulative Theologie' vol. XIII, pp. 1–36, Tübingen, 1844). The level of criticism to which the 'dialectic' is submitted in K. R. Popper's 'Conjectures and Refutations. The Growth of Scientific Knowledge' (London, 1963) ch. 15 is evidently unavoidable, and has a pedigree going back, so far as I am aware, to 'Der verderbliche Einfluss der Hegelschen Philosophie' (Leipzig 1852), by 'Antibarbarus Logicus'. Cf. J. E. Erdmann 'A History of Philosophy' (tr. Hough, 3 vols., London, 1892–8), vol. II, pp. 686–689 (§ 329, 3); J. B. Baillie 'Hegel's Logic' (London, 1901) ch. X.

of his reading in the natural sciences and the formation of many of his distinctive views took place between 1800 and 1815, but he also quotes many books and articles published later than this. In the treatment of light for example (§ 278 Remark), he refers to the discovery of its polarization in 1808[1] but not to the momentous developments in wave theory initiated after 1816 by D. F. J. Arago (1786–1853) and A. J. Fresnel (1788–1827). In the treatment of rain (§ 286), he refers to Lichtenberg's attack on the 'Prüfung der Theorie des Herrn Deluc vom Regen' (Berlin, 1795) by J. D. O. Zylius (1764–1820), as if it had settled a controversy, whereas, by the 1820's, Lichtenberg's views were no longer regarded as worthy of serious consideration. In dealing with the views of H. A. Goeden (1785–1826) on disease (§ 371), he evidently has in mind a systematization of diseases still based on the 'Synopsis nosologiae methodicae' (Edinburgh, 1769) by William Cullen (1710–1790), and he fails to see that Goeden's later work was in tune with the progressive developments of the 1820's.

His actual *mistakes* are few and far between, and bearing in mind Croce's ignorant and ill-founded criticism[2] and the extraordinary reputation of this work, they should perhaps be clearly recorded. The motion of anything but a vertically trajected projectile, even if air resistance and the motion of the earth are not taken into consideration, is a parabola, and never becomes 'simple fall' (§ 266 Addition)[3]. The mean distance of the moon from the earth is not sixty times the earth's diameter (§ 270 Addition).[4] Hegel should have realized that the Moon must turn upon its axis (§ 279 Remark). At that time fourteen satellites of the planets had been definitely identified (Earth 1, Jupiter 4, Saturn 7, Uranus 2), and there was some pretty conclusive evidence that those moving around Jupiter and Saturn had axial rotations.[5] There is therefore no excuse for his having denied the existence of satellitic axial rotation. When he says (§ 300 Addition) that 'The transmission of sound by the earth is remarkable, by putting one's ear to the ground for example, it is possible to hear a cannonade taking place ten or twenty miles away', he is grossly underestimating the

[1] É. L. Malus (1775–1812); see 'Bulletin des Sciences de la Société Philomathique de Paris' vol. I pp. 266–269 (Dec. 1808).

[2] B. Croce 'What is living and what is dead in the philosophy of Hegel' (1906, tr. Ainslie, London, 1915) ch. VIII. He blames Hegel for *rejecting* the natural sciences and yet holding on to their coat-tails. 'It sometimes seems as if Hegel was not in full possession of his thought' (p. 191).

[3] It should, in all fairness, be noted that the passage in which Hegel makes this statement was taken by Michelet from the Jena note-book of 1805/6.

[4] Hegel may have been misled here by the wording of Newton's 'Principia' bk. III prop. iv theorem 4.

[5] 'Phil. Trans. Roy. Soc.' 1790 p. 427; 1792 p. 1; 1797 p. 332.

distance. The cannonade at Mainz in 1792 was heard very clearly near Einbeck, 165 miles away for example, and in 1809 the cannonading of Heligoland was heard near Hanover, 175 miles away. He should not have paid attention to the ornithological fictions of Oliver Goldsmith when he found them refuted by travellers who had actually heard the birds of the Americas singing sweetly (§ 303 Addition).[1] The facts he gives concerning Lorenz Oken (1779–1851) and the theory of the vertebral analogies of the skull (§ 354 Addition) are not strictly accurate. He seems to have based his views on the subject simply on hearsay, and before making them public, should have investigated the matter more carefully. The lizards mentioned in § 356 Addition were discovered at Elden (Eleveden) in Suffolk, not Eldon, and were fifty, not fifteen feet below the surface of the ground.[2] In quoting what G. H. von Schubert (1780–1860) had to say on the testicles of the male Gadfly (§ 368 Addition) he failed to notice a typographical error listed in the 'errata' of the book.[3] In the same passage he quotes a French source in support of the conclusions J. F. Ackermann (1765–1815) had reached as the result of his investigations into the sexual organs of hermaphrodites,[4] and mistranslates 'veramontanum' as 'crista galli'. He does at least question this translation however. He is referring to the elongated cutaneous eminence on the inner surface of the urethra, which occurs where the bulbous part of this tube passes through the prostate. In English writings of the time this was known as the caput gallinaginis or verumontanum, and to German anatomists as 'der Schnepfenkopf'. Hegel may have had in mind the 'Anatomia corporis humani' (Louvain 1683, Germ. tr. Leipzig, 1704) tab. X by Philipp Verheijen (1648–1710) however, in which the feature is referred to as the 'crista galli gallinacei'. 'Göde' (§ 371 Addition) was not the name of Hans Adolf Goeden (1785–1826), and the gentleman did not deserve the drubbing Hegel gave him for reviewing the paragraphs on medicine in the Heidelberg 'Encyclopaedia' (1817) in a critical manner (§ 371 Addition).[5]

[1] See Goldsmith's 'An History of the Earth and Animated Nature' (London, 1774) V pp. 324–325; cf. J. R. Moore 'Goldsmith's degenerate song-birds, an eighteenth century fallacy in ornithology' ('Isis' 1942–43 pp. 324–327).

[2] Alexander Tilloch's 'Philosophical Magazine and Journal' (vol. 48 p. 469, Dec. 1816). The original account of this discovery is in the unpublished proceedings of the 'Bath Philosophical Society' (1816).

[3] 'Ahndungen einer allgemeinen Geschichte des Lebens' (3 vols. Leipzig, 1806, 1807, 1821) vol. I p. 185. This volume was published *while* Hegel was lecturing on the subject at Jena.

[4] 'Infantis androgyni historia et ichnographia' (Jena, 1805), i.e. also published *while* Hegel was lecturing.

[5] 'Critische Bemerkungen ueber Hegel's Begriff vom Wesen der Krankheit und der Heilung' ('Isis' ed. Oken, Jena, 1819 pp. 1127–1138).

An apparent howler on Hegel's part will often be found to have a highly respectable source in the scientific literature of the time, and to be by no means unreasonable once the contemporary state of knowledge and research is borne in mind. In § 330 Addition for instance, Hegel says that, '*Ammonia* has a particular peculiarity, for on the one hand it can be demonstrated that its base is nitrogen, its other constituent being oxygen, but that it also has a metallic base in *ammonium*'. Since the true nature and composition of ammonia were well known by the close of the eighteenth century[1] this characterization might appear to be inexcusable. It is almost certainly based on a paper by Sir Humphry Davy (1778–1829) however.[2] At that time ammonia, potash and soda were taken to be the three alkalies. Davy's discovery that the last two were 'metallic oxides' led him to postulate a *metallic* base to ammonia, and to suspect that the gas might also contain oxygen.[3]

On one occasion at least, political considerations evidently influenced what should have been a purely scientific judgement. In § 355 Addition, Hegel quotes M. F. X. Bichat (1771–1802) in support of the proposition that intelligence has little to do with physical prowess, 'Animals leap with the greatest skill from crag to crag, where the very slightest slip would send them toppling into the abyss, and move with astonishing precision on surfaces scarcely as wide as the extremities of their limbs. Even the ungainliest of animals do not stumble so often as man'.[4] Hegel then proceeds to draw the conclusion that physical is necessarily gained at the expense of spiritual ability, 'When people acquire spiritual and other kinds of aptitudes, and develop a fluent style, ability in music and the fine arts, technical skills, the art of fencing etc., the equilibrium is lost. On the other hand, cruder and purely bodily exercises such as drill, gymnastics, running, climbing, tight-rope walking, jumping and vaulting, preserve this equilibrium. Activities such as these are not conducive to aptitudes of the first kind however, and as they tend to be devoid of thought, they are generally obstacles to mental composure.' There seems to be little justification for this view, and Hegel's entertaining it may well be due to the suspicion with which physical culture societies were regarded by the

[1] See C. W. Scheele (1742–1786) 'Chemische Abhandlung von der Luft und dem Feuer' (Uppsala and Leipzig, 1777, Eng. tr. Kirwan, London, 1780) vol. I p. 196, vol. II p. 75.

[2] 'On the Decomposition and Composition of the Fixed Alkalies' ('Phil. Trans. Roy. Soc.' 1808).

[3] For a sympathetic exposition of Davy's view on this, see Thomas Thomson (1773–1852) 'A System of Chemistry' (5 vols. Edinburgh, 1810) vol. II pp. 4–21; cf. W. Henry (1774–1836) 'Experiments on Ammonia' ('Phil. Trans. Roy. Soc.' 1809 p. 130).

[4] 'Recherches physiologiques sur la Vie et la Mort' (4th ed., ed. Magendie, Paris, 1822) p. 41.

Berlin establishment in the decade following the War of Liberation and the downfall of Napoleon.[1]

Several of the theories defended or accepted by Hegel were criticized at the time and are now very largely defunct. James Hutton (1726–1797) for example, in a paper read to the Royal Society of Edinburgh in 1784, initiated the modern explanation of rain by suggesting that its formation must be regulated by the humidity of the air and the causes which promote mixtures of different aerial currents in the higher atmosphere.[2] J. A. Deluc (1727–1817) contended that the *amounts* of water discharged by the air on certain occasions are too great to be explained from Hutton's hypothesis. He objected strongly to the theory that water is *dissolved* in the air, and contended that when water evaporates, it changes into a new kind of gas, which cannot be detected hygroscopically, but which can change back into water.[3] To many meteorologists of the day, this contention appeared to be confirmed by the *synthesis* of water from 'dephlogisticated' and 'inflammable' air,[4] and by the *decomposition* of water by means of electric sparks, which was first brought about by the Dutch chemist Martin van Marum (1750–1837), working with the great frictional machine in the Teyler Institute at Haarlem in 1787.[5] Hegel accepted Deluc's view and rejected Hutton's (§ 286). In his assessment of animal acids (§ 334 Addition), he makes mention of 'blood acid'. If he has in mind the work of Raymund de Vieussens (1641–1716),[6] who claimed to have discovered an acid in the four ounces of residue left from the evaporation of fifty pounds of blood, he was most certainly out of touch with current research on the subject, for this discovery was then generally acknowledged to have been putative.[7] It is possible however that he is referring to the 'acidum sanguinis' prepared by J. J. Winterl (1732–1809), by slowly

[1] In 1811 F. L. Jahn (1778–1852) founded the first German gymnastic club at Hasenheide near Berlin. He and J. C. F. Guths-Muths (1759–1839) developed such clubs as part of a plan for national regeneration during the French occupation, and many of his gymnasts enlisted in Blücher's army. After the war his movement came into conflict with the authorities cultivating the Holy Alliance. As a result of the Carlsbad decrees (1819) 'curators' such as Hegel's friend C. F. L. Schultz (1781–1834), were appointed to keep watch on the universities, and all gymnastic clubs and student associations were banned.

[2] 'The theory of rain' ('Trans. Roy. Soc. Edin.' vol. I p. 41, 1788).

[3] 'Idées sur la météorologie' (2 vols. London, 1786–1787).

[4] Henry Cavendish (1731–1810) 'Experiments on Air' ('Phil. Trans. Roy. Soc.' Jan. 1784 pp. 119–153).

[5] 'Verhandelingen uitgegeeven door Teylers Tweede Genootschap' (Haarlem, 1787) Stuk iv p. 144.

[6] 'Deux dissertations ... La première touchant l'extraction du sel acide du sang' (Montpellier, 1698).

[7] J. F. John (1782–1847) 'Handwörterbuch der allgemeinen Chemie' (4 vols. Leipzig and Altenburg, 1817–1819) vol. I pp. 115–116; J. F. Pierer (1767–1832) 'Anatomisch-physiologisches Realwörterbuch' vol. I p. 887 (Leipzig and Altenburg, 1816).

treating blood and potash in a sealed container without bringing them to a red heat. According to Winterl alcohol forms a salt with the residue out of which hydrochloric acid precipitates blood acid in the form of a curdled cheese. This experiment remained a matter of interest to chemists until the 1820's.[1] In § 346 Addition Hegel accepts the view that the 'long plumule' of the Trapa Natans or the Four-horned Water Caltrops is *foliar* in nature. This theory had first been put forward by C. L. Willdenow (1765–1812), professor of botany at Berlin,[2] and was widely regarded as being doubtful on account of its necessitating the conclusion that this plant is devoid of a *radicle*. The objections then raised against it have since been confirmed.[3]

Many of the scientific views assessed by Hegel in the 'Philosophy of Nature', although accepted by him and regarded as being free from radical controversies by his contempories, are now only of historial interest. The manner in which they are presented in this work, excepting of course the structuralization to which they are submitted, is therefore of no particular interest, and simply belongs to the general history of the natural sciences. On occasions, Hegel also *criticizes* the accepted views of his day however, and since those who have noticed this have not always been as intimately acquainted with the principles of the 'Encyclopaedia' or the history of the natural sciences as one might have wished, it may be of interest to look in some detail at some of the issues he raises.

An examination of the axioms on which 'pure' mathematics was supposed to rest at the beginning of the last century, makes it abundantly clear that a radical reassessment of them was necessary before the distinction between pure and applied mathematics could be drawn with any certainty.[4] Hegel was certainly justified in arguing therefore (§ 259) that since the mathematics of his day involved the *presupposition* of certain axioms, capable of philosophical assessment, but in fact taken up more or less at random from 'concrete nature', it was not pure in any rigorous or truly philosophical sense.[5]

Eighteenth century astronomers and physicists had tended to ignore the distinction Newton had drawn between the mathematical *representation*

[1] J. C. Schuster (1777–1839) 'System der dualistischen Chemie des Prof. Jakob Joseph Winterly (2 vols. Berlin, 1807) vol. I pp. 398–399. Cf. J. J. Berzelius (1779–1848) 'Om sammansättningar af svafelhaltigen blåsyra salter' ('Kungliga Svenska Vetenskaps Akademiens Handlingar' 1820) pp. 82–99: 'Schweigger's Journal' 1820 vol. 30 pp. 1–67.

[2] P. Usteri (1768–1831) 'Annalen der Botanick' (vol. xvii p. 19, 1788).

[3] Agnes Arber 'Water Plants, a study of aquatic angiosperms' (Cambridge, 1920) p. 207.

[4] See G. S. Klügel (1739–1812) 'Mathematisches Wörterbuch' (7 vols. Leipzig, 1803–1836) vol. III pp. 602–613.

[5] See George Boole (1815–1865) 'An Investigation of the Laws of Thought' (London, 1854) for the subsequent development of this criticism. Leibniz and J. H. Lambert (1728–1777) had both attempted, not very successfully, to develop systems of mathematical logic.

of problems and the physical *reality* of the situations being dealt with.[1] Hegel had seen the importance of this even at the beginning of his career,[2] and often points out that the failure to bear it in mind was hindering advances in the mechanics of his day (§ 266). He praises J. L. Lagrange (1736–1813) for example, for establishing a clear distinction between the purely abstract mode of regarding *functions*, and their applicability to mechanical problems (§ 267).[3] It is indeed his intense awareness of the difference in *quality* between predominantly mathematical thinking and the various levels of complexity to which it is more or less applicable, which constitutes the main value and originality of his treatment of 'Mechanics' in the 'Encyclopaedia'. It should be remembered however, that in this section at least, he criticizes the eighteenth century *interpreters* of Newton rather than Newton himself. This is made particularly clear by the most important and original exposition of the 'Mechanics', the assessment of *gravitation* in § 269. Even the definitions and axioms with which Newton begins the 'Mathematical Principles', admirable and serviceable though they are, are by no means free from difficulties.[4] What is more, he was not primarily concerned with a systematic assessment of his fields of enquiry. Despite its many merits therefore, his work cannot be said to promote any satisfactory degree of precision in the interrelating of *qualitatively* distinct fields of physical enquiry. Its greatness lies rather, in the clarity and vigour with which certain problems are brought within the scope of mathematical calculation. The concept of *force* was one of the means he employed to this end. Even if we allow that he distinguished between its heuristic value and its physical reality however, his use of it in the 'Mathematical Principles' in order to relate the *various* phenomena dealt with to the central principle of the law of gravitation, has to be criticized on account of its having led so easily to the assumption that these phenomena could be exhaustively investigated and fully understood by means of a *single* technique.[5] Hegel recognizes that the law of gravitation embodies the most *comprehensive* generalization the science of his day could make about simply material bodies. He also realizes however, that subordinate to it are

[1] C. Isenkrahe 'Das Räthsel von der Schwerkraft' (Brunswick, 1879); A. Koyré 'Newtonian Studies' (London, 1965).

[2] See his inaugural dissertation 'De Orbitis Planetarum' (Jena, 1801): note 1 p. 372.

[3] 'Théorie des fonctions analytiques' (Paris, 1797). This distinction may be regarded as the starting point of the theory of functions as developed by A. L. Cauchy (1789–1857), G. F. B. Riemann (1826–1866) and K. Weierstrass (1815–1897).

[4] Notes I pp. 308, 319, 321, 323, 324, 334, 336, 349.

[5] A. Koyré op. cit. p. 163, 'Eighteenth-century thought became reconciled to the ununderstandable—with very few exceptions. . . . Later, the problem was very successfully hidden in the concept of the field.'

several fields of *specific* enquiry in which the law itself is not fully apparent. This leads him to treat geometry, arithmetic, motion, matter, gravity, fall etc. as involving disciplines and studies less complex in subject matter and limited in scope than enquiry into the nature of *universal* gravitation itself. Similarly, he takes the solar system to involve still more comprehensive generalizations (Kepler's laws) on account of the *particularity* of its component bodies and the complexity of their motions (§ 270).

The widespread criticism to which the Newtonian calculus was submitted during the eighteenth century,[1] and the fact that Newton himself admitted that bk. I prop. i theorem I of the 'Mathematical Principles' gives rise to a conic section in general rather than an ellipse in particular,[2] was taken by Hegel to be further evidence of the fact that Kepler's first law is essentially more complex than the law of gravitation as such, and that the attempt to *deduce* it from the latter is therefore futile.[3]

Most eighteenth and early nineteenth century text-books attempted to explain the perpendicularity of elevation solely by the ordinary laws of refraction.[4] Hegel's criticism of them, so far as I am aware, was entirely original. By refusing to accept the purely mechanical 'explanations' of his day, and insisting upon what he calls 'the advanced spirituality' of refraction, he may not have added anything to scientific knowledge, but he did at least contribute towards keeping the way open for the demonstration, on the basis of the undulatory theory, that refraction may be more satisfactorily explained from the fact that the *velocity* of light is inversely proportional to the refractive index of the medium through which it passes.[5]

The most famous sections of this work are concerned with a criticism of Newton's 'Opticks', and a defence of Goethe's 'Farbenlehre' (§ 320). It was this criticism rather than the implications of Hegel's general manner of thinking which gave rise to the friendship between the two men. The most worthwhile approach to this subject is undoubtedly that of the *physicist* unblinkered by the presuppositions of his particular field,[6] and

[1] Note I p. 351,

[2] op. cit. bk. I sect. ii.

[3] See also the note on 'De Orbitis Planetarum' (Jena, 1801) I p. 372. Cf. H. C. Corben and Philip Stehle 'Classical Mechanics' (2nd ed. New York and London, 1960) p. 93, 'The most important instance of central motion is that under the influence of an inverse square law of force. This law comprises both gravitational *and electrostatic forces*; the electrostatic forces may be either attractive or repulsive, whereas gravitational forces are always attractive.'

[4] See for example, Charles Hutton (1737–1823) 'A Mathematical and Philosophical Dictionary' (2 vols. London, 1795) vol. II p. 347.

[5] § 318; see the commentary.

[6] Hermann von Helmholtz 'Vorträge und Reden' (4th ed. 2 vols. Brunswick, 1896) vol. I pp. 23–47; Werner Heisenberg 'Wandlungen in den Grundlagen der Naturwissenschaft' (4th ed. Leipzig, 1943) pp. 58–76.

from the physicist's point of view, Goethe's basic fault lies in his rejection of Newton's proposition,[1] that the various colours of bodies arise from their reflecting most copiously this or that kind of light ray.[2] This rejection forced him to deal with the various appearances of colour as involving physiological, physical, chemical and even organic factors, which were not only inessential to the treatment of colour *as such*, but which were not to be satisfactorily explained by the physiology, physics, chemistry and organics of his day, and which were *certainly* not to be explained simply in terms of the opposition between light and darkness.[3]

The great merit of his work in this field is that it consistently exhibits colour as an experience involving *concrete appearances*, although his attempt to refute Newton would seem to imply either that he regarded a purely physical interpretation of colour as being indefensible and unwarranted, or that he considered the 'archetypal phenomenon' to be justified on purely physical grounds. As a *purely physical* explanation of colour however, Newton's theory would appear to be immensely superior to Goethe's, for it still constitutes the broad basis of all modern physical research in the fields of light and optics. When Goethe published 'Zur Farbenlehre', Young's revival of wave theory had yet to be justified, and Malus' 'polarization' constituted the very latest discovery in this field. During the next fifteen years, while Hegel was teaching in Nuremberg, and lecturing at Heidelberg and Berlin, the work done by Biot, Brewster, Arago Fraunhofer and Fresnel etc. brought about the virtual completion of the *geometrical* part of wave theory, and prepared the way for Maxwell's *dynamical* interpretation of light. Goethe chose either to ignore these developments or to attempt a refutation of them in the light of his 'archetypal phenomenon'. Hegel justified his attitude. How then are we to assess Goethe's influence upon Hegel's treatment of light and colours?

Goethe's theory appealed to Hegel because it made it comparatively easy to work out a hierarchical exposition of colour in which justice could be done to both its physical and *spiritual* significance.[4] For Hegel, this spiritual significance involved not simply the 'psychic' factor mentioned by Schopenhauer in his criticism of Goethe,[5] but also the 'intelligible' factor of a dialectical interpretation, employing the fundamental antithesis exhibited by the 'archetypal phenomenon'. Had he accepted Newton's

[1] 'Opticks' bk. I pt. 2 prop. 10.

[2] 'Zur Farbenlehre' ('Polemischer Teil' ed. Matthaei, Weimar, 1958), §§ 610–677.

[3] i.e. the 'archetypal phenomenon'.

[4] See his letter to Goethe, Feb. 20, 1821; printed in Goethe's 'Zur Naturwissenschaft Überhaupt' vol. I sect. iv pp. 212–214, 1962 ed.

[5] 'Goethes Werke—Hamburger Ausgabe' (3rd ed. 1960) vol. XIII pp. 612–613.

theory that white light is a compound of the colours of the spectrum, his treatment of colour would have been much more closely juxtaposed to his treatment of light, and what is more, much more difficult to interpret dialectically. According to Goethe's theory however, it is the various *circumstances* in which light and darkness are combined which give rise to colour. These circumstances involve a *complexity* of physical factors, and consequently, as Hegel took light to constitute the *simplest* level of physics (§ 275–278), he did not treat colour until he had worked out the dialectical exposition of these *further* physical levels which he considered to be involved in its production.

Although this approach is rather more sophisticated than Goethe's, it reproduces many of his errors. It fails for example, to treat colour *as such*, and while honestly purporting to be an essentially physical doctrine, actually misinterprets physical phenomena by bringing psychic and metaphysical considerations into an assessment of them. However, Hegel was undoubtedly convinced that Goethe had refuted Newton on *purely physical grounds*, and was therefore not aware that at this juncture the coincidence of the dialectical method and the archetypal phenomenon was bogus. It has to be admitted therefore, that in the light of his system and knowledge of the facts, he was justified in *placing* and *treating* colour as he did. Consequently, although the treatment of colour is not *intrinsically* erroneous, it is unsatisfactory, not only because Hegel erred in his assessment of the physics of his day, but because he violated (though inadvertently) an important principle of his own system, by introducing *psychic* factors at a level which should have been devoted solely to the treatment of physical phenomena.

In that it consistently exhibits colour as an *experience* involving concrete appearances, Goethe's theory is certainly not without its merits however, and Hegel often shows that he was aware of its true importance. Had he also been aware of Goethe's shortcomings as a *physicist*, he might very easily have anticipated Heinsenberg (loc. cit) by converting the apparent contradiction between the Newtonian and Goethean theories into an exposition of their *complementarity*. His system was well adapted to help him do this; in accordance with its principles, Newton's theory should have been assessed in the 'Philosophy of Nature' and Goethe's presented in the initial stages of the 'Philosophy of Spirit'.

Bearing in mind the state of knowledge at the time, and the sources upon which Hegel draws, it has to be admitted that he gives a perfectly competent and plausible exposition of plant anatomy (§ 346). At the turn of the century, Sprengel, Mirbel, Treviranus and Link had revived interest in the nature and origin of vessels and in the functions of the various tissues, and as a result of their work, these features came to play a role in botanical research which was out of all proportion to their real significance in the construction of the vascular plant. What is more, plant anatomists began to develop a false confidence in the conclusiveness of their researches.[1] By sharpening the antithesis between cells and their 'fluid content' in the cellular tissue, between 'life-vessels' and 'vital-sap' in the vascular system, and between spiral-vessels and wood-sap in the assimilative system, Hegel seems to be preparing the way for the discovery that the vessels also have their origin in cells.[2]

A similar criticism of current views subsequently borne out by later developments is to be found in the remark (§ 353 Addition), dating from 1805–1806, that, 'The sphenoidal bone has a tendency to dominate the centre entirely however, and to completely reduce the skull-bones to a surface which lacks a centre of its own.' S. T. von Sömmerring (1755–1830), in the standard anatomical work of the time,[3] had suggested that it was not a *separate* bone *supporting* the bones of the skull, but a mere *extension* of the occipital bone. Many early nineteenth century anatomists accepted this new interpretation of it, and spoke either of the 'basilary' (Grundbein) or of the 'spheno-occipital bones'.[4] Hegel, like later anatomists, rejected this view.

On occasions he criticizes current views and has been proved correct for reasons other than those he bases his argument on. In § 359 Remark for example, he rejects the opinions of medical writers such as the later Brunonians, Röschlaub and the followers of Schelling, who had made various attempts to explain disease in purely *chemical* terms.[5] He was ready to admit that work of this kind had its value (§ 365), but he objected to its being interpreted as providing a full explanation of organic phenomena. He based this objection on his definition of the Notion of living being (§ 337), according to which the *unity* of the organism is *compatible* with the positing of distinct and transitory (e.g. chemical) moments within it. By the sixties of the last century, the founding of microbiology by

[1] R. H. J. Dutrochet (1776–1847) 'Recherches anatomiques et physiologiques' (Paris, 1824) p. 8, 'Que pourrait-on, en effet, attendre de nouveau de l'observation microscopique des organes des végétaux ...?'

[2] M. J. Schleiden (1804–1881) 'Grundzüge der wissenschaftlichen Botanik' (Leipzig, 1842–1843).

[3] 'Vom Baue des menschlichen Körpers' (6 pts. Frankfurt, 1791–1796) 'Knochenlehre' p. 109 note.

[4] J. F. Meckel (1781–1833) 'Handbuch der menschlichen Anatomie' (4 vols. Halle and Berlin, 1815–1820) § 528.

[5] Cf. B. Hirschel 'Geschichte des Brown'schen Systems und der Erregungstheorie' (Leipzig, 1846).

Pasteur, the discoveries made by Lister and I. Semmelweis (1818–1865) in the field of antiseptic surgery, and the advances made in medical entomology by R. Leuckart (1822–1898) etc. had fully substantiated Hegel's position in so far as he had objected on principle to chemical interpretations of nervous fevers. However, although this subsequent research showed *why* this objection was justified, it did not bear out his reasons for making it, in so far as these reasons were based upon empirical data (cf. § 371).

It is in the *transitions* from one level to the next, in the actual juxtaposings of subject matters, that some of the most fascinating features of the 'Philosophy of Nature' are to be found. As Laszlo Tisza has shown,[1] an important part of a scientist's work consists in assessing, examining and revising these relationships. Scientific breakthroughs occur when discoveries necessitate the revision of the recognized structure of knowledge, the reassessment of complexity relationships. Hegel evidently took immense care over formulating this aspect of the principles he employed throughout the 'Encyclopaedia'. Although many of the transitions to be found in this work were widely recognized at the time and still bear directly upon the general state of knowledge, an understanding of not a few of them demands an intimate acquaintance with extremely specialized and hopelessly dated levels of natural science, and one naturally wonders whether the undergraduates at Jena, Heidelberg and Berlin were equipped to the extent of being able to see the significance of them. In § 314 Addition for example, Hegel concludes the exposition of magnetism and formulates the transition to crystallography by mentioning the ice-spicula. The point he is making here involves a possible relationship between the figuration of a magnetic field,[2] the embryonic aqueous crystallization of hail, sleet and snow,[3] and the crystalline structure of metals and minerals.[4] The ice-spicula is taken to be the most complex expression of magnetic figuration and the simplest level of crystallization. The hierarchical sequence is carefully indicated therefore, but since the knowledge

[1] 'The Conceptual Structure of Physics' ('Reviews of Modern Physics' vol. 35, no. 1, pp. 151–185, Jan. 1963).

[2] See Sir Humphry Davy's numerous papers on the chemical action involved in the functioning of the voltaic pile in 'Phil. Trans. Roy. Soc.' 1807–1810; Michael Faraday on magnetic 'lines of force' in 'Experimental Researches in Electricity' (3 vols. London, 1839, 1844, 1855) § 3237.

[3] 'Jenenser Realphilosophie' 1803/4 I p. 70; 1805/6 II p. 54. Crystallization was supposed to have its origin in an 'invisible germ' or 'constructive force' in water; see J. B. L. de Romé de l'Isle (1736–1790) 'Cristallographie' (3 vols. Paris, 1783) vol. I p. 13.

[4] J. J. Bernhardi (1774–1850) 'Ueber das Kristallisationssystem der chemischen Elemente' ('Schweigger's Journal' 1817 vol. XXI i p. 7). The crystalline structure of metals was fairly well confirmed in Hegel's day; note II p. 334.

of the time had not been consolidated, the value of the transition is suggested but not laboured. A similarly esoteric but well-founded transition is that made in § 321 from colour to odorous matter.[1] It is often the case that well established and widely accepted major transitions from one level to another provide the general framework for plausible and highly original minor ones. The treatment of sound in §§ 300–302 is a good example of this. E. F. F. Chladni (1756–1817), in 'Die Akustik' (Leipzig, 1802), had evidently suggested the transition from cohesion to sound, and J. W. Ritter (1776–1810), through his 'Fragmente aus dem Nachlasse eines jungen Physikers' (2 vols. Heidelberg, 1810), may well have influenced the formulation of the transition from sound to heat. There is no evidence however that the fascinating hierarchical exposition of sound itself had any counterpart in contemporary thinking.

Enough has been said to make it evident that the 'Philosophy of Nature', far from being an arbitrary and irresponsible exposition of partially understood subject matter, is a sensitively structuralized, deeply informed and infinitely rewarding assessment of the whole range of early nineteenth century science. Now that its sources have been indicated and explained and its main features clarified, the reader is at liberty to explore its details to his heart's content. It is to be hoped that those qualified may even be tempted to bring sections of it up to date, and to review its structure and its subject matter in the light of current knowledge.

The reader of recent books on the philosophy of science will probably be struck by the almost complete absence of epistemological issues in Hegel's work. To some extent this is due, as we have noticed, to his formulation of the sphere of 'Logic', in which the *universal* thought determinations or categories involved in the comprehension of the *particularities* of natural science are treated as the subject matter of a *distinct* discipline. The subject matter of the 'Philosophy of Nature' is in fact 'got analytically by an ordinary process of reflection upon the facts which are the common property of every thinker', in precisely the same way as the subject matter of 'Logic' and 'Spirit'. It is *intuited*, and Hegel deals shortly with those who presume to call the usefulness, reliability or

[1] A. F. Fourcroy (1755–1809) suggests that the colour of a dye may be, 'a very subtle body' perhaps not less so than the principle of smells': see 'Elements of Natural History and Chemistry' (tr. Nicholson, 3 vols. London, 1790) vol. III p. 96. Working on the analogy of the propagation of *light* and sound, J. G. Steinbuch postulated the existence of 'odorous rays' (Riechstrahlen): see 'Beitrag zur Physiologie der Sinne' (Nuremberg, 1811) p. 304. The colours of metallic salts, especially oxides, were probably considered by Hegel to be further evidence of the validity of this transition. John Murray (d. 1820), in his 'A System of Chemistry' (4 vols. Edinburgh, 1819) vol. IV pp. 319–336 considers colours, aroma and taste in the same sequence as Hegel. Unlike Hegel however, he does not distinguish between 'odour' and 'fragrancy'.

validity of this procedure in question, 'According to a metaphysics prevalent at the moment,[1] we cannot know things because they are uncompromisingly exterior to us. It might be worth noticing that even the animals, which go out after things, grab, maul, and consume them, are not so stupid as these metaphysicians.' (§ 246 Addition).[2] Strict attention to the principles of the dialectic is therefore regarded by Hegel as providing an analysis radical and comprehensive enough to consolidate the data provided by the working scientist into subject matter worthy of consideration and treatment within the 'Encyclopaedia'. Intuition may be the ultimate source of this subject matter, but the professional know-how of the scientist and the principles of rational exposition as employed by the philosopher are considered by Hegel as being sufficient safeguards against ludicrous misinterpretations of the facts provided by intuition. Looking at the history of 'Hegelianism' one might well conclude that in thinking this he was utterly and completely wrong. Instead of realizing that the 'Encyclopaedia' can only become meaningful once the separate disciplines it includes have been mastered and the question of further relationships arises, professed Hegelians have taken it to imply that there is a short-cut to absolute knowledge via mysticism, obscurantism or the sheer humbug apparent in statements such as those quoted at the beginning of this chapter. Hegel criticizes this attitude severely in the opening pages of these lectures, and it is to be hoped that this book will help to make it clear that what he says not only constitutes a defence of his own position, but is in itself justified. Considering the merits of his work, it says little for the knowledge and ability of those who have professed to interpret it that most of the real advances in knowledge pioneered since the publication of the 'Encyclopaedia' have been brought about by men who have made no claim whatever to being Hegelians. What is more, professed Hegelians have, on the whole, shown themselves to be somewhat incapable, not only of making worthwhile contributions to specific disciplines and demonstrating the relevance of the 'Encyclopaedia' to the specialist, but even of developing a constructive dialogue with their philosophical colleagues. The origin of this state of affairs is not difficult to trace. Pseudo-Hegelian statements concerning epistemological issues in

[1] i.e. Kant's and Fichte's.

[2] R. B. Braithwaite 'Scientific Explanation' (Cambridge, 1953) p. 4 'A philosophical realist and a phenomenalist can perfectly well agree upon the analysis of a law of mechanics in terms of the observable motions of material bodies. They will disagree as to whether or not these observable events themselves require analysis in terms of something epistemologically more primitive. But for the phenomenalist the two stages in his analysis are distinct; and the realist and he can agree to discuss his first stage while agreeing to differ as to whether or not there is a second.'

the natural sciences should not, therefore, be confused with Hegel's *own* way of dealing with them, which simply involves the structuralization of the data provided by informed commonsense, by means of the *principles* of the dialectic.

The further point to be remembered in this connection is that the *psychological* factors involved in epistemological problems are, in accordance with the general structure of the 'Encyclopaedia', to be regarded as constituting part of the subject matter of 'Spirit'. The level of 'Spirit' succeeds that of 'Nature' within the sphere of the 'Encyclopaedia' in that its subject matter involves the more complex quality of *consciousness*. The immediate transition from 'Nature' to 'Spirit', corresponding to the juxtaposition of the Idea and space in the transition from 'Logic' to 'Nature', involves *death*, as the extinction of the physical individual, the most complex level of nature, and *soul* as 'the *substance* or absolute foundation of all the particularizing and individualizing of spirit'.[1] This is also a *major* transition however, in that it initiates the major qualitative change from *particularity* to *singularity*. Consciousness involves not simply universal categories or the particular objects of nature, but a combination of these categories and these objects in the more complex functioning of individuals aware of themselves and their environment. It therefore distinguishes 'Spirit' from 'Logic' and 'Nature' in the same way that the conclusion of a syllogism is distinguished from and yet dependent upon its premises. The broad outlines of Hegel's structuralization of 'Spirit' will be noticed in a subsequent chapter, since they throw important light upon the significance of his development as a dialectical thinker. At present we need only note that the psychological factors involved in epistemological problems are either to be considered as constituting part of the *subject matter* of 'Subjective Spirit',[2] or as being rooted in imperfect philosophical systems.[3] Hegel would also have pointed out moreover, that great care should be taken to distinguish between the logical and psychological aspects of epistemology. In this respect he would, in fact, have agreed wholeheartedly with K. R. Popper: 'The initial stage, the act of conceiving or inventing a theory, seems to me neither to call for logical analysis nor to be susceptible of it. The question how it happens that a new idea occurs to a man—whether it is a musical theme, a dramatic conflict, or a

[1] §§ 375, 376, 388, 389.

[2] See, for example, the treatment of 'sense-perception', 'the intellect', 'thinking' etc. in §§ 413–482; 'Hegel's Philosophy of Mind' (tr. Wallace, Oxford, 1894). The full text of Hegel's treatment of these matters has yet to be translated.

[3] 'Hegel's Lectures on the History of Philosophy' (3 vols. tr. Haldane, London, 1963).

scientific theory—may be of great interest to empirical psychology; but it is irrelevant to the logical analysis of scientific knowledge.'[1]

Within the 'Encyclopaedia' therefore, the universality of 'Logic' is taken to be the presupposition of the particularity of 'Nature', in precisely the same manner as 'Nature' is taken to be the presupposition of the singularity of 'Spirit'. Hegel indicated the relationship between these spheres not by means of panlogism nor yet by means of mystical insight, but by investigating their subject matter, ranging it in order of complexity, and then submitting it to a dialectical exposition involving the consistent use of the principles of levels, hierarchies and spheres. Most of the difficulties raised by his exponents and his critics in respect of this procedure have been of their own making, and have simply reflected their own failure to understand not only the subject matter, but also the principles and the general significance of the 'Encyclopaedia'.

d. DEVELOPMENT

'It must be reserved to Hegel's admirers to make a driveller of him; an adversary will always know that he has to be honoured, for having willed something great, and having failed to accomplish it.'—Kierkegaard.

Hegel did not find it easy to communicate, either as a writer, a lecturer or in private conversation.[2] His works, even at their most lucid, are by no means easy reading, and it could indeed be argued that the first complete and tolerably satisfactory printed account of his system as a whole, was the second edition of the 'Encyclopaedia' (1827), and that it was not until he began his courses at Heidelberg in 1816 that his full capabilities as a teacher began to be recognized. Even towards the end of his life, when fame and recognition might well have developed in him something more of a capacity for relaxed and easy intercourse, he often tended to make an enigmatical impression, even in private conversation. 'One day Goethe announced to his daughter-in-law that there would be a guest for

[1] 'The Logic of Scientific Discovery' (London, 1959) p. 31. With regard to the many excellent works concerned with the logical and psychological aspects of the epistemological issues raised by the natural sciences, particular mention might be made of: P. G. Frank 'The Validation of Scientific Theories' (New York, 1961); C. G. Hempel 'Aspects of Scientific Explanation' (New York, 1965); Stephan Körner 'Experience and Theory' (London, 1966).

[2] His inability to preach effectively may have played a part in his not having entered the church after finishing at Tübingen; see K. Rosenkranz 'Hegel's Leben' (Berlin, 1844) pp. 16–17. In his final report from the Theological Seminary (20th Sept. 1793) the following comment is made, 'Orationem sacram non sine studio elaboravit, in recitanda non magnus orator visus'. Johannes Hoffmeister 'Briefe von und an Hegel' (4 vols. Hamburg, 1952–1960) vol. IV p. 87.

lunch, but did not tell her his name, which he had never omitted to do before, and did not introduce the guest when he arrived. Mute bows on both sides. During the meal Goethe said comparatively little, presumably in order to give free rein to his very talkative guest, who unfolded his thoughts with great logical acumen and in oddly complicated syntax. His increasingly animated exposition, with its quite new terminology, its intellectually elliptical style of expression and its strange philosophical formulae, finally reduced Goethe to complete silence, though the guest did not notice this. The hostess also listened silently, no doubt glancing at her papa (as she always called Goethe) in some surprise. When the meal had come to an end and their guest departed, Goethe asked his daughter-in-law: "Well, how do you like him?" "How very strange he is. I can't make out whether he's brilliant or crazy. He didn't seem to me to be a very clear thinker." Goethe smiled ironically, "Well, well! We have just had lunch with a man who is now the most famous of modern philosophers—Georg Friedrich Wilhelm Hegel."'[1]

In the last thirty years, the systematic analysis of Hegel's terminology and use of language has done much to clarify the meaning of a great deal of his work.[2] It is now no longer possible to regard his style as muddled and wilfully obscure or as expressing purely arbitrary thought-patterns which might be employed for any purpose, or which are regulated by nothing but the final teleology of his system. Once this has been said however, it has to be admitted that there is a difference between his *mature* style as it is employed to convey the thought and exposition of the 'Encyclopaedia' (1817, 1827, 1830), and the manner in which he expressed himself prior to 1806. It was once he had left Jena and taken the job of editing a newspaper at Bamberg (1806–1808) that he began to collect material for the 'Logic',[3] and it is from this period onwards that one is justified in regarding his thought as settled in its broad outlines, and the main features of his style as having been consolidated. The shortened versions of the 'Encyclopaedia' he prepared for his pupils while he was schoolmastering at Nuremberg (1808–1816)[4] may have helped him to

[1] October 17, 1827. At Goethe's request, Hegel stayed at Weimar for two days on his return from a holiday in Paris. F. von Biedermann 'Goethe's Gespräche' (5 vols. Leipzig, 1909–1911) vol. II pp. 476–477; D. Luke and R. Pick 'Goethe, Conversations and Encounters' (London, 1966) p. 170.

[2] I p. 141 et seq.

[3] 'Wissenschaft der Logik' (3 pts. Nuremberg, 1812–1816). W. R. Beyer has claimed that his work as an editor has left its mark upon the abstract and sophisticated terminology of his logical expositions: see 'Zwischen Phänomenologie und Logik' (Frankfurt-on-Main, 1955) p. 219.

[4] 'Philosophische Propädeutik' (ed. Rosenkranz, Stuttgart, 1961), cf. Friedrich Heer 'Hegel und die Jugend' ('Frankfurter Hefte' 22 Jahrgang, Heft 5, pp. 323–332, May 1967). W. R. Beyer, K. Lanig, K. Goldman have shown that the years spent at Nuremberg were happy and rewarding: see 'Hegel in Nürnberg 1808–1816' (Nuremberg, 1966).

develop the conciseness and pithiness of his later phraseology, but they did not bring about any radical change in his general manner of expressing himself. His teaching at Heidelberg (1816–1818) and Berlin (1818–1831) involved extensive developments in the exposition of the *details* of the 'Encyclopaedia', but none in the revision of its general structure or in the purely linguistic features of his lecturing.

It is therefore the period prior to 1806, and the intellectual ferment worked out of his system by the writing of the 'Phenomenology of Spirit' (Bamberg, 1807), which present us with the problematical factors in Hegel's development. It was not until Wilhelm Dilthey published 'Die Jugendgeschichte Hegels' (Berlin, 1905) that any systematic attempt was made to map the main features of this early period, and to throw light upon what Hegel then wrote by relating it to its historical context.[1] His work opened up an extremely fertile field of research, and it is now possible to distinguish fairly clearly between the different stages in Hegel's development and to introduce a certain amount of fact into the discussion of the basic problems by which they are characterized. Since the general significance of the 'Notion' in Hegel's mature expositions and the structuralization of the sphere of 'Spirit' are to be more readily understood once the general history of his early writings is borne in mind, it will probably be of value, before examining these central features of his system, to look in some detail at the main results of the research initiated by Dilthey.[2]

If the 'Encyclopaedia' is accepted, as Hegel evidently intended it to be, as the work on the basis of which his philosophy is finally to be judged, it is the first eighteen years of his life (1770–1788) which have to be regarded as the most significant in respect of his development, since it was then that he

[1] A. L. C. Thomsen (1877–1915), who also distinguished himself by his work on Kant, Feuerbach and Hobbes and by his Danish translation of Hume's 'Natural History of Religion' ('The Monist' XIX, 1909), after working on the Hegel manuscripts in Berlin, produced an excellent but little-known work on the same subject as Dilthey's and at almost the same time: see 'Hegel-udviklingen af hans filosofi til 1806' (Copenhagen, 1905).

[2] T. L. Haering 'Hegel, sein Wollen und sein Werk. Eine chronologische Entwicklungsgeschichte der Gedanken und der Sprache Hegels' (2 vols. Leipzig and Berlin, 1929–1938); Richard Kroner 'Von Kant bis Hegel' (2 vols. Tübingen, 1921–1924); J. Hoffmeister 'Goethe und der deutsche Idealismus' (Leipzig, 1932); Justus Schwarz 'Hegels philosophische Entwicklung' (Frankfurt-on-Main, 1938); Hermann Glockner 'Hegel' (2 vols. Stuttgart, 1954–1958).

G. P. Adams 'The mystical element in Hegel's early theological writings' (Berkeley, 1910), J. G. Gray 'Hegel's Hellenic Ideal' (New York, 1941) and T. M. Knox and R. Kroner 'Hegel's Early Theological Writings' (Chicago, 1948) are the only works in English concerned with this. It should not be inferred however that the nineteenth century was entirely ignorant of Hegel's youth. Karl Rosenkranz (1805–1879) made a great deal of illuminating material available in 'Hegel's Leben' (Berlin, 1844). It has nevertheless been the work of the twentieth century to evaluate this material in a systematic assessment of Hegel's views at different periods. Remnants of the nineteenth century attitude are still to be found in the failure to distinguish between the expositions of the 'Phenomenology' and those of the 'Encyclopaedia' when discussing Hegelianism.

laid the broad foundations of his encyclopaedic range of knowledge, and first displayed the main features of his mature attitude of mind. The similarity between the intellectual attitudes of the first and the last twenty years of his life is indeed quite remarkable, and needs to be submitted to a more careful investigation than is possible here. The move to Berlin, by intensifying the extent to which he was aware of his Swabian origins, almost certainly played an important part in the development of it. Language may well have been a major factor here, for he never lost his broad south German accent, and traces of dialect are to be found even in his published writings.[1] Even in this work for instance, remote as it is from any discussion of purely human differences, he mentions a linguistic peculiarity of his fellow-countrymen in order to illustrate a purely scientific point.[2] Rosenkranz, who had relations in Berlin, and who had lived there intermittently since he was eighteen, has the following to say about the impression Hegel made in Berlin society, 'In Berlin it was certainly the case that much that was attributed to Hegel as an individual was merely Swabian in general, and was not regarded as being in any way peculiar to him so long as he lived more in the south of Germany. This is true of his homely unpretentious manner, his intuitive openness, the pointedness of his speech, the straightforward matter-of-factness and sincerity of his attitude of mind.'[3] It is curious to note how this account of him contrasts with that of his visit to Goethe. Although he felt at home in Berlin therefore, and although it provided the setting for the complete fulfillment of his professional ambitions, it is not surprising to find him thinking back to his early years while he was working there. Some of the topics he discussed with his teachers at the Stuttgart Grammar School reappear in these lectures in a scarcely altered form for example,[4] and the shortest and most poignant of his letters shows to what extent his earliest family life had left its mark upon him. His mother had died on September 21, 1781, and forty four years later he wrote to his sister Christiane from Berlin, 'Today is the anniversary of our mother's death, I keep her always in my mind.'[5]

[1] See the use of the verb 'ausgehen' in § 316 Remark; note II p. 337.

[2] Note II p. 382 § 321 Addition, '(Smell and taste) are very closely related, and are not distinguished in Swabia, so that people there only have four senses. A flower is said to have a "nice *taste*" instead of a "nice *smell*", so that in so far as we also smell with our tongue, the nose tends to be superfluous.'

[3] 'Hegel's Leben' op. cit. p. 22.

[4] See his discussion of a meteorological problem with H. D. von Cless (1741–1820) on July 4, 1785, and the treatment of the same subject in § 287.

[5] Rosenkranz op. cit. p. 4; Johannes Hoffmeister 'Briefe von und an Hegel' (4 vols. Hamburg, 1952–1950) vol. III no. 497. His mother, Maria Magdalena Louisa Fromme (1741–1781) married his father on September 29, 1769.

The most important source for our knowledge of him during these early years in Stuttgart is the diary he kept,[1] and there is no mistaking the similarity between the general attitude of mind apparent in this document and that of the subsequent professor of philosophy. The boy identifies himself with the political status quo of the Duchy of Wurtemberg and deplores the signs of peasant unrest there in precisely the same way as the professor was later to back the Prussian establishment in the enforcement of the Carlsbad Decrees. He writes as follows on June 29, 1785, 'Dear oh dear! Bad news from Hohenheim. The peasants have started. They are a damned lot. They've smashed all the windows in the Duke's castle at Scharnhausen.' As in his later years, his intellectual poise is quite undisturbed by personal problems or social distractions. On June 27, 1785 for example, after analyzing the merits of the Toynbee of the day[2], he notes down the result of a staff meeting at the school, 'The only outcome of it bearing upon our conduct was that we were earnestly admonished to warn our fellow pupils against getting involved in fooling about in lewd and disorderly company. This was with reference to a group of young persons of the male sex aged 16 to 17 and of the female aged 11 to 12, which has been in evidence of late; it is commonly known as the randy club, the nuts etc.[3] The gents take the girls for walks and degrade themselves and waste time in a shameless manner.' He gets on well with his teachers, somewhat better than he did with his colleagues at Berlin in fact, and unlike many adolescents, finds no difficulty in appreciating the various merits of the general *order* into which he has been born. When he left the Grammar School in the late summer of 1788 for example, he chose 'The sorry state of the arts and sciences under the Turks' as the theme of his valedictory oration, in which he attempted to point out how fortunate he and his fellow pupils were to have been fostered in a country so ready to encourage the acquisition of knowledge and the provision of public education.[4] In an essay written on August 7, 1788 he expresses views similar to those soon to be discussed throughout Germany on account of the famous series of letters by Schiller.[5] He contrasts the culture of

[1] Rosenkranz op. cit. pp. 431–448; Johannes Hoffmeister 'Dokumente zu Hegels Entwicklung' (Stuttgart, 1936) pp. 6–61.

[2] J. M. Schröckh (1733–1808) 'Lehrbuch der allgemeinen Weltgeschichte' (3rd ed. Berlin and Stettin, 1777).

[3] 'Doggen-Gesellschaft, Lappländer'. Literally 'mastiff society, Laplanders': see H. Fischer and W. Pfleiderer 'Schwäbisches Wörterbuch' (6 vols. Tübingen, 1901–1936); F. Grose 'A Provincial Glossary' (London, 1811) p. 95.

[4] Hoffmeister 'Dokumente' pp. 52–54.

[5] 'Ueber die Ästhetische Erziehung des Menschen', 'Ueber naive und sentimentalische Dichtung' ('Die Horen' Tübingen, 1795/6): 'Schillers Werke: Nationalausgabe' (ed. Petersen, 35 vols. Weimar, 1943–1964) vols. 20 and 21: tr. Wilkinson and Willoughby (Oxford, 1967).

antiquity, in which, he thinks, there was harmony between man and nature, feeling and thought, love and religion, with the fragmented, formalized and contradictory attitudes of his own day. He then continues, 'Another characteristic of the ancients is that the poets had a gift for describing the external phenomena of visible nature apparent to the senses, that with which they were intimately acquainted. We on the other hand are better informed about the *inner play of forces*, and generally know more of the causes of things than of how they look.'[1]

This *love* of the balance and accord between content and form in classical art was to be expressed again, in a more elaborate manner, forty years later, in the Berlin lectures on Aesthetics. Although Schiller strengthened and confirmed it, it had its origin therefore in the sunny realism of the schoolboy, and it drew its strength not so much from a purely intellectual insight, as from a fundamentally resilient and untroubled frame of mind, which, although it was deepened and transformed by the intellectual turmoil of the years spent at Tübingen, Bern, Frankfurt and Jena, also managed to survive it unscathed. The cultivation of it furthered the development of the rare blend of emotion and intellect, abstract thought and concrete fact so characteristic of his mature thought. During these early years however, it was important mainly in that it provided him with the vision and the peace of mind necessary for devoting the greater part of his time and energy to the acquisition of an enormous fund of miscellaneous knowledge and information. He read voraciously, took copious notes on whatever interested him,[2] and even as a boy, attempted to arrange this wealth of subject matter into an encyclopaedia.[3] If the samples of his extracts and notes published by Hoffmeister are representative of his reading as a whole, his general interests at this time centred mainly upon psychology, education, Egyptology and philosophy. The diary shows however that apart from classical literature,[4] mathe-

[1] 'On some characteristic differences between ancient and modern poets': Hoffmeister 'Dokumente' pp. 48–51; cf. W. Rehm 'Griechentum und Goethezeit' (3rd ed. Bern, 1952).

[2] Hoffmeister loc. cit. pp. 54–166.

[3] The influence upon him of the Swiss mathematician, aesthetician, educationalist and philosopher Johann Georg Sulzer (1720–1779) should be investigated. On March 9 and 10 1787, for example, he made copious extracts from Sulzer's 'Kurzer Begriff aller Wissenschaften und andern Theile der Gelehrsamkeit, worin jeder nach seinem Innhalt, Nutzen und Vollkommenheit kürzlich beschrieben wird' (2nd ed. Leipzig, 1759): see Hoffmeister 'Dokumente' pp. 109–115. Sulzer was deeply influenced by Leibniz and Wolff. On his influence upon the education of his day see R. M. Dahne 'Joh. Georg Sulzer . . . und sein Verhältnis zu den pädagogischen Hauptströmungen seiner Zeit' (Königsee, 1902).

[4] Homer, Aristotle, Demosthenes, Isocrates, Cicero, Plautus, Catullus, Tibullus, Virgil, Livy, Longinus etc.

matics, trigonometry and geometry took up most of his spare time.[1] He read Shakespeare in J. J. Eschenburg's edition (12 vols. Zürich, 1775–1777), and occasionally notes down the impression made upon him by miscellaneous reading such as the 'Cours de belles-lettres' (4 vols. Paris, 1747–1750) by Charles Batteux (1713–1780),[2] or the Richardsonian psychological novel 'Sophiens Reise von Memel nach Sachsen' (2nd ed. Worms, 1776), by J. T. Hermes (1738–1821).[3]

It was, moreover, in these early years that he first displayed the main features of his mature attitude toward religion. The historico-intellectual approach of his Berlin 'Lectures on the Philosophy of Religion',[4] is already evident in an essay 'On the religion of the Greeks and Romans' which he wrote on August 10, 1787,[5] and it comes out clearly in the very first entry in his diary. 'June 26th 1785. Seminary preacher Regier preached at Matins. He read out the Augsburg Confession, and began in fact with the introduction to it before actually preaching. Even if I had remembered nothing else, my historical knowledge would therefore have been increased.'[6]

In October 1788 he began a two year course on philosophy at Tübingen, and it was evidently at this time that he made his first acquaintance with the work of Kant. Johann Friedrich Flatt (1759–1821) was lecturing in the faculty, and in the introductory courses he gave, he was in the habit of emphasizing the relevance of Kant to Christian thinking by comparing his philosophy with that of Descartes, Malebranche, Locke and Leibniz.[7] The effect of his teaching upon Hegel is apparent in the criticism Hegel levels at Kant in the thesis he wrote for his Master of Philosophy in 1790.[8] Characteristically enough he attempts to overcome Kantian dualism by

[1] Mainly the works of A. G. Kästner (1719–1800) and J. F. Lorenz (1738–1807).

[2] Tr. K. W. Ramler 'Einleitung in die schönen Wissenschaften' (4 vols. Vienna, 1770). Hegel takes particular note of the section on epic poetry (vol. II pp. 15–203).

[3] 'I only intended to read a little of "Sophia's Journey" during the afternoon; I was however quite incapable of putting it down until the evening, when I went to the concert.' op. cit. January 1, 1787.

[4] Tr. Spiers and Sanderson (3 vols. London, 1962).

[5] 'Über die Religion der Griechen und Römer' (Hoffmeister, 'Dokumente' pp. 43–48).

[6] Cf. his attitude toward superstition (July 9, 1785) and his comments on the Catholic 'Missa, quam vocant' (Aug. 7, 1785). Herman Nohl has noticed that, after several changes, his *handwriting* reassumes many of its earliest features in his mature works: 'Hegels theologische Jugendschriften' (Tübingen, 1907) p. 402.

[7] Carl von Weizsäcker 'Lehrer und Unterricht an der evangelischtheologischen Facultät der Universität Tübingen von der Reformation bis zur Gegenwart' (Tübingen, 1877) pp. 127–144. On Flatt himself see Karl Flatt 'Einige Züge von dem Bilde des verewigten D. Joh. Fr. Flatt' (Tübingen, 1823).

[8] 'De limite officiorum humanorum, seposita animorum immortalitate' (28 pp. Tübingen 27.ix.1790).

pointing out that despite the distinction drawn between sense and reason, both aspects of knowledge are united in a single subject,[1] and that *purely* moral activity is impossible in that it presupposes psychological phenomena. He also asks whether an acceptance of the absolute imperative of moral duty necessarily requires belief in immortality.

For the next three years Hegel studied theology in the Tübingen seminary, mainly under Gottlob Christian Storr (1746–1805). It was evidently the rigorously logical, dry and somewhat formidable manner in which this man marshalled his immense linguistic and historical learning in order to defend traditional Lutheranism against what he considered to be the pernicious doctrines of the enlightenment, which forced Hegel to spend the greater part of the 1790's thinking over predominantly theological problems. We know from his later letters to Schelling how thoroughly he disapproved of Storr's thought and methods.[2] During his period at Tübingen however, he seems either to have been unwilling to jeopardize his career by criticizing his teacher, or uncertain as to how his views were to be refuted. In his academic work he simply did what was necessary. For his thesis he chose a purely historical subject,[3] and merely concentrated upon handling his sources with the same scrupulous exactness and pedantry as that displayed by Storr in developing dogma out of Biblical exegesis. There are no letters dating from this period, and the early fragments published by Nohl cannot be precisely dated with any certainty.[4] We do know that Hegel read Rousseau and the Greek tragedies at this time however, and that his favourite hobby was botany.[5] It was not the dons therefore, but his friendships, and especially those with Hölderlin and Schelling which provided the positive intellectual stimu-

[1] 'sensus cum ratione sic quasi coaluit, ut vis utraque *unum* constituat subjectum'.

[2] Hoffmeister 'Briefe' vol. I nos. 6–8 (Dec. 1794–Jan. 1795): 'How are things in Tübingen apart from this? Until there's someone like Reinhold or Fichte lecturing there, nothing worthwhile will come out of the place . . . I haven't yet heard of any other attacks upon Kant's doctrine of religion apart from Storr's, although it will undoubtedly have to face them. The influence of it is certainly not great as yet, and will take time to become fully apparent . . . There is no shaking orthodoxy so long as the profession of it brings civil advantages by being involved in the whole structure of a state . . . I feel however that it would be interesting . . . to disturb the antlike industry of the theologians as much as possible, to make nothing easy for them, to chase them out of every corner and to allow them no refuge, until they have nowhere else to turn, and are forced to display their nakedness to the light of day.'

[3] 'De ecclesiae Wirtembergicae renascentis calamitatibus' (Tübingen, June, 1793).

[4] Herman Nohl 'Hegels theologische Jugendschriften' (Tübingen, 1907). For the latest views on the chronology of Hegel's early works, see Gisela Schüler 'Zur Chronologie von Hegels Jugendschriften' in 'Hegel-Studien' vol. 2 (ed. Nicolin and Pöggeler, Bonn, 1963) pp. 111–159. Cf. Gunnar Aspelin 'Hegels Tübinger Fragment. Eine Psychologisch-Ideengeschichtliche Untersuchung' in Lunds Universitets Årsskrift N.F. Avd. I Bd. 28 Nr. 7 (Lund, 1933).

[5] Hoffmeister 'Dokumente' p. 31. M. Sartorius shared it with him.

lation of these years.[1] Hölderlin had already begun to write 'Hyperion' before he left the seminary, Schelling was soon to make his mark as a philosopher, and it was the fervent discussions on Hellas, Christianity, Plato, Spinoza, Kant, Schiller, Jacobi etc. which took place whenever this circle came together, which were the greatest formative influence upon Hegel's intellectual development during his student years.

The Lutheran church in Wurtemberg was, throughout the eighteenth century, in a somewhat difficult situation. The effect of Pietism upon it after 1688 had led to severe internal strains, and by the middle of the century it looked as though it might well break apart. In 1777 Christian Friedrich von Schnurrer (1742–1822) was appointed principal of the Tübingen seminary, and the teachers he collected about him had as their main objective the reconciliation of Pietism with orthodox Lutheranism, and the defence of Christian doctrine against the destructive criticism levelled against it by the men of the enlightenment. Storr joined the faculty in 1786 and Flatt the theological faculty in 1792, and it was these two men who formed the nucleus of what is now known as the older Tübingen school.[2] Fichte's anonymous 'Essay towards a Critique of all Revelation',[3] which was thought at first to have been by Kant, appeared in 1792, and Kant's 'Religion within the bounds of mere reason' in 1793.[4] The Kantian works referred to by Flatt and Storr in the lectures heard by Hegel were therefore those that had appeared by 1790.[5] They accepted Kant's distinction between phenomena and noumena, and used it to establish the plausibility of theological propositions. They argued for example, that although three persons are not equal to one in the world of phenomena, the possibility of their being so as Divine Persons or noumena cannot be denied, since, as Kant has shown, we can know nothing of the noumenal world except that there everything is in all respects different from what prevails in the case of phenomena. They concluded from this that theology cannot possibly expect or fear anything from philosophy, and

[1] J. Hoffmeister 'Hölderlin und Hegel' (Tübingen, 1931); cf. Th. Haering 'Hölderlin und Hegel in Frankfurt' (Tübingen, 1943): O. Pöggeler 'Hegel und die Grieschische Tragödie' ('Hegel-Studien', Bonn, 1964) pp. 285–305.

[2] C. von Weizsäcker op. cit.; H. Hermelink 'Geschichte der evangelischen Kirche in Württemberg von der Reformation bis zur Gegenwart' (Stuttgart and Tübingen, 1949). A ducal commission for the reform of the seminary was appointed in March 1792 and its recommendations put into effect by decree on May 22, 1794.

[3] 'Versuch einer Kritik aller Offenbarung' (Königsberg, 1792).

[4] 'Die Religion innerhalb der Grenzen der blossen Vernunft' (Königsberg, 1793) tr. Greene and Hudson ed. Silker (New York, 1960).

[5] 'Kritik der reinen Vernunft' (Riga, 1781); 'Grundlegung zur Metaphysik der Sitten' (2nd ed. Riga, 1786); 'Kritik der praktischen Vernunft' (Riga, 1788); 'Kritik der Urteilskraft' (Berlin and Liebau, 1790).

that the only valid basis it can have is that of *supernatural* revelation, made evident by the Scriptures. They therefore took it to be the task of the theologians to establish the historical validity of the Bible, to acknowledge it as the sole source and law book of Christianity, and to make use of the deductive method in resolving its statements into a systematic exposition of Christian dogma.[1] The strength of their position is undeniable, and for two decades at least it enabled them to infuse new life into the Lutheranism of the Duchy. The reaction against them gave a powerful impetus to romanticism however, and their Biblical scholarship was soon to be discredited by advances which brought to light the historical and linguistic complexity of the texts from which they had extracted their dogma. To Hegel however, it was not only the rather obvious pedantry and spiritual shortsightedness of the manner in which they handled religion which was objectionable, but the way in which they managed to travesty Kant. In distinguishing between phenomena and noumena, Kant had insisted that noumena were not to be divorced from 'their complex, the intelligible world', and that the distinction should not be used to give plausibility to the extravagances of the imagination.[2] It would of course have been difficult to argue that the Scriptures on which Storr and Flatt based their arguments were simply to be regarded as extravagances of the

[1] Otto Pfleiderer 'The Development of Theology in Germany since Kant' (tr. J. F. Smith, London, 1893); J. J. Herzog 'Realencyklopädie für protestantische Theologie und Kirche' (3rd ed. 24 vols. Leipzig, 1896–1913) vol. 20 pp. 148–159. Storr's most important works are: 'Observationes quaedam ad comparandam Kantianam disciplinam cum christiana doctrina pertinantes' (1792, tr. Süskind, Tübingen, 1794), and 'Doctrinae christianae pars theoretica e sacris litteris repetita' (1793, tr. C. C. Flatt, Stuttgart, 1803). After he had been discredited in Germany, he was translated into English: see 'An Elementary Course of Biblical Theology' (London, 1838 tr. Schmucker in 'Ward's Library of Standard Divinity'), 'Expositions of the Epistles of Paul' (tr. R. Johnston, Edinburgh, 1842), 'On the parables of Christ' (Edinburgh, 1835).

As an example of his work, see the treatment of the Trinity in the 'Observationes' (Germ. tr. p. 7), 'As for the doctrine of the Trinity, the impossibility of giving a positive definition of the distinction between Father, and Son, and Holy Spirit, is no sufficient reason for denying the distinction itself, of which the Bible assures us; for reason, when left to herself, sets before us objects concerning which we indeed know *that* they exist (τὸ ὅτι), but concerning whose nature we have no positive knowledge. We can only distinguish between them and some false representations, or determine what they are not; but of their intrinsic nature, *how* they are (τὸ πῶς) we have not the slightest knowledge'. Cf. Carl Daub (1763–1836) 'Theologumena, sive doctrinae de religione christiana ex natura Dei perspecta repetendae capita potiora' (Heidelberg, 1806). Storr evidently published 'Die Lehre von der Dreieinigkeit' (1776), but I have been unable to trace the work: see F. G. Süskind and J. F. Flatt 'G. C. Storrs Sonn- und Festtagspredigten' (2 vols. Tübingen, 1808), vol. II p. 37.

[2] 'Prolegomena to any Future Metaphysic' (1783, tr. Mahaffy, London, 1889) §§ 32–35, 'Experience must therefore contain all the objects for our concepts; but beyond it no concepts have any signification, as there is no intuition for their basis. The imagination may perhaps be forgiven for occasional extravagance, and for not keeping carefully within the limits of experience, since it at least gains life and vigour by such flights, and since it is always easier to moderate its boldness, than to stimulate its languor. But the understanding which ought to *think* can never be forgiven for substituting *extravagance*; for we depend upon it alone for assistance to set bounds, when necessary, to the extravagance of the imagination.'

imagination. Nevertheless, it was equally apparent that, in the light of the Kantian position, they could lay no special claim to constituting knowledge of the Divine. What, then, were the implications of Kantianism for religion? Fichte answered this by concentrating upon Kant's 'Critique of Practical Reason' and emphasizing the importance of belief in revelation as a factor in the *moral* development of mankind. He took the possibility of revelation to depend upon the moral nature of man and not vice versa, and argued that if there is a revelation at all, its content must coincide with that of the moral law.[1] Kant expressed his approval of Fichte's work, and when he published his own views on the matter, they were found to be similar to those of his admirer.[2]

That Hegel appreciated the importance of these developments is apparent from his first extensive theological essay 'The Life of Jesus',[3] in which the significance of Christ's teaching is stated in Kantian terms, 'Act on the maxim which you can at the same time will to be a universal law among men. This is the fundamental law of morality—the content of all legislation and of the sacred books of all nations'.[4] He seems however to have sensed the limitations of Kant's treatment of religion at a very early stage. His knowledge of the church and of history in general made him intensely aware of the individualistic and ahistorical bias in Kantian thinking. He realized that religion is not simply rooted in individual moral experience, and that the church is not merely a community of mutually recognizing moral entities. He appreciated the value of Kantian morality as the fulfillment of the divinity in man, but he deplored man's limitation of his knowledge of God to morality. He had criticized Flatt's exposition of Kantian morality in that it had seemed to him to belittle the importance of psychology. In the very first sentence of 'The Life of Jesus' he acknowledges the need for something more than a Kantian definition of God, 'Pure reason, incapable of all bounds, is the Godhead itself—The plan of the world in general is therefore ordered in accordance with reason; it is by reason that man is taught to know his vocation, an absolute purpose

[1] 'Versuch einer Kritik aller Offenbarung' (Königsberg, 1792): cf. R. Adamson 'Fichte' (Edinburgh and London, 1881) pp. 25–35.

[2] 'Die Religion innerhalb der Grenzen der blossen Vernunft' (Königsberg, 1793) tr. Greene and Hudson ed. Silber (New York, 1960): cf. A. Seth 'The Development from Kant to Hegel' (London, 1882) pp. 89–170, C. C. J. Webb 'Kant's Philosophy of Religion' (Oxford, 1926), F. E. England 'Kant's Conception of God' (London, 1929).

[3] Nohl op. cit. pp. 73–136. This work was written at Bern between May 9 and July 24, 1795. F. Rosenzweig 'Hegel und der Staat' (2 vols. Munich and Berlin, 1920) vol. I p. 17 was one of the first to emphasize that Hegel's early interest in Kant was theological and religious rather than theoretical and philosophical. Cf. Herbert Wacker 'Das Verhältnis des jungen Hegel zu Kant' (Berlin, 1932), Ingtraud Goerland 'Die Kantkritik des jungen Hegel' (Frankfurt, 1966).

[4] op. cit. p. 87.

in his life; it is indeed often obscured, but it has never been extinguished, and a faint glimmer of it has always survived, even in darkness.'[1]

It was this need which led him to investigate the manner in which Christ's life and teaching, the fulfillment of Kantian morality, have given rise to the institutionalization of religion in a church,[2] and to deplore the extent to which formalized theology and its ecclesiastical proponents had become divorced from the warmth and spontaneity of life, the needs and capabilities of humanity, 'If someone has not had this systematic web (of casuistry) woven round him from his youth up, if he has come to know human nature by other means, by observing the experience of others or by following his own feelings, and if he now becomes acquainted with the system and is supposed to live in accordance with it, he finds himself in a world bewitched. In a man brought up under the system he can find no essential features like his own; instead of trying to find anything natural in him, he would be better to look for it in oriental fairy stories or in our chivalry romances. Indeed he would be less in error if he proposed to make these poetic fantasies the basis of a system of physics or these productions of our own era the basis of a psychology . . . Think of the innumerable hypocrites in any church which has a system of this kind. They have mastered all the requisite knowledge, acquired the prescribed feelings, obeyed the church's decrees. They live and move in church activities. We may well raise the question: What strength can be ascribed to them if they observe and do all that the church requires and yet remain villains and traitors into the bargain? Just as lack of the means to satisfy physical needs robs us, as animals, of life, so too, if we are robbed of the power to enjoy freedom of mind, our reason dies, and once we are in that position we no more feel the lack of it or a longing for it than the dead body longs for food and drink . . . Our public religion, like many of our customs, appeals in these matters, as well as in the fasts and mournings of Lent and the finery and feasting of Easter Day, to rules for feelings, and these rules are supposed to be universally valid. This is why there is so much hollowness, so much spiritlessness in our usages; feeling has gone out of them, even though the rule still prescribes that we should have it. Casuistry and monastical asceticism have been hit by nothing so much as by the development of a moral sense in mankind and the better knowledge of the human soul.'[3]

[1] Nohl op. cit. p. 75.

[2] 'Die Positivität der christlichen Religion': Nohl pp. 137–239: extracts tr. Knox and Kroner op. cit. pp. 67–181: written at Bern between November 2, 1795 and April 20, 1796.

[3] Knox and Kroner op. cit. pp. 137–139: Nohl op. cit. pp. 206–208.

In 'The Spirit of Christianity', which Hegel wrote at Frankfurt during the winter of 1798-9,[1] the same theme is developed with reference to the Jews. Unlike Kierkegaard in 'Fear and Trembling',[2] he deplores Abraham's absolute faith in a *transcendent* God, 'The whole world Abraham regarded as simply his opposite; if he did not take it to be a nullity, he looked on it as sustained by the God who was alien to it. Nothing in nature was supposed to have any part in God; everything was simply under God's mastery.'[3] He then illustrates the consequences of such an attitude with reference to the history of this people, 'The subsequent circumstances of the Jewish people up to the mean, abject, wretched circumstances in which they still are today, have all of them been simply circumstances and elaborations of their original fate. By this fate, an infinite power which they set over against themselves and could never conquer—they have been maltreated and will be continually maltreated until they appease it by the spirit of beauty and so annul it by reconciliation . . . The great tragedy of the Jewish people is no Greek tragedy; it can rouse neither terror nor pity, for both of these arise only out of the fate which follows from the inevitable slip of a beautiful character; it can arouse horror alone. The fate of the Jewish people is the fate of Macbeth, who stepped out of nature itself, clung to alien Beings, and so in their service had to trample and slay everything holy in human nature, had at last to be forsaken by his gods (since these were objects and he their slave) and be dashed to pieces on his faith itself.'[4]

Christ is regarded as the reconciliation of God and man, the fulfillment of the law, 'Over against commands which required a bare service of the Lord, a direct slavery, an obedience without joy, without pleasure or love . . . Jesus set their precise opposite, a human urge and so a human need.'[5] The significance of the Three Persons of the Trinity as the figuration of the atonement of God, Man and Spirit is discussed,[6] and after a consideration of St. John ch. I the essential *spirituality* of religion is asserted, 'Nowhere more than in the communication of the divine is it necessary

[1] 'Der Geist des Christentums und sein Schicksal': Nohl op. cit. pp. 241–342; Knox and Kroner op. cit. pp. 182–301.

[2] 'Frygt og Bæven' (Copenhagen, 1843). Kierkegaard regarded this work as a criticism of the relationship between religion and philosophy formulated by Hegel. He probably had in mind the 'Encyclopaedia' § 63 or the 'Philosophy of Right' § 270 however. This work was unknown to him. See F. J. Billeskov Jansen 'Søren Kierkegaard. Værker i Udvalg' (4 vols. Copenhagen, 1950) vol. IV p. 131.

[3] Knox and Kroner op. cit. p. 187; Nohl op. cit. p. 247.

[4] Knox and Kroner pp. 199–205: Nohl pp. 256–260.

[5] Knox and Kroner p. 206: Nohl p. 262.

[6] Knox and Kroner pp. 257–281: Nohl pp. 306–324; cf. L. W. Grensted 'A Short History of the Doctrine of the Atonement' (Manchester, 1920).

for the recipient to grasp the communication with the depths of his own spirit. Nowhere is it less possible to learn, to assimilate passively, because everything expressed about the divine in the language of reflection is *eo ipso* contradictory; and the passive spiritless assimilation of such an expression not only leaves the deeper spirit empty but also distracts the intellect which assimilates it and for which it is a contradiction.'[1] The resurrection, or the emergence of 'Spirit' from 'Nature', is taken to be the necessary preparation for the Feast of Ascension, or the recognition of the holding of the particular within the universal by means of the singular,[2] 'Thus any expectation that the actual body associated with the Jesus who had been glorified and deified would be raised to divinity on the strength of miraculous deeds wrought by him in the flesh is so entirely unfulfilled that it rather intensifies all the more the harshness of thus attaching an actual body to him. Nevertheless, this harshness is all the greater for us than for the members of the first Christian community, the more intellectual we are in comparison with them. They were breathed upon by the oriental spirit; the separation of spirit and body was less complete for them; they regarded fewer things as objects and so handed fewer things over to intellectual treatment. Where we have intellectual cognition of a determinate fact or a historical objectivity, they often see spirit; where we place only spirit unalloyed, there they look on spirit as embodied. An instance of the latter type of outlook is their way of taking what we call immortality, and in particular the immortality of the soul. To them it appears as a resurrection of the body. Both outlooks are extremes, and the Greek spirit lies between them. Our extreme is the outlook of reason which sets a soul—something negative in the sight of every intellect—over against the intellect's object, the dead body. The early Christian extreme is the outlook, so to say, of a positive capacity of reason to posit the body as living while at the same time it has taken it for dead. Between these extremes is the Greek view that body and soul persist together in one living shape.'[3]

It was this conclusion which rounded off the *theological* speculations of the 1790's. For the next seven years Hegel attempted to interpret his earlier encyclopaedic interests in the light of it, and it was out of these attempts that his mature system was to emerge. On his father's death in

[1] Knox and Kroner p. 256: Nohl p. 306.

[2] Cf. Aquinas 'Summa Theologica' iii pp. 54–56; W. Milligan 'The Resurrection of Our Lord' (Edinburgh, 1881), 'The Ascension and Heavenly Priesthood of our Lord' (London, 1892); J. W. Schmidt-Japing 'Die Bedeutung der Person Jesu im Denken des jungen Hegel' (Göttingen, 1924).

[3] Knox and Kroner pp. 297–298: Nohl p. 339. A. T. B. Peperzak 'Le jeune Hegel et la vision morale du monde' (The Hague, 1960).

January 1799 he inherited enough money[1] to enable him to think of qualifying himself for a university career. He contacted Schelling, and it was almost certainly the renewal of their friendship which encouraged him to put his views to the test by attempting an assessment of *natural phenomena* in the light of the general principles he had evolved from his theological studies.[2] The immediate outcome of this was the 'Dissertatio philosophica de Orbitis Planetarum' (Jena, 1801) already noticed. In the autumn of 1801 he began lecturing at Jena on Logic and Metaphysics to an audience of eleven. Between then and the autumn of 1802, and probably as a general preparation for these lectures and with a view to publication, he wrote out his first attempt at a comprehensive system.[3] Like the dissertation this work shows how clearly the necessity of hierarchical thinking was apparent to him at this time. It also has a rather loose triadic structure moreover, and contains considerable evidence of an attempt to demonstrate the importance of *syllogistic* thinking in a systematic exposition of its subject matter.[4] Under the heading of '*Logic*' a progression is made from the simple relations of quality and quantity to the more complex relationships of the judgement and the syllogism, and finally to definition, division and cognition. 'Metaphysics' is regarded as being more complex than logic in that it involves not only abstract categories but also the 'thing-in-itself'. In somewhat Kantian terms cognition is then expounded as a system of principles, and this is followed by a metaphysics of objectivity, and finally by a metaphysics of subjectivity involving the ego and 'absolute spirit'. Under the heading of '*Nature*' Hegel then deals with a *logically contingent* subject matter, progressing from the aether, appearance and motion, to mechanics, matter and physics. There is therefore no organics and no '*Spirit*', probably because he still felt himself to be unequal to the task of structuralizing these spheres in the light of the principles he was attempting to employ. From what is written

[1] 3154 goulds, i.e. £367 in the English currency of the time.

[2] Schelling published his 'System of Transcendental Idealism' in March 1800, and we know that Hegel studied it in Frankfurt (Rosenkranz p. 149). Hegel's corresponding speculations are to be found in 'Fragment of a System' (Sept. 14, 1800), which is concerned mainly with the problem of unifying the opposites which reflective thinking has to acknowledge as separate i.e. the eternal and the temporal, God and man, subject and object, etc. It is in his conception of *life* that he finds the key to their union. Knox and Kroner pp. 309–319, Nohl pp. 343–351. See his letter to Schelling of November 2, 1800 ('Briefe' no. 29), and his plan for an encyclopaedia, probably written in the early months of 1797: F. Rosenzweig 'Das älteste Systemprogramm des deutschen Idealismus'. (Heidelberg Akademie der Wissenschaften: Philosophisch-historische Klasse: 1917 Abh. 5). This fragment shows the influence of Plato and Hölderlin, but contains no treatment of 'Nature'.

[3] 'Jenenser Logik, Metaphysik und Naturphilosophie' (ed. G. Lasson, Leipzig, 1923); 'Philosophische Bibliothek' (Felix Meiner Verlag, Hamburg, 1967).

[4] Hermann Schmitz 'Hegel als Denker der Individualität' (Meisenheim, 1957) pp. 122–126.

however, it is evident that he intended to show the significance of the third and most comprehensive major sphere in the exposition of the whole.

In the lectures of 1803–1804 he evidently repeated the work on '*Logic*' done in 1801–1802, and concentrated upon his exposition of the natural sciences, treating this sphere at the four main levels of mechanics, chemism, physics and organics. He also made a fairly extensive but clearly incomplete attempt at working out the levels of consciousness into a philosophy of '*Spirit*'.[1] In 1805–1806[2] he again omitted to revise the '*Logic*'. Although he also retained the four main levels indicated in the previous lectures in his treatment of the natural sciences, he now submitted this section to a thorough revision, dealing with it in more detail, and attempting to give greater precision to its triadic structure. The most interesting feature of these lectures is however the first formulation of the broad outlines of the mature philosophy of '*Spirit*', progressions being made from subjective spirit to politics, and finally to art, religion and philosophy.

By 1801 therefore, Hegel had decided that in a philosophical encyclopaedia a progression would have to be made from simpler to more complex phenomena, that this would involve a broad division of its subject matter into *logical* considerations simpler in content than natural phenomena, *nature* itself, in the assessment of which logical considerations would evidently involve contingency, and still more complex spiritual considerations, and that it was the most complex sphere of *Spirit* which held the key to the philosophical exposition of the whole. The broad outline of his mature system was therefore already apparent to him, and while lecturing and writing at Jena he concentrated upon developing first the 'Logic', then 'Nature' and finally 'Spirit'. What he evidently lacked at this time however, was a central standpoint and principle which would enable him to demonstrate the interrelatedness of these three spheres, the identity of subject matter and structure in his expositions, the truth of 'the Greek view that body and soul persist together in one living shape'. He came to realize that this would involve the establishment of a teleological standpoint for the assessment of *Spirit*, and that in that he had not yet attempted this, he could not even regard himself as expounding the *whole* sphere of knowledge, since what was necessarily to be conceived of

[1] 'Jenenser Realphilosophie I' (ed. Hoffmeister, Leipzig, 1932); cf. Schmitz op. cit. pp. 126–133.

[2] 'Jenenser Realphilosophie II' (ed. Hoffmeister, Leipzig, 1931); cf. Schmitz op. cit. pp. 133–138. Michelet inserted extracts from these lectures in the edition of the 'Philosophy of Nature' he brought out in 1842.

as a totality was evidently limited by the imperfect integration of what he was bound to regard as constituting the parts of it.[1]

It was the attempt he made to solve this problem in the 'Phenomenology of Spirit' (Bamberg, 1807) which concluded his development as a thinker. Before proceeding to assess this work however, it may be of value to compare the 'Philosophy of Nature' with the corresponding works by Schelling and his followers, since it was certainly Schelling who encouraged him to develop this sphere of the 'Encyclopaedia' at Jena, and although the connection between them at this time is well known, it is, in general, imperfectly understood. On July 30, 1814 Hegel wrote as follows to H. E. G. Paulus (1761–1851), professor of philosophy and theology at Heidelberg,[2] 'You know that I have concerned myself extensively, not only with classical literature, but also with mathematics, and of late with higher analysis, differential calculus, physics, natural history, chemistry, in order to be able to deal with the charlatanry of physiophilosophy, which philosophizes without knowledge, by means of imagination, and which treats empty conceits and even absurdities as thoughts. This might at least serve to recommend me in a negative manner.' The same tone prevails in the opening pages of these lectures. It is indeed probable that Hegel had become aware of the worthlessness of much of Schelling's speculation as early as the summer of 1800, when he was studying his 'System of Transcendental Idealism'[3] at Frankfurt, and that he only co-operated with him in the early years at Jena in order to facilitate his initiation into university teaching. It must at least most certainly be emphasized, that it is only in its *superficial* features that the 'Philosophy of Nature' resembles the corresponding Schellingian writings. Like these works, it communicates an attempt to assess the natural sciences, but there the similarity ends. The dissertation of 1801, Hegel's first published work on this subject, has most of the main features of his mature attitude to natural science, and as has been noticed, his first *comprehensive* treatment of this sphere (1801–1802), in that it is preceded by a logic and a metaphysic, emphasizes the importance of strictly hierarchical thinking, was evidently meant to be succeeded by a philosophy of spirit, and makes minimal use of such favourite Schellingian concepts as polarity, magnetism, galvanism etc., also bears a very close resemblance to his

[1] W. van Dooren 'Het Totaliteitsbegrip bij Hegel en zijn Voorgangers' (Assen, 1965). On the development of Hegel's views at Jena see K. Rosenkranz 'Hegel's Leben' (Berlin, 1844) pp. 178–198; H. Glockner 'Hegel' (2 vols. Stuttgart, 1954–1958) vol. II ch. 6.

[2] Hoffmeister 'Briefe' vol. II no. 235.

[3] 'System des transcendentalen Idealismus' (Tübingen, March 1800).

mature work.[1] It may be said quite confidently therefore, that the diatribe with which these lectures begin is not simply a matter of the pot calling the kettle black. The sober and meticulous structuralization of the accomplishments of the natural sciences which distinguishes Hegel's work is indeed a far cry from the spirit which swept Herder, the spiritual progenitor of the Schellingians, as he sailed from Riga in the early summer of 1769. 'It was on the ship therefore that I became a philosopher—a philosopher however who had as yet barely learnt how to philosophize from nature without books and instruments. If I had been able to do this, under a mast, on the wide ocean, what a standpoint it would have been for philosophizing upon the sky, sun, stars, moon, air, wind, sea, rain, current, fish and the depths of the sea, for discovering first-hand the physical nature of it all! Philosopher of nature, that should be your standpoint with the youth whom you instruct. Stand by him on the wide sea and *show* him facts and realities, use no words in explaining them, but let him grasp it all of his own accord.'[2]

Herder's attitude, as pictured here, had a great influence upon the young Schelling's intuitive approach toward the natural sciences, and for two decades at least it looked as though this brand of realistic romanticism might revolutionize scientific thought. Hegel, like Goethe, evidently appreciated the living wholeness of the insights it fostered[3] and saw the value of it as a corrective to the subjectivism endemic to the age, but his awareness of its defects was evidently well known, even before the publication of the 'Phenomenology'.[4] The brilliance of the rhetoric it inspired gave rise to an enthusiasm which it was often unable to sustain through the labours of painstaking research. On occasions, the vision was maintained, but found to be irrelevant to the details that had to be dealt with. Irresponsible and fantastic theories were therefore promulgated, cautious, sober and systematic research flouted. The collapse of the scientific method seemed possible, chaos seemed imminent. There was however no denying the brilliance of many who propounded the new doctrine. In Wordsworth, Novalis, Oehlenschläger and Kellgren the romantic view of nature brought forth exquisite poetry and nothing more,

[1] 'Jenenser Logik' etc. op. cit.

[2] 'Journal meiner Reise im Jahre 1769' (ed. Gillies, Oxford, 1947). For the germ of the idea of a somewhat more systematic philosophy of nature, see his 'Vom Erkennen und Empfinden der menschlichen Seele' (Riga, 1778), in 'Herders Sämmtliche Werke' (ed. B. Suphan, 33 vols. Berlin, 1877–1913) vol. 8 pp. 165–333.

[3] § 246 Addition; O. Pöggeler 'Hegels Kritik der Romantik' (Bonn, 1956).

[4] See his early characterization of intuitive thinking as 'the darkness in which all cats are grey' (sic). H. Steffens 'Was ich erlebte' (10 vols. Breslau, 1840–1844) vol. IV p. 312.

but in the addresses of Schelling and Steffens the audience was urged in a new and exciting manner to throw itself into the precise *investigation* of natural phenomena. In the autumn of 1802 Steffens began his famous lectures in Copenhagen.[1] 'Reason, the well-spring in which freedom and necessity are inseparably mingled, is that which is most central to us. It is the divinity by which *each* is united with all, the growing toward that which is sublime, the noble shoot that awakens us, the ray of eternal clarity that rouses us, the deep motivating principle of all our higher desires. It was with our very existence that a divinity gave us the ordering principle involved within the organization of a whole interacting everlastingly with all its parts. To raise that shoot, to cause it to grow, is the constant wish of every nobler nature. He feels in his heart that this is the immovable point around which everything moves, the changeless amid all change—the source of everything known.'[2]

Schelling influenced natural scientists as Hegel never did.[3] As the result of the enthusiasms stimulated by his teaching, J. J. Wagner and J. F. Fries attempted to reduce all the laws of the natural sciences to mathematics, J. E. von Berger developed pantheistic views out of his work as an astronomer, J. W. Ritter and H. C. Ørsted made important discoveries relating to electricity and magnetism, F. B. von Baader distinguished himself as a mineralogist, H. F. Link and C. G. Nees von Esenbeck made their names as botanists, G. H. von Schubert published reliable works on botany, zoology and natural history in general, and a whole host of doctors, K. G. Carus, K. A. Eschenmayer, K. R. Hoffmann, A. F. Marcus, A. Roeschlaub, J. P. V. Troxler, K. J. A. Windischmann etc. propounded more or less eccentric views on medical matters. Oken's popularization of science by means of his periodical 'Isis', and his founding of the 'Association of German Naturalists and Physicians' in 1822, should also be put to the credit of the Schellingians. His work had a direct influence upon *British* affairs through the encyclopaedic ambitions of Coleridge and the founding of the British Association for the Advancement of Science in 1831.[4]

English readers, who are probably acquainted with the translation of

[1] Grundtvigianism, which, apart from Marxism, is the only truly popular and socially effective movement to have arisen out of German romanticism, owes much to these lectures.

[2] 'Indledning til philosophiske Forelæsninger' (Copenhagen, 1803) pp. 183–184.

[3] Heinrich Knittermeyer 'Schelling und die Romantische Schule' (Munich, 1929).

[4] 'To give a stronger impulse and a more systematic direction to scientific inquiry, to obtain a greater degree of science, and a removal of those disadvantages which impede its progress, and to promote the intercourse of the cultivators of science with one another and with foreign philosophers.' —W. V. Harcourt (1789–1871).

Oken's main work on the philosophy of nature,[1] will probably be surprised to learn that many Schellingians produced reliable scientific works later in life. By 1815 the essentially sterile nature of Schelling's early views had been acknowledged by most working scientists, although some of his disciples continued to speak well of them as late as the 1850's. Hegel, as we have noticed, had taken an independent attitude to the natural sciences from the very beginning of his public career. However, since his 'Philosophy of Nature' was not designed primarily in order to *revolutionize* scientific research, since it was too abstruse to capture the imagination easily, and since the scientists who acknowledged their debt to him remained very minor figures,[2] his work tended to be lumped together with Schelling's, and to fall with it into the disrepute with which all subsequent evaluations of it have had to contend.

Kant's warning that noumena should not be divorced from 'their complex, the intelligible world' is heeded in Hegel's early work at Jena. He acknowledges the importance of formulating levels, hierarchies and spheres as clearly and precisely as possible, and of so demonstrating the Notion, the essential structure of knowledge. He notices the seductiveness of mysticism, of closing one's eyes, which is particularly pernicious in that it is not entirely valueless, 'There is indeed a *turbid something* which is not quite feeling or science, it is a speculative feeling or the Idea, and although it is unable to free itself from phantasy and feeling, it is also no longer merely one or the other of these. I have in mind *mysticism*, or rather the *oriental* as well as the *Jacob-Boehmian* attempts to demonstrate the Idea . . . The *lucid* element is the universal, the *Notion*, which, in its all-exhibiting revelation, is as deep as it is extensive.'[3] Although his encyclopaedic work at this time is fragmentary, and although his dissatisfaction with it is apparent in his constant revision, there is, nevertheless, a very clear affinity between his Jena lectures and the mature 'Encyclopaedia'. How then are we to explain the 'Phenomenology', which, to a Kantian, can hardly appear as anything better than a nightmare? It is true that the work has a rather loose triadic structure, and that a general progression is made from basic subject matter such as sense certainty, perception, understand-

[1] 'Elements of Physiophilosophy by Lorenz Oken' (tr. A. Tulk, London, 1847). The book is a shocking assemblage of ludicrous thoughts and inane observations. § 3593, from the section on psychology, provides a fair example of its verbiage: 'Gazing upon a Snail one believes that he finds the prophesying goddess sitting upon the tripod. What majesty is in a creeping Snail, what reflection, what earnestness; what timidity, and yet at the same time what confidence! Surely a Snail is an exalted symbol of mind slumbering deeply within itself.'

[2] L. D. von Henning (1791–1866), G. F. Pohl (1788–1849).

[3] Hoffmeister 'Dokumente' pp. 338–339.

ing etc. to clearly complex considerations such as morality, religion and absolute knowledge. Natural science is considered after scepticism and the 'unhappy consciousness' however, and is the immediate antecedent of pleasure and necessity, the law of the heart and virtue etc.[1] What are we to make of this? It can hardly be argued that this sequence corresponds to anything in heaven, earth, or the waters under the earth. A scientist might well object to having the general nature and relatedness of the natural sciences travestied and caricatured in this manner, in what is evidently a Bottom's dream, especially when he is also told that these intellectual antics are being perpetrated in the name of an absolute philosophy, transcending at some amazingly high level his rather more pedestrian accomplishments. After reading the reference to a botanical matter in the preface,[2] Goethe wrote as follows to his friend T. J. Seebeck (1770–1831), 'To say anything more monstrous is indeed not possible. It seems to me quite unworthy of a rational man to want to annihilate the eternal reality of nature by means of a miserable sophistical joke . . . When a distinguished thinker manages to contradict and obliterate an idea by means of ingenious and mutually self-nullifying words and phrases, one knows not what to say'.[3]

There is indeed no commoner evidence of the complete misinterpretation of Hegelianism than that provided by those who, though evidently ignorant of both the origin and the import of the 'Phenomenology', persist in proclaiming its merits. They would be better advised to admit that they know not what they say. Most of the ridicule to which these would-be Hegelians have been justly submitted has its origin in a very healthy awareness of what is ostensibly ludicrous in this work, and in the shrewd suspicion that those claiming to have found a bottom to it are themselves somniloquent.

During the winter of 1801/2, as we have seen, Hegel lectured on Logic, Metaphysics and Nature, and had evidently planned to develop a philosophy of 'Spirit'. In the summer of 1802 he gave notice of a forthcoming

[1] 'The Phenomenology of Mind' (tr. J. B. Baillie, London, 1931) pp. 241–412.

[2] Goethe quotes the following (op. cit. p. 68), 'The bud disappears when the blossom breaks through, and we might say that the former is refuted by the latter; in the same way when the fruit comes, the blossom may be explained to be a false form of the plant's existence, for the fruit appears as its true nature in place of the blossom. These stages are not merely differentiated; they supplant one another as being incompatible with one another. But the ceaseless activity of their own inherent nature makes them at the same time moments of an organic unity, where they not merely do not contradict one another, but where one is as necessary as the other; and this equal necessity of all moments constitutes alone and thereby the life of the whole.' Seebeck evidently managed to clarify the matter somewhat: see Goethe's letter of January 15, 1813: 'Werke' IV Abtheilung 23 Band (Weimar, 1900).

[3] November 28, 1812: see Goethe's 'Werke' IV Abtheilung 23 Band (Weimar, 1900).

text-book, to accompany his lectures, entitled 'Logic and Metaphysics, or Systema reflexionis et rationis'.[1] This failed to appear, although it was repeatedly advertized by him. Finally, in the winter of 1805/6 his friend Friedrich Immanuel Niethammer (1766–1848) arranged for such a work to be published by J. A. Goebhard (d. 1813) of Bamberg. There can be little doubt that Hegel originally intended this to be the first edition of his 'Encyclopaedia', and that the lectures of 1805/6 give a fairly clear idea of the initial plan and general foundation of it. The 'Logic' of 1801/2 was evidently to constitute the basis of the first part, the 'Nature' of 1803/6 that of the second part, and the 'Spirit' of 1805/6 that of the third part.[2] Printing began in February 1806, and he had arranged to have half the manuscript in the printer's hands by Easter. He soon found however, not only that he was quite unable to work his material out systematically, but that he was getting hopelessly behind schedule. By the August of 1806 he had sent off barely half the work,[3] and it was evidently at that time that he first decided to call it not a 'System of Sciences' but a 'Phenomenology'.[4] The second half of the book was written in the incredibly short period of two months (Aug.–Oct. 1806). The preface was completed by the new year, and sent to the publisher on January 16, 1807.

These circumstances explain a great deal. The obscurity of Hegel's style evidently has its origin in the rapidity with which he wrote. The excessive unevenness in the execution of the work and its somewhat enigmatical character is presumably the result of his having been forced to change his conception of it while he was actually writing. It is valuable therefore, not as a *systematic* exposition of levels, hierarchies and spheres,

[1] The circumstances under which the 'Phenomenology' was conceived and written were only made known thirty years ago: see Theodor Haering 'Die Entstehungsgeschichte der Phänomenologie des Geistes', in B. Wigersma 'Verhandlungen des dritten Hegelkongresses' (Tübingen and Haarlem, 1934); 'Phänomenologie des Geistes' (ed. Hoffmeister, Leipzig, 1937), introduction.

[2] Otto Pöggeler 'Zur Deutung der Phänomenologie des Geistes' in 'Hegel-Studien' vol. I pp. 255–294 (Bonn, 1961) p. 279. Pöggeler corrects some of the details in Haering's reconstruction of the events leading up to the publication of the work. He shows for example that Hegel had begun to write it by the early summer of 1805, i.e. before the contract with Goebhard had been signed. See H. Schmitz 'Die Vorbereitung von Hegels Phänomenologie des Geistes in seiner "Jenenser Logik"' ('Zeitschrift fur philosophische Forschung'. 14, 1960. 16–39).

[3] Baillie's translation pp. 131–412.

[4] See his lecture notice for 1806/7 published August 1806, 'logicum et metaphysicam sive philosophiam speculativam praemissa phaenomenologia, ex libro suo "System der Wissenschaften" proxime prodituro, Parte prima'. J. H. Lambert (1728–1777), in his 'Neues Organon, oder Gedanken über die Erforschung und Bezeichnung des Wahren, und dessen Unterscheidung vom Irrthum und Schein' (2 vols. Leipzig, 1764) pt. IV had defined 'phenomenology' as the, 'theory of appearance and of its influence upon the correctness and incorrectness of human knowledge'. Kant, in the 'Metaphysischen Anfangsgründe der Naturwissenschaft' (1786) pt. IV, regards it as being the mode in which motion makes its appearance. Hegel subsequently used it to describe a sphere of subjective spirit ('Encyclopaedia' §§ 413–439).

as is the 'Encyclopaedia', but as a broad and somewhat rough survey of certain *spiritual* phenomena. In that the natural sciences, like psychological, epistemological, historical, ethical, social, moral and religious phenomena, are the object of thought, there is no reason why they should not be brought within this survey. In the 'Phenomenology' Hegel is not however attempting to do justice to the precise interrelatedness of the *subject matter* of 'Logic', 'Nature' and 'Spirit'. He is concerned primarily, if not exclusively, with various modes of *consciousness*, and the extent to which they approximate to the standpoint from which 'Spirit' might be structuralized. It has to be admitted however that his account of this standpoint is woefully inadequate,[1] and in that this work has led so many unacquainted with both the structure and the subject matter of the 'Encyclopaedia' to interpret Hegelianism as a philosophical game, devoid of rules, and best played blindfold in a state of blissful ignorance, its influence is to be deplored.[2]

Hegel therefore concluded his development by *preparing the way* for rounding off the exposition of the 'Encyclopaedia' by a full-scale *structuralization* of 'Spirit'.[3] It was not until the Berlin period however that he found the time and the opportunity to show what this entailed. Tracing his development is important, in that it enables one to place his early works in perspective, and in that it helps one to see how easily what he was attempting to communicate in his mature works, can be misunderstood or even completely overlooked by those who are unaware of its origin.

e. THE NOTION

'There is surely a peece of Divinity in us, something that was before the Elements, and owes no homage unto the Sun.'—Sir Thomas Browne.

---

[1] Baillie's translation pp. 789–808.

[2] There are competent surveys of the main arguments of the 'Phenomenology' in J. N. Findlay 'Hegel, a Re-examination' (London, 1958) and G. R. G. Mure 'The Philosophy of Hegel' (London, 1965). Since the war, the French have published works designed to make it more intelligible, see, Jean Hyppolite 'Genèse et Structure de la Phénoménologie' (Paris, 1946), Alexandre Kojève 'Introduction à la Lecture de Hegel' (Gallimard, 1947). See also: G. Stiehler 'Die Dialektik in Hegels "Phänomenologie des Geistes"' (Berlin, 1964), J. Loewenberg 'Hegel's Phenomenology' (La Salle, 1965). R. K. Maurer, in 'Hegel und das Ende der Geschichte' (Stuttgart, 1965) has the merit of investigating the apparent historicity of the work. L. Flam, in 'De Bewustwording Beschouwingen bij de "Fenomenologie van de Geest"' (Brussels, 1966) concentrates upon its moral, social and political aspects. The real significance of the work is not widely recognized.

[3] Otto Pöggeler op. cit. 'Hegel-Studien' (Bonn, 1961) pp. 282–283, 'In opposition to the usual interpretation of the Hegelian text, I should like to propose the following: that the actual science of Spirit is not the Logic, but the philosophy of Spirit.' This is undoubtedly justified, and is now widely accepted. For a classical exposition of the former view see Jean Hyppolite 'Logique et Existence. Essai sur la logique de Hegel' (Paris, 1953).

It is perhaps rather curious that although most continental scholars are now agreed as to the general nature of the various stages in Hegel's *development*, they still hold widely different opinions as to what constitutes the basic motivation of this development and the central feature of his mature *thought*. Despite his careful analysis of Spinoza,[1] and the forthright manner in which oriental *pantheism* of the Hindu or Spinozistic kind is rejected as inadequate to the full capabilities of philosophy in the final sections of the 'Encyclopaedia',[2] even the nineteenth century assertion that his thought is pantheistic in tone, is still repeated by some of them.[3] Theodor Steinbüchel[4] came closer to the truth of the matter when he saw the basic problem of Hegel's philosophy as an attempt to establish the relationship between the universal and the particular, and characterized it as being *panentheistic* in intention i.e. as an attempt to demonstrate not simply that God is everything, nor yet that He transcends everything, but that while He is indeed transcendent, everything is *in* Him.[5] Hermann Schmitz has concentrated upon the nature of the *dialectic* as being central to Hegel's thinking,[6] and attempted to show that it has its origin in the syllogism and the total incompatibility of subject and predicate found in the infinite judgement.[7] More recently, Jörg Splett has attempted to show how the logicalization of the Christian Trinity throws light upon both the ultimate 'telos' and the ubiquitous structuralization of Hegel's work.[8]

Although the value of such approaches is not to be denied, it seems likely that the most valuable contribution to the solution of this problem made in the last decade has come from Otto Pöggeler, who has suggested that the central principle of Hegelianism is to be found neither in the

[1] See the references collected in Glockner's 'Hegel-Lexikon', which show that Hegel's predominant attitude was appreciative but critical. See especially the 'History of Philosophy' pt. III sect. ii ch. 1 div. A.

[2] § 573.

[3] For one of the earliest assertions of this kind see F. C. Baur (1792–1860) 'Die christliche Lehre von der Dreieinigkeit' (3 vols. Tübingen, 1841–1843) vol. III p. 911.

[4] 'Das Grundproblem der Hegelschen Philosophie' (Bonn, 1933).

[5] R. C. Whittmore 'Hegel as Panentheist' (New Orleans, 1960); Erik Schmidt 'Hegels Lehre von Gott' (Gütersloh, 1952); K. C. F. Krause (1781–1832) first made this point: see J. E. Erdmann 'A History of Philosophy' (3 vols. London, 1807–1899) vol. II pp. 669–679. Goethe expresses the idea very neatly:

'Denn alles Drängen, alles Ringen
Ist ewige Ruh' in Gott dem Herrn.'

[6] 'Hegel als Denker der Individualität' (Meisenheim, 1957).

[7] 'The mind is no elephant', 'A lion is no table' etc., propositions which are correct but absurd: 'Encyclopaedia' § 173. Schmitz links these somewhat abstract considerations with the concept of *alienation* as it is characterized in the 'Phenomenology' (B, IV, b, 3) under the heading of the unhappy consciousness.

[8] 'Die Trinitätslehre G. W. F. Hegels' (Munich, 1965); cf. J. Hessen 'Hegels Trinitätslehre. Zugleich eine Einführung in sein System' (Freiburg, 1922).

'Logic' nor in any of the particular levels of 'Spirit', but in 'Spirit' regarded as a *whole*. This suggestion, if it is not simply taken to imply the vague and somewhat dangerous truism that spirit as such has certain powers of synthesis, would appear to lead us to the very centre of the problem. Properly considered, it enables us to draw together the valuable but fragmentary insights of various interpreters, and to establish a vantage point from which the whole lay-out of the Hegelian system may be profitably viewed and accurately assessed.[1]

It is evident from the Jena writings, that so long as Hegel was unable to establish the nodal point in the hierarchy of knowledge which could provide him with the broad framework for the structuralization of 'Spirit', he had difficulty in dealing with this sphere. This was a particularly serious obstacle to the whole development of his thought, for since 'Spirit' constitutes the most complex of the three major levels of knowledge, it is also from this nodal point that the entire 'Encyclopaedia' must derive its unity. Hegel realized moreover, that since the final levels of 'Spirit' would have to be exhibited as concluding the whole *cycle* of knowledge, they would also have to be exhibited as initiating it, that is to say, as constituting the immediate presuppositions of the simplest categories of the 'Logic'. As a result of the various attempts he made at working out an 'Encyclopaedia', he became intensely aware of the fact that a mere enumeration of levels of complexity was unlikely ever to yield the nodal point he required. In the 'Phenomenology of Spirit' therefore, he set out to establish its features and general significance by what amounted to a process of elimination. Taking the general complexity of 'Spirit' as distinct from the comparative simplicity of 'Nature' and 'Logic' as his point of departure, he attempted to show the relative inadequacy of various spiritual phenomena to the fulfillment of what was required. As is well known, this led him to the definition of what he calls 'Absolute Knowledge'. It has to be admitted however, that partly on account of the rapidity with which he was forced to write this work, and partly on account of the imperfection of his preliminary assessments, this level is poorly defined, and the general significance of it inadequately expressed. One might reasonably have expected of him that he would have given a more explicit and rounded account of it in the 'Encyclopaedia', but it can hardly be said that he managed to do so.[2]

The final levels of the hierarchy of 'Spirit' are therefore central to any

[1] 'Zur Deutung der Phänomenologie des Geistes' in 'Hegel-Studien' vol. I pp. 255–294 (Bonn, 1961).

[2] §§ 572–577.

understanding of the overall significance of Hegel's work. Before proceeding to examine this crucial section of the 'Encyclopaedia' in some detail however, it may be of value to make a few general remarks about the method he employs in developing his system, since the principles elicited at this final level of it are intimately involved in the structure of the whole.

It has, firstly, to be remembered, that when he presents a phenomenon as concluding and rounding off a sphere, he has to exhibit it not only as the most *complex* level of that particular hierarchy, but as including within itself and having as its presupposition all the simpler levels constituting the qualitative unity of which it is the culmination. In the 'Philosophy of Nature', as throughout the whole of the 'Encyclopaedia', he brings immense erudition, great intellectual acumen and not a little ingenuity to bear upon the task of indicating phenomena capable of fulfilling these requirements. If, therefore, we are not intimately acquainted with early nineteenth century knowledge, it will often be difficult for us to appreciate the significance of his work. If we do manage to overcome this handicap however, we shall soon discover that the judgements involved in the selections he makes are never unworthy of serious consideration. Able and accomplished though they invariably are however, they are necessarily based upon the subject matter available to him, and even the major transitions of the 'Encyclopaedia' are therefore open to revision. It is not often realized however, that even a level as important as the 'Absolute Idea' finds its particular place in the system and concludes the 'Logic' simply because it was the most complex category Hegel was able to *intuite* from the subject matter available to him. Consequently, although he does his best to show why he regards it as presupposing and including all the abstract universals by which it is preceded, he does not rule out the possibility of its being revised or redefined by subsequent thinkers.[1] The rounding off of the sphere of 'Nature' provides us with a closely analagous example. Since Hegel regards death as presupposing all the stages of development and complexity in the animal organism, the most complex of all natural phenomena, he presents it here as the most complex of all *particularities*, and consequently as the immediate presupposition of consciousness or 'Spirit', in which *singularity* involves both universals and particularities. The formulation of this transition is by no means inapposite to current experience and knowledge, and may still quite reasonably be regarded as having its value. Although we may even be convinced that there is no reason why it should not be regarded as *proof* against any

[1] 'Encyclopaedia' §§ 236–244.

further revision however, it would be unwise of us to regard the formulation of it as final, even if only for the very general reason that the manner in which knowledge enables a philosopher to *illustrate* the structure of the 'Encyclopaedia' is perpetually changing.[1]

We have already noticed that it is sections of the 'Encyclopaedia' such as these, in which transitions are made from one *sphere* to another, which tend to be the most controversial. In that they simply involve progressions in degree of complexity, they should of course present us with little difficulty once we have an elementary idea of the basic structure of the work. In that they also have to be regarded as concluding and initiating *qualitative* differences varying widely in degree of *comprehensiveness* however, they will quite obviously always be the focal points of legitimate and valuable differences of opinion. Nor is this so only in the case of major transitions such as those from 'Logic' to 'Nature' and from 'Nature' to 'Spirit'. The whole range of subject matter surveyed within the 'Encyclopaedia', down to its most minute details, must be regarded as being open to discussion, reinterpretation and revision of this kind. Once this has been said however, it should be added that this infinite revisability in no way affects the *structure* of the work. A modern physicist for example, although he will certainly differ from Hegel in his interpretation of the subject matter of his particular discipline, will have little difficulty in discovering the merits of his structuralization of it.

We have no direct evidence of the method Hegel employed in assimilating and arranging his material. When he was writing the 'Encyclopaedia' and preparing the lectures he based upon it however, it seems as though he made a preliminary survey of his subject matter, ranging it in general order of complexity, and *then* looked through it for the nodal points which might be presented as the concluding and initiating levels of the various spheres. A certain amount of evidence in support of this view may be adduced from the 'Philosophy of Nature'. In the treatment of Sound for example,[2] the major transitions demarkating the sphere as a whole were evidently suggested by the science of the day. The brilliant exposition of acoustic phenomena worked out between these nodal points is entirely original however, and is evidently the outcome of nothing but Hegel's thorough grasp of the subject matter, and the principles common to the 'Encyclopaedia' as a whole.

Before examining the manner in which these principles are combined in the final levels of 'Spirit', we should perhaps take careful note of their

[1] §§ 375–376.
[2] §§ 300–302.

precise nature. We have already noticed that it is very easy to misassess and misunderstand the ubiquitous levels, hierarchies and spheres of the Hegelian system, in that they have a *dual* nature. This is also true of the Idea, the Notion and the dialectic, the principles which derive their significance from the final 'telos' of the system. They are all to be regarded as *principles*, and as being distinct from their subject matter, on account of their being identical throughout the 'Encyclopaedia' and constituting the *general structure* of 'Logic', 'Nature' and 'Spirit'. In that they are also completely devoid of identity however, constituting as they do an integral part of an endlessly *varied* and varying subject matter, they are also to be regarded as perpetually changing and infinitely revisable. They may be said therefore to be mere theoretical *abstractions* in so far as they are lacking in subject matter, and to be utterly *unthinkable* in so far as any attempt is made to deny their *purely* structural nature. One might say, that although they have to be recognized, they also have to be illustrated, and that both the recognition and the illustration must be very largely meaningless in so far as it is supposed that one may be separated from the other. They are universal and changeless in that they are always relevant to an understanding of any kind of subject matter. They are particular and changing in that they are always strictly irrelevant to the *actual* acquisition of knowledge. Although Hegel often speaks of them in a striking and memorable manner, he is never very explicit in his treatment of them, and never goes out of his way to explain them. The following passage is typical of his utterances on the subject, 'As thoughts invade the limitless multiformity of nature, its richness is impoverished, its springtimes die and there is a fading in the play of its colours. That which in nature was noisy with life, falls silent in the quietude of thought; its warm abundance, which shaped itself into a thousand intriguing wonders, withers into arid forms and shapeless generalities, which resemble a dull northern fog.'[1]

Since the principles of the 'Encyclopaedia', as principles, are changeless abstractions, the apparent *movement* in the work, from one subject matter to another, motivated as it is simply by the need to illustrate the basic structure, is merely the result of Hegel's having had to communicate by means of the printed word and lecture in a manner acceptable to undergraduates. Theodor Litt has therefore done great service to a more

[1] § 246 Addition. Cf. the famous passage in the preface to the 'Philosophy of Right', 'When philosophy paints its grey in grey, then has a shape of life grown old. By philosophy's grey in grey it cannot be rejuvenated but only understood. The owl of Minerva spreads its wings only with the falling of the dusk.'

'Grau, teurer Freund, ist alle Theorie,
Und grün des Lebens goldner Baum.'

general understanding of Hegelianism by pointing out that the subject matter of the 'Encyclopaedia' may, with rather more profit, be considered in the *converse* order to that in which it is presented.[1] Since Hegel chose to deal with the levels in order of increasing complexity, progressions are made which certainly give his expositions the appearance of being teleological. A close examination of them will make it evident however that their apparently teleological nature is merely the result of his having been unable to talk intelligibly about everything at once. The main purpose of his work is not to *progress* to a certain end, but to *exhibit* the form of the 'Encyclopaedia' as a whole by eliciting the structure of its various spheres. In so far as it is helpful or necessary to think in terms of ends however, the various hierarchies might perhaps be said to display an *immanent* teleology.

The sphere of 'Spirit' is like every other in the 'Encyclopaedia' in that the significance of the level which rounds it off can only be fully understood with reference to the hierarchy by which it is preceded. In this case Hegel formulates a progression from what would now be called psychology ('Subjective Spirit'), to the law, ethics, the social sciences and history, and finally to aesthetics, religion and philosophy.[2] The *principles* involved in this exposition are in no way peculiar to it, so that the *structure* that emerges from them has no particular features and significance of its own. Although it can hardly be claimed that there is a widespread appreciation of the value of this structure, many have been intrigued by the subject matter of the sphere, with the result that Hegel's expositions of the law, conscience, constitutions, war, world history, painting, music, poetry, Hinduism, Buddhism, Judaism, Plato, Aristotle, Bacon, Jacob Boehme etc. etc. etc. are undoubtedly the best known and most widely discussed features of his work. This is not the place to embark upon the fascinating procedure of investigating the sources, judgements and assessments which gave rise to the actual levels, hierarchies and spheres formulated here. Since the final section of spirit contains the key to the understanding of the whole 'Encyclopaedia' however, it is essential that it should be carefully examined, its significance firmly grasped, and the general implications of it clearly presented.

Hegel formulates this level in §§ 572–577 of the 'Encyclopaedia' and

[1] 'Hegel, Versuch einer kritischen Erneuerung' (Heidelberg, 1953).

[2] 'Philosophy of Mind' (tr. Wallace, Oxford, 1894). The 'Philosophy of Subjective Spirit has not yet been translated in its entirety. 'Philosophy of Right' (tr. Knox, Oxford, 1962); 'Philosophy of History' (tr. Sibree, Dover Publ., 1956); 'Philosophy of Fine Art' (tr. Osmaston, London, 1916); 'Philosophy of Religion' (tr. Spiers and Sanderson, London, 1895); 'History of Philosophy' (tr. Haldane, London, 1892).

calls it, quite simply, 'Philosophy'. He does not make it easy for us to grasp its significance however. The lectures on 'Philosophy', which should have clarified the general meaning of it do not in fact do so, since they treat their subject historically, not speculatively, and despite their vague triadic structure cannot therefore be regarded as a completely integral part of the 'Encyclopaedia'. When attempting to expound the central principle of Hegelianism therefore, we are left with these jejune paragraphs, the enigmatic utterances concluding the 'Phenomenology', and a genial reference to 'Hamlet' at the end of the 'Lectures on the History of Philosophy'.[1]

Despite their limitations however, these sources, if they are carefully considered *in their context*, do not provide an entirely inadequate basis for the task in hand. The paragraphs in the 'Encyclopaedia' are the most satisfactory, and from these it is quite evident that Hegel's thought at this juncture is essentially *syllogistic*. An examination of them will make it apparent that the major spheres of 'Logic', 'Nature' and 'Spirit' are here interpreted as the qualitative *unities* of universality, particularity and singularity, and are regarded by Hegel as constituting the premises and conclusions of a wholly triadic and syllogistic exposition. The ultimate origins of these entities are, at this level, admittedly remote, but since the attempt is being made simply to exhibit their combination while maintaining their distinctness, and since their formulation has already been submitted to a thoroughgoing and rigorous analysis, this is by no means a procedure which, in this section of the 'Encyclopaedia', is entirely inappropriate. It is pointed out that there are three possible ways of regarding or demonstrating their combination. In the first instance, 'Logic' may be regarded as being combined with 'Spirit' through the mediation of 'Nature'. If this general proposition is illustrated by a particular case, it might for example be stated that the *category* of measure is *known* to me on account of its *occurring* in a chemical combination (§ 575). In the second instance, 'Nature' is combined with 'Logic' through the mediation of 'Spirit'. A particular case of this would be the *occurrence* of a chemical combination, *known* to me and so giving rise to the formulation of the *category* of measure (§ 576). In the third instance, the syllogism, 'is the Idea of philosophy, which has *self-knowing reason*, the absolutely-universal, for its *middle term*: a middle which divides itself into *Spirit* and *Nature*, making the former its presupposition, as the process of the *subjective* activity of the Idea, and the latter its universal extreme, as the process of the *implicit*, objective being of the Idea'. In the particular instance of this case, my

[1] op. cit. vol. III p. 547.

subjective *recognition* of measure, and the *occurrence* of it in chemical combinations, are regarded as the premises of the universality of it as a *category* (§ 577).

In these three syllogisms therefore, Hegel attempts to exhibit the universal *principles* involved in the three possible ways of regarding knowledge. As the German text is explicit enough on the point, it must be the inaccuracy of Wallace's translation of § 574[1] which has led British thinkers to regard the 'Logic' *as such* as constituting the middle term of this final syllogism. Hegel makes no mention whatever of the 'logical system' fabricated by Wallace. What he actually says is that, 'This Notion of philosophy is the *self-thinking* Idea, the truth aware of itself (§ 236). It is that which is logical, in the sense that it is universality *verified* within concrete content as in its actuality.' The point he is evidently making here is that levels, hierarchies and spheres, the components of the *Idea*, like the categories of the 'Logic', are universal in that they are not to be confined to particular instances or subjective thinking. As a confirmation of the correctness of Pöggeler's thesis that it is 'Spirit' and not 'Logic' which constitutes the focal point of the 'Encyclopaedia', it should be noted moreover that it is not the *Absolute* Idea of the 'Logic',[2] but the *self-thinking* Idea of Spirit which is presented by Hegel as exhibiting the unity of the whole cycle of knowledge.

When he refers to them as 'that which is logical', Hegel shows that he regards these central principles formulated in the final levels of 'Spirit' as differing very little, if at all, from purely logical categories. On account of their extreme abstraction and generality they are indeed well suited to be regarded as the immediate antecedent of pure Being, the most elementary category of the 'Logic'. On the other hand, since it is the *intellectual* manipulation of them which gives rise to the unity of the whole 'Encyclopaedia', he is also clearly justified in regarding them as the most complex of all *spiritual* phenomena. Taken as a whole therefore, this may well be regarded as the most satisfactory of the three major transitions he formulates.

What then is the part played by the Idea, the Notion and the dialectic in Hegel's thinking? The Idea is, one might say, the fulfillment of all the levels, hierarchies and spheres formulated throughout the 'Encyclopaedia'. It is therefore also the coincidence of the *subject matter* of the work with its central *principle*. 'The Idea is what is true *in and for itself*, it is *the absolute*

[1] 'The Philosophy of Mind' op. cit. p. 196.
[2] 'Encyclopaedia' §§ 236–244.

unity of the Notion and objectivity. The ideal nature of its content is merely the way in which the Notion exhibits itself in the form of external existence, and, by keeping this shape in its power through enclosing it within its ideality, maintains itself within it.'[1] It is therefore a unity in precisely the same manner as the syllogism is, that is to say by being the fulfillment of its premises in a conclusion. In the case of the Idea however, 'Logic', 'Nature' and 'Spirit' constitute the component parts. It find its complete fulfillment in the final levels of 'Spirit', but it is also evident wherever the subject matter of the 'Encyclopaedia' *coincides* with its apparently teleological triadicity, 'The eternal life of nature consists firstly in the Idea displaying itself in each sphere to whatever extent finitude makes possible, just as every drop of water yields an image of the sun. Secondly, it consists in the dialectic of the Notion, which breaks through the limitation of this sphere, and since it only finds partial satisfaction in such an inadequate element, necessarily passes over into a higher stage.'[2] Within the sphere of nature, the phenomenon corresponding to the Absolute Idea of the 'Logic' and the self-thinking Idea of 'Spirit' is life, 'As the union of the Notion with exteriorized existence, in which the Notion maintains itself, life constitutes the Idea . . . Life is not merely the resolution of the opposition between the Notion and reality, but of oppositions in general. Life has being where inner and outer, cause and effect, end and means, subjectivity and objectivity etc., are one and the same.'[3] Nature in general, on account of its materiality, tends to be regarded as falling short of this however, 'The ancients grasped *matter* in general as non-ens, and nature has also been regarded as the Idea's *falling short* of itself, for in this external shape the Idea is inadequate to itself.'[4] In a much quoted passage Hegel expands upon this with reference to the system as a whole, 'Nature has yielded itself as the Idea in the form of *otherness*. Since the *Idea* is therefore the negative of itself, or *external to itself*, nature is not merely external relative to this Idea (and to the subjective existence of the same, spirit), but is embodied as nature in the determination of *externality*.'[5] The animal, as the most complex of natural phenomena and the initiator of 'Spirit' is regarded by him as the *existent* Idea, 'In so far as the animal's members are simply moments of its form, and are perpetually negating their independence, and withdrawing into a unity which is the reality of the Notion, and is for the Notion, the animal

[1] 'Encyclopaedia' § 213.
[2] § 252 Addition.
[3] § 337 Addition.
[4] § 248 Remark.
[5] § 247.

is the existent Idea. If a finger is cut off, a process of chemical decomposition sets in, and it is no longer a finger. The unity which is produced has being for the implicit unity of the animal. This implicit unity is the soul or Notion, which is present in the body in so far as the body constitutes the process of idealization.'[1] As such it initiates the *idealization* of nature, 'The animal organism is the microcosm, the centre of nature which has become for itself. Within it, the whole of inorganic nature has recapitulated itself, and is idealized, and it is this that has to be demonstrated by the more detailed exposition of it.'[2] Reflective and finally dialectical thinking are the means by which this is subsequently achieved.

The extent to which finitude makes it possible for the Idea to display itself in each sphere of the 'Encyclopaedia' is of course limited. Consequently, despite the immanence of Hegel's teleology and the care with which the various levels, hierarchies and spheres are formulated, there is nearly always some sort of dispartity between the Idea as such and the particular sphere being expounded. The ultimate coincidence has to be postulated and borne in mind, and the general framework of one's exposition is clearly regulated by the need to formulate levels, range them in hierarchies and round them off within spheres, but the identity of subject matter and structure will, more often than not, be a matter of theory rather than accomplishment and practice. To the extent that the philosopher is therefore obliged to recognize a difference between the actual form of rationalized knowledge and the ideal in the light of which it is to be regarded as rational, Hegel refers not to the Idea, but to the Notion. He explains this concept as follows, 'The *Notion* as Notion contains the following three moments or functional parts. The first is *universality*—meaning that is is in free equality with itself in its specific character. The second is *particularity*—that is, the specific character in which the universal continues in serene equality with itself. The third is *singularity*—meaning the reflection-into-self of the specific characters of universality and particularity;—which negative self-unity has *complete and original determinateness*, without any loss of self-identity or universality.'[3] Since the subject matter of a sphere such as 'Nature' does not yield a reflection of the triadic structure of the 'Idea' in the course of any piecemeal examination of it, the Notion is therefore invoked in order to substantiate its triadic division into the universality of the 'Mechanics', the particularity of the 'Physics' and the singularity of 'Organics', 'This division follows from the

[1] § 350 Addition.
[2] § 352 Addition.
[3] 'Encyclopaedia' §§ 160–165.

standpoint of the Notion as it is grasped in its totality, and displays the diremption of the Notion in its determinations. As it exhibits its determinations in this diremption, and yet only allows them independence as moments, it realizes itself in this, and so posits itself as Idea. The Notion not only exhibits its moments and expresses itself in its differences however, but also leads these apparently independent stages back into their ideality and unity. By leading them back into itself, it in fact turns them for the first time into the concrete Notion, the Idea, and truth.'[1] Precisely the same procedure is adopted in the structuralization of all the subsidiary spheres of 'Nature', and, indeed, of the 'Encyclopaedia' as a whole. On occasions however Hegel recognizes that he is met halfway by the subject matter itself, 'Magnetism is one of the determinations which inevitably became prominent when the *Notion* began to be aware of itself in determinate nature, and grasped the Idea of a *philosophy of nature*. This came about because the magnet exhibits the nature of the Notion, both in a simple straightforward way, and in its developed form as syllogism (§ 181). Its poles are the sensibly existent ends of a real line such as a rod, or a dimensionally more extended body. Their reality as poles is of an ideal nature however; it is not sensibly mechanistic, for the poles are simply indivisible. The point of indifference, which constitutes their substantial existence, is their unity as determinations of the Notion, and consequently it is from this unity alone that they derive their significance and their existence.'[2]

No feature of the Hegelian system is better known or less understood than the *dialectic*. In a famous conversation, recorded by Eckermann, Goethe tackled Hegel on the subject during the latter's visit to Weimar on October 18, 1827.[3] 'Hegel is here; Goethe has a very high esteem for him personally, though he does not greatly relish some of the fruits of his philosophy, and this evening he gave a tea party in his honour. In the course of the conversation, the nature of the dialectic was discussed.'

'Basically,' said Hegel, 'it is nothing more than the regulated and methodical cultivation of the spirit of contradiction, which is a gift common to everyone, and particularly valuable for distinguishing the true from the false.'

'But let us hope,' interposed Goethe, 'that such intellectual arts and skills are not too much misused for the purpose of turning falsehood into truth and truth into falsehood!'

[1] § 252 Addition.
[2] § 312 Remark.
[3] F. von Biedermann 'Goethe's Gespräche' (5 vols. Leipzig, 1909–1911) vol. III pp. 477–478.

'That does sometimes happen,' replied Hegel, 'but only with people who are spiritually sick.'

'Well,' said Goethe, 'I personally recommend the study of nature as preventive of that disease. For in nature we are dealing with something which is infinitely and eternally true, and which immediately rejects as inadequate everyone who does not show complete integrity and honesty in the way he observes and treats his subject. And I am certain that the study of nature would be a wholesome remedy for many a dialectical sufferer.'

The dialectic derives its significance and validity solely and exclusively from the triadicity of the self-thinking Idea. It has its ultimate origin therefore in the threefold division of knowledge, and it is applicable to the various spheres of the 'Encyclopaedia' only in so far as the attempt is being made to elicit a reflection of the Idea from them 'to whatever extent their finitude makes possible'. As Hegel presented his work, it appears as a triadic progression, *within each sphere*, from what is implicit or universal, to what is for itself or particular, and finally to what is in-and-for-itself or singular. It might just as well have been presented in the converse sequence however, and this might in fact have been a more satisfactory manner of procedure, since it *is* from the final triad that the whole pattern derives its significance. The great advantage of the method Hegel adopted is however that whereas it makes it difficult to see the significance of the triads while following only the details of his work, once the final levels of 'Spirit' are under consideration, the generalizations one is forced to make are fully qualified and substantiated, and, consequently, the validity of the overall exposition is so much the more apparent than it would have been had a *beginning* been made with these extreme abstractions.

It should be remembered that the Idea, the Notion and the dialectic, like the level, the hierarchy and the sphere, are *principles*, dual in nature, essentially distinct from their subject matter, but also constituting an integral part of it. *Practically* considered, they imply therefore that the exposition of a philosophical encyclopaedia involves three distinct disciplines. Firstly, the subject matter has to be intuited and understood for its own sake in precisely the same way as it is by the ordinary non-philosophical specialist. Secondly, the qualitative differences so often overlooked in the usual treatment of this subject matter have to be elicited and formulated as a system of levels, hierarchies and spheres. Here, as we have noticed, Hegel's work has much more in common with that of our contemporaries than it had with the predominantly alphabetical systematizations being developed in his own day. Thirdly, these principles, as elicited from their subject matter, have to be demonstrated as contributing to the definition and fulfillment of the 'self-thinking Idea' by being submitted to a dialectical interpretation. Although this third requirement does not justify any distortion or misrepresentation of the subject matter of the 'Encyclopaedia', it does invalidate the claims of all imperfect thinking to final philosophical validity, in that it demands that the structure of *each* sphere should be regarded as the fulfillment of its subject matter, and not vice versa.[1]

It will, perhaps, have become apparent, that the central problems faced by Hegel in his attempt to structuralize 'Spirit', bear a close resemblance to those in which a theologian becomes involved when he attempts to make intelligible remarks about the being and attributes of God. Hegel recognized the similarity, and in both the 'Phenomenology' and the 'Encyclopaedia' there is an immediate juxtapositioning of the theological and philosophical disciplines. Religious considerations, as we have seen, played an important part in his development, and largely on account of the effect they had upon Kierkegaard and Feuerbach, his mature views on religion have exercised a profound influence upon modern theology, and have helped, directly or indirectly, to form many of the current opinions on the subject. The manner in which his philosophical system was regarded by churchmen and theologians was by no means a matter of indifference to him moreover, and towards the end of his life, in a review of a book by Göschel, he makes it evident that he was then willing, and even pleased, to have it regarded as a restatement in philosophical terms, of the truths of Christianity.[2] This is not the place to enter upon a critical analysis of the famous 'Lectures on the Philosophy of Religion', but the relevance of the central principle of this work to current theology, and an indication of the manner in which religion is assessed within the 'Encyclopaedia', may, perhaps, form a fitting conclusion to this chapter.

Viewed from the standpoint of his mature system, the main development in Hegel's thinking during the 1790's was the shift from an interest

[1] An examination of Hegelianism in the light of Hans Vaihinger's theory of *fictionalism* would be a stimulating undertaking, and might do much to establish a general recognition of the value and validity of the central principles of the 'Encyclopaedia'. See 'Die Philosophie des Als-Ob. System der theoretischen, praktischen und religiösen Fiktionen der Menschheit auf Grund eines idealistischen Positivismus' (Berlin, 1911), 'The Philosophy of "As If"' (tr. C. K. Ogden, New York, 1924).

[2] Karl Friedrich Göschel (1784–1861) 'Aphorismen über Nichtwissen und absolutes Wissen im Verhältnisse zur christlichen Glaubenserkenntnis' (Berlin, 1829). The review appeared in the official organ of orthodox Hegelianism, 'Jahrbücher für wissenschaftliche Kritik' 1829 nos. 99–102, 105–106. 'Vermischte Schriften aus der Berliner Zeit' (ed. Glockner, Stuttgart, 1958) vol. 20 pp. 276–313.

in the *ethical* and *theological* implications of Kant's thought to preoccupation with the *encyclopaedic* potentials of Schelling's. The basic judgement motivating this change seems to have been that whereas ethical, social and religious matters must necessarily fall within the purview of an encyclopaedic interest, the converse is not the case. This judgement reappears in the mature exposition of 'Spirit', in which, as we have seen, philosophy and not religion is regarded as constituting the closest approximation to the 'Logic'. This simply implies that Hegel regarded philosophers as more fitted for expounding the significance of the major transition from 'Spirit' to 'Logic' than theologians. He evidently thought that although theology and philosophy are concerned with very similar subject matters, that of the former being God and man's relationship to God, and that of the latter being knowledge and man's ability to acquire and master it, it would be unreasonable to expect a theologian to make a contribution to philosophy unless he were able to distinguish between the two disciplines. He concluded therefore, that the essential difference between a theologian and a philosophical encyclopaedist is that whereas the latter is obliged to concern himself with religion, the former is by no means obliged to expound his world-view encyclopaedically. He makes this difference quite clear on several occasions. In the review just mentioned for example, he quotes with approval Göschel's remark that, 'Spirit searches all things, including the depths of the Godhead.'[1] In the peroration to his inaugural lecture given at Berlin on October 22, 1818 he develops the same theme, 'I make bold to wish and hope that I shall succeed in winning and deserving your confidence along the way that we have before us. To begin with, however, I can ask nothing of you but this, that you should bring with you confidence in science, belief in reason, confidence and belief in yourselves. The spirit of truth, faith in the power of thought, is essential to the study of philosophy; man should honour himself, and regard himself as worthy of the highest. He cannot overvalue the greatness and power of thought. The closed essence of the universe harbours no force capable of resisting the spirit of knowledge, to whose eyes it must disclose and reveal itself, and for whose delight it must lay forth its riches and its depths.'[2] Remarks such as these naturally brought Fichte's fate upon him, and for a while at least, he was suspected of atheism by the Prussian government. In 1821 for example, when the king by an order in cabinet made a minister responsible for seeing that

[1] 'Denn der Geist erforschet alle Dinge, auch die Tiefen der Gottheit'. op.cit. p. 157.

[2] Franz Wiedmann 'G. W. F. Hegel in Selbstzeugnissen und Bilddokumenten' (Hamburg, 1965) p. 69.

the Okenian philosophy of nature and 'similar doctrines leading to atheism' were not promulgated in the universities of Prussia, Hegel felt himself to be threatened.[1] Glockner has noticed however, that despite the treatment of mediaeval scholasticism in the lectures on the 'History of Philosophy', and despite his lifelong profession of staunch Lutheranism, it is the speculative theological systems of the middle ages, writings such as the 'Summa contra gentiles' and the 'Summa theologica' of St. Thomas Aquinas, which provide the closest approximation to the interpretation of religion found in his works.[2]

The key to this interpetation is his assessment of the doctrine of the Christian Trinity as this dogma has been accepted throughout the Western Church since 1054.[3] As the triadic syllogistic unity of the self-thinking Idea is regarded by him as constituting the most complex level of 'Spirit', the fullest and completest formulation of the central principle of philosophy, so the Trinitarian doctrine of the co-equality of the Three Divine Persons in one Substance is regarded by him as constituting the most complex level of 'Religion', the fullest and completest formulation of the central principle of theology. The philosophical principle, once the significance of it is grasped, implies the attitude to its subject matter made explicit in the 'Encyclopaedia'. The theological doctrine, once put into practice, implies the life and activity of the Christian community. To force the encyclopaedic labours demanded by a recognition of the significance of the Idea upon a Christian community would be to kill it. To reduce philosophy solely to the life and activity of the Christian community would be to stifle it. Properly understood therefore, the disciplines of theology and philosophy are complementary. Philosophy derives its full stature, depth, nobility and certainty from the spiritual life of a wholesome Christian community. This community, in its turn, may rest assured of nothing but respect and confirmation from any fully valid philosophy.

As might have been expected, the expression of views such as these involved Hegel in several bitter controversies, which he would probably have been better advised to have avoided. Despite the appreciation he

[1] Letter to Neithammer June 9, 1821: 'Briefe' (ed. Hoffmeister no. 390, vol. II pp. 269–273). Cf. Friedrich Heer 'Hegel und die Jugend' ('Frankfurter Hefte' 22 Jahrgung, Heft 5, May 1967 pp. 323–332); R. Garaudy 'Gott ist tot' (Berlin, 1965).

[2] Hermann Glockner 'Hegel' (2 vols. Stuttgart, 1958) vol. II pp. 562–567.

[3] On the 'Filioque' addition to the Creed and the doctrine of Double Procession see J. N. D. Kelly 'Early Christian Creeds' (London, 1964), H. B. Swete 'On the History of the Doctrnie of the Procession of the Holy Spirit' (Cambridge, 1876). See the important analysis of the 'Divine *Triangle*' in J. Hoffmeister 'Dokumente zu Hegels Entwicklung' (Stuttgart, 1936) pp. 303–306.

shows of the part played by feeling and aesthetic experience in religion for example,[1] he managed to make an enemy of Schleiermacher, and despite the astonishing insight into many of the non-Christian religions displayed in his lectures, he tended, when not actually speaking from the cathedra, to hold unswervingly to the Lutheranism and the uncompromising intellectualism of his youth.[2] This may have been due in part to what he had suffered under the tutelage of Storr, and there can be little doubt, that despite the general principles of his system and his realistic and accurate knowledge of mankind, he hoped that he would not remain the sole expositor and proponent of the 'self-thinking Idea'.

To what extent is his treatment of theology and his assessment of Christianity relevant to current scholarship and the present state of affairs? If, for the sake of brevity and convenience, we may take this question to touch principally upon the central doctrine of the Trinity, the following observations may prove to be acceptable as an answer to it.

Largely on account of his having read a work by Tholuck,[3] Hegel took a great interest in the non- and pre-Christian origins of Trinitarian theology. Tholuck had indicated the occurrence of the divine triad in Arabic, Parsee and pagan Greek thought, and in his lectures on religion Hegel paid particular attention to the corresponding Hindu doctrine of the trimurti.[4] Recent scholarship has tended to confirm the view that the conception of the triadicity of the Deity was not derived solely from the New Testament or even from the Judaeo-Christian tradition.[5] What is more, the church has not been very successful in controlling the interpretation of the dogma at a popular level. It was not until 1334 that the observance of the Sunday following Whitsun as a feast in celebration of the Trinity was universally enjoined by the Pope,[6] and it can hardly be claimed that the festival enjoys the popularity it deserves. It captured the popular imagination in England largely on account of its having been

[1] 'Lectures on the Philosophy of Religion' op. cit. p. 3.

[2] Anton Günther (1783–1863) attempted to interpret *Roman Catholic* sacramentalism in terms of Hegelianism. All his works were condemned by the Index in 1857, and he submitted to the decision.

[3] 'Encyclopaedia' introd. 2nd ed. F. A. G. Tholuck (1799–1877) 'Die spekulative Trinitätslehre des späteren Orients' (Berlin, 1826).

[4] op. cit. vol. II pp. 11–30.

[5] Hermann Usener (1834–1905) 'Dreiheit' ('Rheinisches Museum für Philologie' N.F. vol. 58, 1903); the article by K. E. Kirk in A. E. J. Rawlinson 'Essays on the Trinity' (London, 1928); J. R. Illingworth 'The Doctrine of the Trinity' (London, 1907); A. R. Johnson 'The One and the Many in the Israelite conception of God' (Cardiff, 1942); A. W. Wainwright 'The Trinity in the New Testament' (London, 1962).

[6] P. Browe 'Zur Geschichte des Dreifaltigkeitsfestes' ('Archiv für Liturgiewissenschaft' i, pp. 65–81, 1950).

the day on which St. Thomas à Becket was consecrated bishop in 1162,[1] and many curious perversions of Trinitarian theology have flourished here.[2] Nor has the situation been any different in Germany,[3] or on the continent at large.[4] Hegel is therefore undoubtedly justified in refusing to regard Trinitarian thought of the popular kind as exclusively Christian, or as in any way adequate to an expression of the central truth of Christianity.

Hegel takes the culminating embodiment of the Christian acknowledgement of the Trinity to be the life of the Christian community.[5] This was by no means an original interpretation of the dogma. Daniel Waterland (1683–1743) for example, propounded it in the course of his attempt to make Trinitarian thinking intelligible to the Socinians, Deists and Arianizers of his day, 'If religious practice in any measure depends upon a previous knowledge of God (as undoubtedly it does) then certainly, for the like reason, the perfection of that practice depends upon the perfection of such knowledge . . . If God be Father, Son and Holy Ghost, the duties owing to God, will be duties owing under that trine distinction; which must be paid accordingly: and whoever leaves out any of the three out of his idea of God, comes so far short of knowing God perfectly, and of serving him in proportion of the manifestations made of him . . . The belief of the doctrine of the Trinity (supposing it true) is no slight or insignificant theory, no barren notion or speculation; since it has a direct influence upon the dispositions of our minds, and upon our happiness hereafter. I make not this an argument of the truth of the doctrine . . . but of the importance of it . . . And I add, that if it may have such influence upon us, in creating proper dispositions, that comes to the same

[1] See Margery Brews' Valentine letter to John Paston (Feb. 1477), 'No more to yowe at this tyme, but the Holy Trinite hafe yowe in kepyng.' 'The Paston Letters' (ed. Gairdner, 3 vols. Westminster, 1900) vol. III p. 170.

[2] See 'The Castle of Perseverance' (c. 1425) which opens with speeches by the *infernal* Trinity of Mundus (the world), Belyal (the devil) and Caro (the flesh). 'The Macro Plays' (ed. Furnivall and Pollard, E.E.T.S. Extra Series no. XCL, London, 1904).

[3] German folk-lore relating to the Trinity, some of it from Swabia, is surveyed by E. Hoffmann-Krayer and H. Bächtold-Stäubli in 'Handwörterbuch des deutschen Aberglaubens' (10 vols. Berlin and Leipzig, 1927–1942) vol. II pp. 430–435.

[4] Usener, op. cit., has no very high opinion of the ultimate origin of popular triadic thinking, 'It can be confirmed that even today there are peoples who have developed no numerical concept greater than two, and that there are others for whom their highest number, three, means the same as many.' St. Antoninus (1389–1459), in his 'Summa Theologica' (ed. Ballerini, Verona, 1740) inveighs against the pictorial representation of the Trinity as a three-headed body as 'monstrum in verum natura'. Urban VIII had similar pictures burnt on August 11, 1628: cf. J. Molanus (1553–1585) 'Oratio de Agnis Dei' (Louvain, 1771) p. 486, 'Bullarium Benedicti XIV' (1768) vol. I p. 345b.

[5] 'Philosophy of Religion' pt. III c.iii, 'The Idea in the element of the Church or Spiritual Community; the kingdom of the Spirit.'

as to say, that it raises and improves our virtues, and all virtue is practical.'[1] This interpretation has become particularly popular among English theologians since Professor Hodgson endorsed it in the Croall Lectures of 1942–1943. He expresses it as follows, 'This doctrine had its origin not in philosophical speculation, but in the fidelity of the Christian community to the revelation it had received . . . The doctrine of the Trinity, the distinctively Christian doctrine of God, gives its character to the distinctively Christian way of worshipping and serving God; it guides our paths by giving us the pattern unity for individual and social life; it illuminates and deepens our hope of immortality; it enables us to see God and man in their right proportion as Creator and created.'[2] More recently, John Wren-Lewis has also emphasized that, 'the doctrine is no abstract theologians' puzzle but a practical and concrete design for living.'[3]

The Church defines dogma for the purpose of transmission, not explanation, the whole spirit of which procedure is therefore essentially negative, an avowal that no attempt should be made to explain what is essentially inexplicable.[4] It must certainly be admitted that despite the brilliance and acumen with which St. Augustine and St. Thomas Aquinas have developed the psychological theory of the Trinity,[5] Hegel is, in the main, correct when he characterizes expositions of this kind as exercises in thought, the validity of which tends to be confined to its *theological* context, and the persuasiveness of which tends to depend upon the reader's sharing in its presuppositions, many of which remain rationally unsubstantiated.[6] F. C. Baur (1792–1860), taking this insight as his point of departure, surveyed and the whole history of orthodox Trinitarian doctrine in a magnificently detailed and perceptive manner, showing that it could hardly be regarded as in any sense philosophically or even theologically consistent.[7] English theology provides no exception to this.

[1] 'The Importance of the Doctrine of the Holy Trinity asserted in reply to some late pamphlets' (London, 1734) ch. II pp. 35–77: Collected Works (10 vols. Oxford, 1823).

[2] 'The Doctrine of the Trinity' (London, 1943) p. 193.

[3] 'Modern Philosophy and the doctrine of the Trinity' ('The Philosophical Quarterly' vol. 5, 1955, pp. 214–224).

[4] J. R. Illingworth 'The Doctrine of the Trinity apologetically considered' (London, 1907).

[5] Officially, the predominant theory in the West, according to which the two processes of the Divine Life are compared to the analogical processes of human self-knowledge and self-love. The Son is generated as the act of thinking on the part of the Father, the Holy Ghost proceeds from the mutual love of the Father and the Son. St. Augustine 'The Trinity' (tr. McKenna, Washington, 1963); St. Thomas 'The Summa Theologica' (tr. English Dominicans, 20 vols. London, 1911–1925) vol. 2 pp. 1–207.

[6] 'History of Philosophy' pt. 2 sect. ii.

[7] 'Die christliche Lehre von der Dreieinigkeit und Menschwerdung Gottes in ihrer geschichtlichen Entwicklung' (3 vols. Tübingen, 1841–1843): on Hegel, vol. III pp. 886–933.

R. C. Moberly manages, it is true, to introduce some philosophical consistency into the consideration of the doctrine,[1] but his work has not been influential, and most modern English theologians would probably agree with Claude Welch when he says that, 'Whatever may be concluded about other doctrines, the doctrine of the Trinity has rightly been considered to be wholly a doctrine of revelation, as regards both its historical basis and its role in systematic theology.'[2] Consequently, although a student of classical Greek, a philosopher and a modern scientist would all have to qualify their acceptance of the interpretation put upon 'homoousin' and 'hypostasis' at Nicaea and Constantinople, it is essential that the Christian theologian should not do so, since for him this interpretation embodies a truth concerning the 'Three Persons in one Substance' which is of *absolute* importance.[3]

Hegel singles out Jacob Boehme, with his theory of the Supreme Spirit before the creation, the seven nature spirits, and the regeneration of man through Christ, as typical of thinkers steeped in the truths of Christianity, attempting to give truth a speculative form, but failing to do so in any very satisfactory manner on account of their only being able to think in terms of sensuous images. As we have seen, he regards the principles of his 'Encyclopaedia' as the only means by which Boehme's handicaps may be completely overcome.[4]

Hegel's assessment of religion is therefore of great general interest, since it not only provides a means by which constructive dialogues might be opened up between the various religions, but also one by which theologians might communicate meaningfully with other specialists. The institutionalized and self-conscious use of the general *philosophical* principles of his system within predominantly *religious* contexts might well prove to be a mixed blessing however, since it would at least have a *tendency* to stultify the spontaneity and human idiosyncrasy which are as

[1] 'Atonement and Personality' (London, 1901) ch. VIII.

[2] 'The Trinity in Contemporary Theology' (London, 1953) p. 243; cf. C. C. Richardson 'The Doctrine of the Trinity' (New York, 1958).

[3] At the Council of Nicaea (325) and possibly also at that of Constantinople (381), the dogma of the Trinity was defined in its basic outlines in order to counteract certain heresies. The real distinction of the Three Divine Persons was affirmed against Sabellianism, and a recognition of their co-equality and co-eternity maintained in the face of Arianism and Macedonianism. Jules Lebreton 'Histoire du Dogme de la Trinité' (8th ed. 2 vols. Paris, 1927–1928); G. L. Prestige 'God in Patristic Thought' (London, 1952); J. N. D. Kelly 'Early Christian Creeds' (London, 1964).

[4] 'History of Philosophy' pt. 3 sect. i, B: cf. G. W. Allen's article on Boehme in the 'Encyclopaedia of Religion and Ethics' vol. II pp. 778–784 (ed. Hastings, Edinburgh, 1909). Alexandre Koyré, 'La philosophie de Jacob Boehme' (Paris, 1929) does not think that Boehme can be regarded as propounding any sort of *system*.

essential to the life of a Christian community as they are to the work of an artist.

f. THE IDEA OF NATURE

'If theory had to depend entirely upon experience, there would never be any.'—Novalis.

Since there never has been any general appreciation of the 'Encyclopaedia', it can hardly be regarded as very surprising that the application of its principles to an assessment of the natural sciences should have involved Hegel in a criticism of several widely accepted ways of thinking. We have already noticed the value of his attempts to indicate the importance of the qualitative differences he regarded as being unjustifiably overlooked by the *natural scientists* of his day. These lectures also contain explicit as well as implied criticisms of several vaguer and more *general attitudes* to natural phenomena however, and since it might be argued with some justice that several of these are still flourishing, it may be of interest to take note of them.

Although the relevance of *astronomy* to theological or philosophical considerations is somewhat difficult to define with any precision, it is, quite understandably, *felt* to be of very considerable importance. Like Paley, Hegel tended to belittle the intellectual content of this feeling, and to concentrate solely upon an analysis of the actual subject matter of the discipline. He then came to the conclusion, that whereas stellar astronomy might reasonably be regarded as presupposing the subject matter of mathematical and finite mechanics (§§ 254–267), it could not reasonably be regarded as involving anything as *complex* as the solar system or physics (§ 268–273), let alone organic phenomena. Subsequent developments have made it impossible for us to regard it in quite this manner, but the general significance of the assessment would still appear to be relevant to our emotional if not to our purely intellectual manner of regarding stellar phenomena. 'The host of stars . . . should not be put on a level with the solar system, which for us is the primary knowable system of real rationality within the heavens. The stars may be admired for their repose, but in worth they are not to be regarded as the equals of the concrete individual body. The content of space explodes into an infinite number of matters; this can delight the eye, but it is only the first breaking forth of matter, and this eruption of light is as unworthy of wonder as an eruption on the skin or a swarm of flies. The tranquillity of these stars means more to the heart, for the contemplation of their peace and simplicity calms the passions. Their world is not so interesting from a philosophical point of view as it is to the sentiments however. As a plurality within immeasurable spaces it is of no significance to reason; it is externality, emptiness, negative infinity. Reason knows itself to be above this, for the wonder is merely negative, an uplifting of the mind which remains strictly limited.'[1]

The assessment on the basis of which the planets are regarded as the most complex phenomena of the solar system[2] and the Earth as the most complex of the planets, is similar to this in that it is also likely to give rise to emotional rather than intellectual objections. 'The planet is the veritable prius, the subjectivity in which these differences are merely moments of an ideal nature, and in which life first has determinate being. The Sun is subservient to the planets, just as the Sun, Moon, comets and stars in general, are merely aspects of the Earth. The Sun therefore has neither engendered nor thrown off the planets; the whole solar system is an entirety, for the Sun and the planets are engendered reciprocally . . . It is the property of the Earth or of organic being to digest the completely universal astral powers which appear to have independence as heavenly bodies, and to bring them under the sway of individuality, so that these gigantic members reduce themselves to moments. Quality, in its totality, is individuality, as the infinite form which is one with itself. If there is any talk of pride of place, it must be this our Earth which we regard as supreme. If one reflects quantitatively, one can certainly let the Earth sink away beneath one as, 'a drop in the ocean of infinitude'; size, however, is a very external determination. We now come to stand upon the Earth therefore, which is not only our physical, but also our spiritual home.'[3]

The assessment on the basis of which animation and sentience are regarded as initiating a sphere which is 'higher'[4] than that of physics or inorganic nature is closely analogous, in that it also involves a rejection of durability or size and an acceptance of complexity as the deciding factor in the dialectical progression. This transition is particularly interesting and valuable in that it presupposes the acceptance of the view that life is the *culmination* of inorganic nature, and the avoidance of the homely

[1] § 268 Addition.
[2] § 270.
[3] § 280 Addition.
[4] Hegel does use this adjective to convey the concept; see § 312 Remark, 'Nature is the Idea in the element of extrinsicality, and like the understanding, it holds fast to the *dispersed* moments of the Notion and so expresses their reality. In higher things however, it unites the different forms of the Notion into the highest concretion of unity.'

but blind alley opened up by the opinion that inorganic subsistence is the ultimate outcome of all life. 'The sentience of individuality is to the same extent immediately *exclusive* however, and maintains a state of tension with an inorganic nature to which it is opposed as to its *external* condition and material . . . The basic division, or expulsion of the Sun and everything else, constitutes the precise standpoint of animation. The *Idea* of life is in itself this unconscious creativeness, it is an expansion of nature, which in animation has returned into its truth. For the individual however, inorganic nature is a presupposition with which it is confronted, and it is this which gives rise to the finitude of living being. The individual is for itself, but as the organic being has this negativity within itself, the connection here is absolute, indivisible, internal, and essential. Externality is determined only as having being for organic being; organic being is that which maintains itself in opposition to it'.[1] Similarly, since consciousness or 'Spirit' is regarded as being the most complex outcome of organic existence, the entire sphere of 'Nature' is, in the structure of the whole 'Encyclopaedia', to be regarded as the antecedent or presupposition of it. 'This is the *transition from natural being into spirit*; nature has found its consummation in living being, and has made its peace by shifting into a higher sphere. Spirit has therefore issued forth from nature. The purpose of nature is to extinguish itself, and to break through its rind of immediate and sensuous being, to consume itself like a Phoenix in order to emerge from this externality rejuvenated as spirit'.[2]

In that the application of the principles of the 'Encyclopaedia' to the natural sciences has given rise to the formulation of transitions such as these, the work might be regarded as constituting a counter-Copernican revolution in the general history of European thought. Advances in our knowledge of astronomical space since the sixteenth century, and in our awareness of the extent of geological time since the nineteenth, have certainly made it appear reasonable to ridicule the idea that organic existence and consciousness might be regarded as the culmination of nature. What is more, if we are thinking solely in terms of size and duration, of the *extent* of space and time, there would appear to be little point in arguing that this is not a ridiculous idea. To say that Hegelianism has countered Copernicanism is therefore merely to say that a view of the universe in which the Earth is not regarded as the centre is *compatible* with a view of knowledge in which not only the Earth, but also organic

[1] § 357 and Addition.
[2] § 376 Addition.

life and consciousness are regarded as more complex and therefore of more significance and importance than stars and galaxies etc.[1] If it is borne in mind that it is impossible for anyone regarding natural phenomena to deny the *consciousness* involved in his consideration of them, and that the *quality* of this awareness must imply that any meaningful interpretation of nature necessarily involves a consideration not only of size and extent but also of relative *complexity*, the emotional and intellectual disturbances set up by an attempt to see or deny the full significance of relative space and time, will tend to disappear.

The *logical categories* involved in these disturbances are dealt with by Hegel in §§ 94–104 of the 'Encyclopaedia'. Infinity for example, is presented as having determinate being and limit as its immediate antecedents and being-for-self as its immediate sequent, infinite progression as having quantum and number as its immediate antecedents and quantitative ratio and measure as its immediate sequents. These transitions, like the rest of the 'Encyclopaedia', imply therefore, that any consideration of experience as a whole involves not simply reference to nature, the content of space and time, but also an investigation of the relative complexity of categories and of the general significance of 'Spirit'. The extent to which popular opinion would tend to question their validity is therefore the extent to which it habitually regards knowledge in a purely *piecemeal* manner, and so necessarily fails in any attempt it makes to treat it as a whole.

Hegel regards the subject matter of the 'Philosophy of Nature' as being the *confirmed* and *consolidated* content of the data provided by the natural sciences. He shows very little interest in the procedure of weighing and evaluating the relative merits of various theories, and only refers to it in order to indicate his reasons for regarding and assessing the subject matter as he does. He is by no means blind to the necessary imperfection of all empirical knowledge, and he recognizes that it needs constant revision, but he never fails to object to the framing of *hypotheses* in so far as he regards these imperfect productions of 'Spirit' as giving rise to distorted interpretations of natural phenomena. He is even reluctant to admit that they may be employed profitably in a heuristic manner in order to facilitate research, and he always insists that they can serve no further purpose once the knowledge they relate to has been confirmed and consolidated. It is this attitude which gives rise to his invective against

[1] Cf. J. W. Oliver 'Kant's Copernican Analogy: an examination of a re-examination' ('Kant-Studien' vol. 55 sect. 4 pp. 505–511, 1964).

the proliferation of forces, the postulation of bundles of light rays, atoms, pores, the latency of heat, Newton's theory of colours etc. He objects to these concepts primarily for *scientific* reasons, that is to say, because he regards them as having no foundation in the subject matter they are meant to make intelligible. Thinking which is given to this kind of fictionalizing, which fails to recognize the significance of formulating levels, hierarchies and spheres, and which relies upon various more or less invalid or inappropriate models in order to communicate its interpretations of natural phenomena, is characterized by him as the *understanding*. 'If the thought-determinations are vitiated by a rigid antithesis, i.e. if they are only of a *finite* nature, they are not adequate to the absoluteness of truth, which is both in and for itself, and truth is therefore unable to enter into thought. Thought of this kind, which can bring forth only *limited* determinations, and which has no other means of procedure, is what in the stricter sense of the word is termed *understanding*. The *finitude* of these thought-determinations is, moreover, to be grasped in a double manner. In one respect they are simply *subjective*, and the antithesis of an objective clings permanently to them. In the other, their *content* is always restricted, so that they persist in antithesis to one another and still more to the Absolute.'[1]

The merits and demerits of the standpoints he takes on account of this attitude toward hypotheses have been fully treated in the commentary. He regards it as the prerogative of any informed and thinking person to call in question the concepts of specialists if he suspects them of being purely hypothetical, 'The professionals only allow validity to the peculiar idiom of certain theories etc., they completely overlook what others say, and treat it as if it had not been said. People of this kind often want to form a closed circle, to be in exclusive possession of science, and to extirpate other forms of judgement; jurists are an example of this. The law is for everyone however, and so is colour. A closed circle such as this develops certain intellectual habits, which have a straitening effect. If one is not automatized by these habits one is supposed to be uninitiated, for only the club members are supposed to understand the matter. This is not a false supposition, for as one does not employ the metaphysical category of the *understanding* according to which they consider the matter ought to be regarded, one certainly does not understand what they understand. Philosophers are usually cold shouldered, although it is in fact their task to criticize these categories.'[2]

[1] 'Encyclopaedia' § 25.
[2] § 320 Addition. Cf. § 276 Remark, § 286 Addition, § 298 Remark.

Hegel often characterizes the concepts of the understanding as the products of 'reflection'. His criticism of the philosophy of reflection first became widely known on account of his early Jena writings, which were published when the nature and extent of his differences with Schelling were still very largely unrecognized. At that time it was mainly directed at what he regarded as the artificial Kantian and Fichtean distinction between the thinking subject and the thing-in-itself.[1] He realized later that his attitude tended to involve an unwarranted simplification of the views of these thinkers. Nevertheless, to talk of the determinations and philosophy of 'reflection' became a convenient way of characterizing an attitude of mind which simply *reflected* the subject matter of knowledge piecemeal instead of assessing it rationally, and it was for this reason that the word became part of his technical vocabulary.[2] As it is used in the 'Encyclopaedia' therefore, it refers to the tacit or self-conscious recognition of a distinction between the subject matter of this work and knowledge. The use of it therefore implies a precise indication of the *origin* of the particular concepts of the understanding being criticized. The predominant *categories* involved in reflective thinking are analyzed and assessed in the 'Logic' under the heading of 'Essence'. 'The standpoint of essence is, in general, that of reflection. The word "reflection" has its origin in optics, where it refers to light, in its rectilinear progression, impinging upon a mirroring surface and being thrown back from it. We have here a duality, the being of an immediacy, and secondly, a mediated or posited factor. Now it is precisely a duality such as this which occurs when we reflect, or, as we also say, *think back* upon an object, since we are then attempting to comprehend it as mediated, not as it is in its immediacy. The task or aim of philosophy is often taken to be the ascertainment of the essence of things, and this is merely regarded as meaning that instead of leaving them in their immediacy, they have to be shown to be mediated by or grounded in something else. In this case, the immediate being of things is conceived of as a rind or curtain behind which essence is concealed.'[3] Reflective is also sharply distinguished from dialectical thinking, 'In its proper determinateness, dialectic is however the true and peculiar nature of the determinations of the understanding, of things, and of the finite in general. Reflection differs from it mainly because it transcends isolated determinateness and its relatedness by positing this determinateness in relation-

[1] Herman Glockner 'Hegel' (2 vols. Stuttgart, 1958) vol. II pp. 187–191.

[2] See the various shades of meaning attached to it listed in Glockner's 'Hegel-Lexikon' (2 vols. Stuttgart, 1957).

[3] 'Encyclopaedia' § 112 Addition.

ship while maintaining the validity of its isolation. Dialectic transcends in an *immanent* manner however, so that the one-sidedness and limitedness of the determinations of the understanding shows itself in its true light as the negation of these determinations. All that is finite is self-sublating. That which is dialectical therefore constitutes the moving spirit of scientific progress, the only principle by means of which *immanent connection and necessity* may enter the content of science; the true as opposed to the external sublation of that which is finite lies therefore in the dialectic in general.'[1]

Although he recognizes therefore, that consciousness or 'Spirit' *in general* has the power to self-consciously synthesize 'Logic' and 'Nature', Hegel distinguishes very carefully between the *various* attitudes to the subject matter of the natural sciences which this power has given rise to. He points out that not all levels of 'Spirit' are capable of assessing it with equal validity and rationality, 'The natural unity of thought and intuition found in a child or an animal is no more than feeling, it is not spirituality. Man must have eaten of the tree of the knowledge of good and evil, he must have gone through the labour and activity of thought in order to be what he is, i.e. the subjugator of the separation of what is his, from nature.'[2] As has already been noticed, consciousness is regarded by him as becoming capable of assessing nature rationally once it has grasped the significance of the Idea and the Notion, 'Nature is *implicitly* a living whole; more closely considered, the movement through its different stages consists of the Idea *positing* itself as what it is *implicitly*, i.e. the Idea passes *into itself* by proceeding out of its immediacy and externality, which is *death*. It does this primarily in order to take on *living* being, but also in order to transcend this determinateness, in which it is merely life, and to bring itself forth into the existence of spirit, which constitutes the truth and ultimate purpose of nature, and the true actuality of the Idea.'[3]

This is not the place to enter upon a detailed analysis of the careful expositions of various attitudes to the subject matter of the natural sciences given in the lectures on 'Subjective Spirit', 'Aesthetics', 'Religion' etc. As has been noticed, most of the *epistemological* issues raised in current philosophies of science would have been regarded by Hegel as constituting the subject matter of psychology rather than that of 'Nature'. His analyses of the attitude of various peoples and of the artist to 'nature', and of the theologian to the 'Creation' need not detain us here. Since, however, the

[1] 'Encyclopaedia' § 81 Remark.
[2] § 246 Addition.
[3] § 251.

lectures on the 'History of Philosophy'[1] contain detailed criticism and assessments of the philosophies of nature he considers as approximating most closely to his own, some indication of the relevant contents of this work may provide a fitting conclusion to this chapter.

Naturally enough, he takes the threefold division of the subject matter of the 'Encyclopaedia' and the interpretation of this in the light of the self-thinking Idea as being, in principle, the ultimate accomplishment of philosophy. In these lectures therefore, he attempts to show the extent to which the philosophers of the past have formulated systems approximating to this ideal. In doing this it was not however convenient for him simply to adopt the general procedure of the 'Encyclopaedia', for if he had lectured in a purely *speculative* manner, his audiences would have found his expositions somewhat bewildering. They would have involved the analysis of the various philosophical systems without reference to their historical contexts, and would probably also have necessitated their being dismembered, for very few of them are wholly consistent in merit and principle. He therefore decided to give the subject an *historical* framework, and to allow his criticism of the various philosophies to arise out of a simply chronological method of presentation. The result is highly satisfying, the uncomplicated historical sequence of the subject matter being readily intelligible, and the criticisms deriving point and crispness from their speculative origin. It is however somewhat misleading, and many critics have, understandably but quite mistakenly, taken the work to imply that Hegel regarded the world *historical* process as finding its final culmination in the Berlin lecture rooms of 1818–1831.

A perusal of this work soon makes it apparent that it is the philosophical systems of ancient Greece which Hegel regards as approximating most closely to his own. Thus, the subject matter of his own '*Logic*' is seen as being anticipated and prefigured in the Greek attempts to define the *nous*. Thales is therefore praised as the first true philosopher of nature in that he attempted to present water as the *principle* of all things. Heraclitus's formulation of the universal principle of flux from being and non-being is, of course, singled out for special appreciation. It is however the 'Metaphysics' of Aristotle which Hegel regards as constituting the closest approximation to the 'Logic'. Similarly, the various Greek attempts to define the significance of the elements etc., are regarded as prefigurations of the 'Philosophy of *Nature*'. Once again it is the relevant Aristotelian work, the 'Physics', which receives the most exhaustive treatment. Hegel

[1] (3 vols. tr. Haldane and Simson, London, 1963).

praises it for presenting nature as determined by the conceptions of end and necessity, but criticizes it, as he does the whole Aristotelian system, for allowing 'the different parts to fall into a series of independently determined conceptions', and failing to exhibit the nous as permeating all empirical manifestation.[1] Greek anticipations of the 'Philosophy of *Spirit*' are found in the treatment of the soul by Leucippus and Democritus, Plato's 'Republic', Aristotle's psychology, ethics and politics, and in the ethical doctrines of the Stoics and Epicureans etc.

It is in the juxtaposing of Bacon and Boehme in his consideration of the intellectual history of the early seventeenth century, that Hegel indicates the most interesting anticipation of his 'Philosophy of Nature' in *modern* philosophy.[2] The Lord Chancellor of England and the shoemaker of Görlitz are presented as formulating the two fundamental principles of any final philosophy of nature, i.e. the understanding of its subject matter and the appreciation of its structure. He characterizes the central significance of Bacon's work as follows: 'He did not merely bring forth opinions and sentiments, he did not merely express himself regarding the sciences dogmatically, as a fine gentleman might, but he went into the matter closely, and established a method in respect of scientific knowledge . . . He set forth the general principles of procedure in an empirical philosophy. The spirit of his philosophy is to take experience as the true and only source of knowledge, and then to regulate the thought concerning it. Knowledge from experience stands in opposition to knowledge arising from the speculative Notion, and the opposition is apprehended in so acute a manner that the knowledge proceeding from the Notion is ashamed of the knowledge from experience, just as this again takes up a position of antagonism to the knowledge through the Notion . . . The Notion is an essential matter, but as such its finite side is just as essential . . . This particularity must be worked out on its own account; we must become acquainted with empirical nature, both with the physical and the human. The merit of modern times is to have accomplished or furthered these ends; it was in the highest degree unsatisfactory when the ancients attempted the work.' The corresponding appreciation of Boehme is one of the most fascinatingly perceptive expositions of the whole work. The crux of it is as follows: 'Boehme's chief, and one may even say, his only thought—the thought that permeates all his works—is that of perceiving the holy Trinity in everything, and recognizing everything as

[1] op. cit. vol. II p. 156; cf. pp. 153–179.
[2] op. cit. vol. III pp. 170–216.

its revelation and manifestation, so that it is the universal principle in which and through which everything exists; in such a way, moreover, that all things have this divine Trinity in themselves, not as a Trinity pertaining to the ordinary conception, but as the real Trinity of the absolute Idea. Everything that exists is, according to Boehme, this three-fold alone, and this three-fold is everything. To him the universe is thus one divine life and revelation of God in all things.'

For Hegel, as we have seen, the Idea of Nature involves a combination of the Baconian and the Boehmian attitudes to natural phenomena. Despite the searching criticism of Newtonian mechanics and optics contained in these lectures, the *basic* inspiration of the work may therefore be regarded as differing little, if at all, from that of the 'Principia Mathematica'.

g. CRITICS

'Cantate serenissimae
Triumphum philosophiae.'
—Robert Burton 'Philosophaster.'

The fate of these lectures in the hands of their critics has been somewhat singular. There can be very few works of this importance that have remained so completely unappreciated for so long. When Michelet finally published them in full in 1842, most of the purely scientific material they deal with was already ten to forty years out of date, and even the specialists were no longer completely familiar with the details of it. The general public had known of the broad outlines of the work since 1817, but only from the condensed paragraphs and remarks of the published 'Encyclopaedia', and taken by themselves, these abstruse and highly technical passages were necessarily unintelligible to those acquainted with neither the natural sciences nor the general principles of Hegelianism. During the 1830's there were therefore complete and radical misunderstandings of the work; F. C. Sibbern (1785–1872) for example, Kierkegaard's tutor at Copenhagen, published acute but wholly irrelevant criticisms of what he considered to be Hegel's views on certain natural phenomena.

The situation did not change appreciably once the full text had appeared, for despite the care with which it had been prepared, the explanatory comments with which it was accompanied were quite inadequate to the needs of the day. No one was both willing and able to undertake the daunting task of explaining it in detail and relating its principles to the state of current knowledge. As time passed and the undertaking became more difficult, scientists and philosophers therefore tended to class it with the corresponding Schellingian writings, and to regard it as obsolete. Michelet, Rosenkranz and Vera, despite the courage and persistence with which they attempted to expound the merits of it, had neither the knowledge nor the ability to save it from sinking into the oblivion in which it has remained ever since. The structure forced upon our university education by the need for specialists has tended to seal its fate. Professional philosophers are not required to be as well acquainted with the natural sciences as they should be, and very few of them indeed ever acquire a working knowledge of the details and minutiae of the histories of these disciplines. What is more, natural scientists, since Whewell, have not been in the habit of reading Hegel, and have ceased even to dream of taking all scientific knowledge as their province. Since this state of affairs is widely recognized, few will be surprised to learn that apart from some valuable dissertations on *special* aspects of the work which have appeared in Germany in the last decade or so, worthwhile criticism of it is extremely rare.

In order to throw the maximum amount of light upon the nature of Hegel's expositions, criticisms of them should, in the normal course of events, be presented in a *rational* sequence. In this case however it will be more fitting simply to arrange the relevant publications in chronological order. This list contains everything relevant with which I am acquainted, it does not however pretend to be exhaustive.

1800–1831

During Hegel's lifetime, neither his followers nor his opponents paid much attention to the work.

W. T. Krug — 'Briefe über die Wissenschaftslehre' (Leipzig, 1800).

W. T. Krug — 'Briefe über den neuesten Idealism' (Leipzig, 1801).

W. T. Krug — 'Entwurf eines neuen Organons der Philosophie' (Meissen and Lübben, 1801).

H. A. Goeden — 'Critische Bemerkungen ueber Hegels Begriff vom Wesen der Krankheit und der Heilung.' (Oken's 'Isis' pp. 1127–1138, Jena, 1819).

F. W. J. Schelling — 'Munich Lectures 1827': 'Werke' (ed. Schröter, 12 vols. Munich, 1927–1954) vol. 5 pp. 196–234.

Huelsemann — 'Ueber die Hegelsche Lehre oder absolutes Wissen und moderner Pantheismus' (Leipzig, 1829).

C. H. Weisse — 'Ueber den gegenwärtigen Standpunkt der philosophischen Wissenschaft' (Leipzig, 1829).

1832–1860

The predominant attitude of this period was *critical*. Specialists such as Wilde and Schleiden called the soundness of Hegel's knowledge of the natural sciences in question, and philosophers such as Schelling, Weisse and Borelius raised problems regarding the general principles of his system. Michelet and Rosenkranz, who were alone in defending the value of the 'Philosophy of Nature' among the philosophers, also failed to interest the natural scientists in it.

C. F. Goeschel — 'Hegel und seine Zeit. Mit Rücksicht auf Göthe' (Berlin, 1832).

C. H. Bachmann — 'Ueber Hegels System' (Leipzig, 1833).

F. W. J. Schelling — Introduction to H. Beckers 'Victor Cousin über französische und deutsche Philosophie' (Stuttgart and Tübingen, 1834); 'Werke' suppl. vol. 4 pp. 445–468.

C. H. Bachmann — 'Anti-Hegel' (Jena, 1835).

C. H. Weisse — 'Grundzüge der Metaphysik' (Hamburg, 1835).

C. L. Michelet — 'Geschichte der letzten Systeme der Philosophie in Deutschland von Kant bis Hegel' (2 pts. Berlin, 1837).

C. L. Michelet — 'Zugeständnisse der neuesten Physik in Bezug auf Göthe's Farbenlehre' ('Hallische Jahrbücher für deutsche Wissenschaft und Kunst' ed. Ruge and Echtermeyer nos. 305–307, Dec. 1838).

F. C. Sibbern — 'Bemaerkninger og Undersøgelser, fornemmelig betreffende Hegels Philosophie, betragtet i Forhold til vor Tid.' (Copenhagen, 1838) pp. 17–21.

C. L. Michelet — 'Schelling und Hegel' (Berlin, 1839).

J. C. F. Rosenkranz — 'Kritische Erläuterungen des Hegel'schen Systems' (Königsberg, 1840).

F. W. J. Schelling — 'Erste Vorlesung in Berlin. 15 November, 1841' (Stuttgart and Tübingen, 1841).

J. Schaller — 'Geschichte der Naturphilosophie' (2 vols. Leipzig and Halle, 1841–1846).

J. Salat — 'Schelling und Hegel' (Heidelberg, 1842).

C. F. E. Trahndorff — 'Schelling und Hegel, oder das System Hegels als letztes Resultat des Grundirrthums in allem bisherigen Philosophiren erwiesen' (Berlin, 1842).

G. A. Gabler — 'Die Hegelsche Philosophie' (Berlin, 1843).

C. L. Michelet — 'Entwickelungsgeschichte der neuesten deutschen Philosophie' (Berlin, 1843).

E. F. Vogel — 'Schelling oder Hegel oder Keiner von Beiden?' (Leipzig, 1843).

E. Wilde — 'Geschichte der Optik' (2 pts. Berlin, 1843) II pp. 153–218.

K. G. Reuschle — 'Die Naturphilosophie und die Physik' ('Jahrbücher der Gegenwart' 1843–1844).

J. C. F. Rosenkranz — 'Ueber Schelling und Hegel' (Königsberg, 1843).

M. J. Schleiden — 'Schelling's und Hegel's Verhältniss zur Naturwissenschaft' (Leipzig, 1844).

C. H. Weisse — 'Hegel und das Newtonische Gesetz der Kraftwirkung' ('Zeitschrift für Philosophie und spekulative Theologie' vol. XIII pp. 1–3, Tübingen, 1844).

K. P. Fischer — 'Speculative Charakteristik und Kritik des Hegel'schen Systems' (Erlangen, 1845) pt. IV pp. 332–372.

C. L. W. Heyder — 'Kritische Darstellung . . . der Aristotelischen und Hegel'schen Dialektik' (Erlangen, 1845).

A. J. Matter — 'Schelling ou la Philosophie de la Nature' (Paris, 1845).

F. A. Trendelenburg — 'Geschichte der Kategorienlehre' (Berlin, 1846).

C. L. Menzzer — 'Die Naturphilosophie und der Hegelianismus' ('Allgemeine Literatur-Zeitung' Oct. 1847).

J. B. Stallo — 'General Principles of the philosophy of Nature . . . embracing the philosophical systems of Schelling and Hegel' (Boston, 1848).

J. C. F. Rosenkranz — 'Studien' (5 pts. Berlin, 1839–1848) pt. 5.

F. Rehm — 'Göthe und Hegel. Eine historische Parallele' (Oels, 1849).

J. C. F. Rosenkranz — 'System der Wissenschaft' (Königsberg, 1850) pp. 158–362.

F. W. J. Schelling — 'Abhandlung über die Quelle der ewigen Wahrheiten' ('Gesammtsitzung der Akademie der Wissenschaften zu Berlin' 17 Jan. 1850); 'Werke' vol. 5.

J. J. Borelius — 'I hvad afseende är Hegel pantheist' (Uppsala, 1851).

S. Ribbing — 'Eristiska Blad I' (Uppsala, 1852).

J. C. F. Rosenkranz	'Meine Reform der Hegelschen Philosophie' (Königsberg, 1852).
H. Schwarz	'Versuch einer Philosophie der Mathematik verbunden mit einer Kritik der Ausstellungen Hegel's über den Zweck und die Natur der höheren Analysis' (Halle, 1853).
F. Dorguth	'Das Licht der wahrhaften kosmischen dem Irrlichte der Hegel'schen Dialektik gegenüber' (Magdeburg, 1854).
A. Vera	'Introduction à la Philosophie de Hégel' (Paris and Strassburg, 1855).
A. Vera	'An Inquiry into speculative and experimental science, with special reference to Mr. Calderwood and Professor Ferrier's recent publications, and to Hegel's doctrine' (London, 1856).
F. C. B. Dahl	'Om Naturbegrebets Grundmomenter' (Copenhagen, 1859).
W. Whewell	'On the Philosophy of Discovery' (London, 1860) ch XXIV ii.

1861–1900

Various more or less unsuccessful attempts were made to show the relevance or irrelevance of Hegelianism to the natural sciences. Vera's translation had little effect upon either philosophers or working scientists.

F. A. Trendelenburg	'Logische Untersuchungen' (2 vols. Leipzig, 1862).
A. Vera	'Philosophie de la Nature, de Hégel, traduite pour la première fois et accompagnée d'une introduction et d'un commentaire perpétuel' (3 vols. Paris, 1863–1866).
J. C. F. Rosenkranz	'Hegel's Naturphilosophie und die Bearbeitung derselben durch den Italienischen Philosophen A. Vera' (Berlin, 1868).
W. R. Smith	'Hegel and the metaphysics of the fluxional calculus' ('Transactions of the Royal Society of Edinburgh' vol. XXV pp. 491–511, 1869).
J. C. F. Rosenkranz	'Erläuterungen zu Hegels Encyclopädie der philosophischen Wissenschaften' (Leipzig, 1870).
F. Chlebik	'Kraft und Stoff, oder der Dynamismus der Atome aus Hegel'schen Prämissen abgeleitet' (Berlin, 1873).
C. L. Michelet	'Hegel und der Empirismus' (Berlin, 1873).

J. H. Stirling	'Whewell and Hegel and Hegel and Mr. W. R. Smith, a vindication in a physio-mathematical regard' (London, 1873).
C. L. Michelet	'Das System der Philosophie als exacter Wissenschaft' (5 vols. Berlin, 1876).
F. Engels	'Dialektik und Natur' (written 1872–1882; ed. Riazonov, 1927; tr. and ed. C. Dutt, preface and notes J. B. S. Haldane, London, 1940).
C. L. Michelet	'Herbert Spencer's System der Philosophie und sein Verhältniss zur deutschen Philosophie' ('Berlin Philosophische Gesellschaft' 1882).
S. Alexander	'Hegel's Conception of Nature' ('Mind' 1886 pp. 495–523).
C. L. Michelet	'Historisch-kritische Darstellung der dialektischen Methode Hegel's' (Leipzig, 1888).
G. J. P. J. Bolland	'Het objectiveerend standpunkt van natuuropvatting en zijn eenzijdigheid' ('Theol. Tijdschrift', 1889).
G. Kent	'Die Lehre Hegels vom Wesen der Erfahrung und ihre Bedeutung für das Erkennen' ('Christiania Videnskabs-Forhandlinger' 1891 no. 5).
D. G. Ritchie	'Darwin and Hegel, with other philosophical studies' (London, 1893).
J. M. E. McTaggart	'Studies in Hegelian Dialectic' (Cambridge, 1896).

1901–1930

The isolated and fragmentary attempts to relate Hegelianism to current scientific developments continued, and there was an emergence of the first truly *historical* approach to Hegel's views.

A. Bullinger	'Hegels Naturphilosophie in vollem Recht gegenüber ihren Kritikastern' (Munich, 1903).
Anon.	'Hegel not Haeckel; or, "The riddle of the universe solved"' (Birmingham and Dublin, 1906).
G. J. P. J. Bolland	'Hegel's Encyklopädie' (Leyden, 1906).
J. Clay	'Natuurphilosophie en atomistiek' ('Tijdschrift voor Wijsbegeerte' 1907).
B. Croce	'What is living and what is dead of the philosophy of Hegel' (Bari, 1907, tr. D. Ainslie, London, 1915).
G. J. P. J. Bolland	'De Natuur. Proeve van centraliteit der wetenschap' (Leyden, 1908).
O. D. Chwolson	'Hegel, Haeckel, Kossuth, und das zwölfte Gebot' (Brunswick, 1908).

O. Closs — 'Kepler und Newton und das Problem der Gravitation in der Kantischen, Schellingschen und Hegelschen Naturphilosophie' (Heidelberg, 1908).

O. Closs — 'Das Problem der Gravitation in Schellings und Hegels Jenaer Zeit' (Heidelberg, 1908).

G. J. P. J. Bolland — 'Zuivere rede' (Leyden, 1909).

J. Fischer — 'Die Hegelsche Logik und der Goethesche Faust' ('Archiv für Philosophie' vol. 22, sect. i, no. 3, 1909).

G. W. Cunningham — 'Thought and Reality in Hegel's System' (New York, 1910).

M. Kelly — 'Hegel's Charlatanism Exposed' (London, 1911).

A. K. Phalén — 'Das Erkenntnisproblem in Hegels Philosophie' (Dissertation, Uppsala, 1912).

H. W. Ph. E. v. d. Bergh van Eysinga — 'Beschouwingen over de anorganische natuur' ('Tijdschrift voor Wijsbegeerte' 1913).

C. Siegel — 'Geschichte der deutschen Naturphilosophie' (Leipzig, 1913).

C. Siegel — 'Goethe und die spekulative Naturphilosophie' ('Kantstudien' 19, 1914 pp. 488–496).

R. Weimar — 'Hegel und die "ganz" moderne Naturwissenschaft' ('Hegel Archiv' ed. G. Lasson, Leipzig, 1914) pp. 48–55.

G. J. P. J. Bolland — 'De Boeken der spreuken' (Leyden, 1915).

J. d'Aulnis de Bourouill — 'De logica van Hegel en zijn bewijs van de valwet der lichamen.' ('Akademie van Wetenschappen—Medelingen', 1915).

J. v. d. Bergh van Eysinge-Elias — 'De logica van Hegel en zijn bewijs van de valwet der lichamen' ('Tijdschrift voor Wijsbegeerte', 1915).

H. L. Vernhout — 'Natuurleer en zuivere rede in het systeem van Hegel en Bolland' ('Tijdschrift voor Wijsbegeerte', 1917).

F. Sedlák — 'Pure Thought and the Riddle of the Universe' (London, 1919).

J. Hessing — 'Het verband van natuurwetenschappen en wijsbegeerte.' ('Tijdschrift voor Wijsbegeerte' 1921).

J. M. E. McTaggart — 'The Nature of Existence' (2 vols. Cambridge, 1921–1927).

B. Wigersma — 'De denkwijze der natuurwetenschap' ('De Idee', 1924).

R. Honegger — 'Goethe und Hegel' ('Jahrbuch der Goethe-Gesellschaft' vol. XI pp. 38–111, Weimar, 1925).

G. F. Hemens — 'Relativity and the Hegelian Philosophy' (2 pts. Twickenham, 1928).

N. Hartmann — 'Die Philosophie des deutschen Idealismus' (2 pts. Berlin, 1923–1929), pt. II pp. 282–295.

SINCE 1930

The *general cultural* background of Hegel's work has become more fully understood, and there have been interesting attempts to assess the value of some of the details of the 'Mechanics', but there has been no attempt to place the subject matter as a whole in its historical context, and very little appreciation of the general principles of Hegelianism in their relation to the natural sciences.

R. Berthelot — 'Science et philosophie chez Goethe' (Paris, 1932).

J. Artzt — 'Der Substanzbegriff bei Kant und Hegel' (Dissertation, Freiburg-im-Breisgau, 1933).

N. Hartmann — 'Aristoteles und Hegel' (2nd ed. Erfurt, 1933).

J. Schubert — 'Goethe und Hegel' (Leipzig, 1933).

H. Falkenheim — 'Goethe und Hegel' (Tübingen, 1934).

C. Schilling — 'Natur und Wahrheit' (Munich, 1934).

H. Franz — 'Von Herder bis Hegel' (Frankfurt-on-Main, 1938).

J. Hessing — 'De natuur' (A series of articles in 'De Idee' 1938–1942).

W. von Baeyer — 'Seele, Leben, Zeit und Begriff in Hegels Philosophie' (Würzburg, 1939).

W. Bauchert — 'Begriff und Gestalt bei Hegel' (Dissertation, Kiel, 1940).

G. R. G. Mure — 'Introduction to Hegel' (Oxford, 1940).

L. Hoyack — 'Eenige belangrijke gezichtspunkten uit de natuurphilosophie van Hegel' ('Uitzicht' IV, 1943).

B. Wigersma — 'Natuurphilosophie; de geometrische, mechanische en astronomische kategorieën' (Bussum, 1943).

R. G. Collingwood — 'The Idea of Nature' (Oxford, 1945) pt. II, iii.

E. E. Harris — 'The Philosophy of Nature in Hegel's System' ('The Review of Metaphysics' Dec. 1949, vol. III pp. 213–228).

M. Heidegger — 'Holzwege: Hegels Begriff der Erfahrung' (Frankfurt-on-Main, 1950).

N. Altwicker — 'Der Begriff der Zeit im philosophischen System Hegels' (Dissertation, Frankfurt-on-Main, 1951).

H. Kobligk — 'Denken und Zeit, Beiträge zu einer Interpretation des Hegelschen Zeitbegriffes' (Dissertation, Kiel, 1952).

T. Litt — 'Hegel. Versuch einer kritischen Erneuerung' (Heidelberg, 1953).

P. P. Wiener — 'Readings in the Philosophy of Science' (New York, 1953) pp. 366–387.

J. N. Findlay — 'Hegel: a Re-examination' (London, 1958) ch. 9.

H. Braun — 'Realität und Reflexion. Studien zu Hegels Philosophie der Natur' (Dissertation, Heidelberg, 1960).

Soviet Academy of Sciences — 'Geschichte der Philosophie' (Moscow, 1957; Germ. tr. 5 vols. Berlin, 1960–1963) vol. II pp. 87–90.

M. Behm — 'Hegels spekulative Deutung der Infinitesimalrechnung' (Dissertation, Cologne, 1963).

K. R. Popper — 'Conjectures and Refutations' (London, 1963) ch. 15.

K. H. Volkmann-Schlück — 'Die Entäusserung der Idee zur Natur' ('Hegel-Studien', Bonn, 1964).

Anon. — 'Abriss der Geschichte der Philosophie' (Moscow, 1960, Germ. tr. Wietz Verlag, Berlin, 1966) pp. 252–255.

h. TEXT AND SOURCES

'Nullus est liber tam malus, ut non aliqua parte prosit'.
—Pliny.

The text of the 'Philosophy of Nature' translated here is that prepared by K. L. Michelet and published in 1842 as volume VII pt. i of the eighteen volume Berlin edition of Hegel's complete works, issued between 1832 and 1845. Hermann Glockner reproduced this text, without altering it, as volume 9 of the 'Sämtliche Werke' (26 vols. Stuttgart, 1927–1940), and it is the fourth printing of this edition (1965) which has been used for the translation.

The foundations of Michelet's work are the three editions of the 'Encyclopaedia' that appeared at Heidelberg in Hegel's lifetime (1817, 1827, 1830). They differ widely in many important respects, and no less than 3600 significant alterations first appeared in 1830. The critical edition of the 'Encyclopaedia' prepared by Nicolin and Pöggeler (1959) has therefore been used in order to check on Michelet's handling of his printed sources.[1] Those remnants of the 1817 text reproduced in 1830 have been distinguished from the rest of the work,[2] and where the 1959 text has not been found acceptable, the reasons for deviating from it have been indicated in the commentary.

The 'Additions' were put together by Michelet from various manuscript sources, only one of which, the Jena lecture notes of 1805–1806, has since been published.[3] The passages in his text originating from this manuscript have been indicated, and any difficulties which the two versions give rise to have been discussed in the commentary. Most of the material from which these 'additions' were formed consisted of lecture notes from the Berlin period (1819–1830). Only one of the manuscripts has been traced,[4] and a perusal of it has not necessitated any revision of Michelet's work.

Apart from the removal of errors, the most important result of this textual analysis is the light it throws upon Hegel's response or lack of response to the changing state of the natural sciences. It is to be hoped therefore, that English readers will now be able to assess this aspect of his work with greater certainty than has been possible hitherto. The forthcoming German edition will also indicate the various sources and dates of the component parts of Michelet's text.[5] The four major components are distinguished in the translation as follows:

i. passages dating from 1817, *reproduced* in 1830:
ii. **passages first printed in either 1827 or 1830:**
iii. lecture material from the *Berlin* period 1819–1830:
iv. lecture material from the *Jena* period of 1805–1806.

Errata

in the German text (Glockner's edition Stuttgart, 1965)

Page 2, line 2 — Substitute a comma for the full stop after genießen.

[1] F. Nicolin and O. Pöggeler 'Hegels Enzyklopädie der philosophischen Wissenschaften im Grundrisse (1830)'. (Hamburg, 1959).

[2] The 1827 'Encyclopaedia' has never been reprinted. The 1817 edition has however been reproduced in volume 6 of the 'Sämtliche Werke' (ed. Glockner, 26 vols. Stuttgart, 1927–1940).

[3] J. Hoffmeister 'Jenenser Realphilosophie II' (Leipzig, 1931). Michelet knew nothing of the earlier manuscripts of 1801–1802: see 'Jenenser Logik, Metaphysik und Naturphilosophie' (ed. G. Lasson, Leipzig, 1923) and 1803–1804: see 'Jenenser Realphilosophie I' (ed. Hoffmeister, Leipzig, 1932).

[4] The notes taken down by K. G. von Griesheim (1798–1854) during the winter of 1823–1824. A microfilm of them has been supplied by the 'Staatsbibliothek der Stiftung Preussischer Kulturbesitz', 1 Berlin 33, Archivstrasse 12–14: see 'Handschriftenabteilung' Ms. germ. qu. 542.

[5] Heinz Heimsoeth 'Die Hegel-Ausgabe der Deutschen Forschungsgemeinschaft' ('Kant-Studien' 51 pp. 506–511, 1959–1960): F. Nicolin 'Die neue Hegel-Gesamtausgabe. Voraussetzungen und Ziele' ('Hegel-Studien' 1 pp. 295–313, 1961), 'Philologische Aufgaben der Hegelforschung' ('Heidelberger Hegel-Tage' ed. Gadamer, Bonn, 1964 pp. 327–337).

Page 13, line 1	For einer read ſeiner.
Page 24, „ 9	For 2 read 3.
Page 35, „ 24	For hat read haben.
Page 40, „ 25	For iſt read ſind. (?)
Page 52, „ 1	For vorgeſteut read vorgeſtellt.
Page 52, „ 18	Insert iſt after ewig.
Page 57, „ 24	For duas read dyas.
Page 72, „ 18	For nichtige read Richtige.
Page 88, „ 7	Insert iſt after zurückgegangen.
Page 88, „ 11	For der read aller.
Page 102, „ 5	For um ebenſo read er ein um ſo.
Page 102, „ 6	For iſt, indem ſie read iſt ſie als.
Page 112, „ 16	For Geſchindigkeit read Geſchwindigkeit.
Page 123, „ 30	Insert iſt after gut.
Page 131, „ 32	For Maaße read Maße.
Page 143, „ 19	For von read an.
Page 143, „ 31	For auch read aus.
Page 145, „ 1	For werden read worden.
Page 145, „ 13	For Sphären read Sphäre.
Page 145, „ 13	For auflöſen read auflöſt.
Page 145, „ 14	For Bewegungen read Bewegung.
Page 145, „ 15	For ihnen read ihr.
Page 145, „ 15	For haben read hat.
Page 145, „ 16	For bewegen read bewegt.
Page 145, „ 31	Delete the comma after Daſeyn nach.
Page 146, „ 26	For Rotation read Nutation.
Page 147, „ 16	For höheres Inſichſeyn read Höheres in ſich.
Page 147, „ 21	For da dieſes nur read es iſt nur.
Page 147, „ 32	For alſo ſeine Kraft hat read ſeine Kraft alſo ſein Negatives hat.
Page 148, „ 6	For ſchon read teils.
Page 152, „ 4	Substitute a semicolon for the comma after identiſch.
Page 152, „ 5	For Qualitativen; read Qualitativen,.
Page 153, „ 6	For welcher vorher read der vorher.
Page 157, „ 6	For eine read reine.
Page 170, „ 9	For ein eandere read eine andere.
Page 175, „ 1	For die Kometen read dieſe Körper.
Page 176, „ 7	For Atmoſphäre read Luft.
Page 176, „ 12	Insert Prozeßes after allgemeinen.
Page 183, „ 8	For Paracelſus read die Alten.
Page 183, „ 9	For alle irdiſchen Körper beſtehen read der irdiſche Körper beſtehe.
Page 187, „ 3	Delete the comma after Standpunkt.

Page 190, line 16 For quantite read quantité.
Page 192, „ 33 For vroduciren read produciren.
Page 206, „ 13 Insert a full stop after auf.
Page 207, „ 29 For seinen read ihren.
Page 227, „ 7 For Gestalteten read gestalteten.
Page 229, „ 7 Insert Michelet's note on p. 231 before ‚Gegen'. (Cf. 1827 ed. p. 281 lines 3–4).
Page 231, „ 7 Delete Michelet's note.
Page 236, „ 3 For ist read sind. (?)
Page 246, „ 14 For anschägt read anschlägt.
Page 249, „ 10 Insert a full stop after wird.
Page 249, „ 13 For Eine Saite read eine Seite.
Page 249, „ 26 For fortgehen read fortgeht.
Page 265, „ 16 For Wänne read Wärme.
Page 266, „ 23 For gesetzt read gesetzt.
Page 268, „ 26 For list read ist.
Page 278, „ 17 For attrahirt read angezogen.
Page 278, „ 20 For die allenthalben der ganze Magnetismus ist read das allenthalben als dies Ganze ist.
Page 281, „ 32 For Magnetismus read Magnet.
Page 282, „ 17 For dieselbe Maße read dasselbe Volumen.
Page 292, „ 2 For Magnetismus read Ton des Magnets.
Page 292, „ 16 For Gebilden read Gebilde.
Page 292, „ 17 For sie da sind read es da ist.
Page 296, „ 1 For die Flächen desselben sich die 'molécules intégrantes' read diesen sich die Moleküle.
Page 306, „ 28 For anerkennend read anerkennt.
Page 308, „ 26 For Traitede read Traité de.
Page 313, „ 18 For CDAB read CDAB.
Page 319, „ 11 Insert a full stop after gehoben.
Page 333, „ 18 For ind n read indem.
Page 334, „ 32 For kann read hat.
Page 335, „ 1 Insert hat after gezeigt.
Page 335, „ 2 For von read mit.
Page 335, „ 3 For hierin read hierum.
Page 335, „ 4 Insert es ist after sondern.
Page 335, „ 5 Insert der before als.
Page 335, „ 5 Delete the comma after Beider.
Page 335, „ 6 Delete stellt.
Page 335, „ 7 For dar read darstellt.
Page 342, „ 30 Insert [1] before the note.
Page 346, „ 22 For des read seines.
Page 347, „ 33 For Prisma read Prismas.

Page 348, line 12	For in read an.
Page 348, „ 17	Insert iſt after ſchwärzeſten.
Page 348, „ 24	For nämlich read nun.
Page 349, „ 2	Insert Negative, als das after wahrhaft.
Page 352, „ 12	For pſychologiſchen read phyſiologiſchen.
Page 355, „ 30	For ä erlich read äußerlich.
Page 356, „ 17	For herausgetreten read Herausgetretne.
Page 356, „ 18	Delete der.
Page 356, „ 19	For oder read in der.
Page 361, „ 8	Insert ſich als after zuerſt.
Page 375, „ 24	For j read jeder.
Page 382, „ 8	For Λ read A.
Page 389, „ 29	For ie read die.
Page 401, „ 19	Insert a semicolon after identiſch, and a comma after Kali.
Page 421, „ 31	For findet man read finde ich.
Page 426, „ 23	For dieß eine Zeit lang read es eine Zeitlang (Schwefelbaryt).
Page 426, „ 25	For Das erſte Verbrennliche read Das eigentlich Brennliche.
Page 433, „ 19	Insert a full stop after Sitz.
Page 434, „ 19	For ſind read iſt.
Page 437, „ 13	For ehmals read ehemals.
Page 442, „ 21	For er read es.
Page 442, „ 28	For Härte und Kryſtalliſation read Härte (Kryſtalliſation).
Page 442, „ 32	For ein Mittelgeſchmack read Mittel, Geſchmack.
Page 443, „ 6	For phyſiſchen Körper read Phyſiſchen.
Page 459, „ 34	Insert [1] before Aus.
Page 463, „ 31	Insert hat after erhalten.
Page 463, „ 31	Insert iſt after gegenübergetreten.
Page 468, „ 8	For ungeheure read üppige.
Page 468, „ 19	For ſtumme read ſtumpfe.
Page 471, „ 6	For beſtimmter read beſtimmte.
Page 479, „ 33	For ſich einzeln finden read einzelner ſind.
Page 483, „ 27	For Dieſer periodiſche Wechſel tritt read Dieſe periodiſchen Wechſel treten.
Page 484, „ 20	For verwandelt read individualiſiert.
Page 487, „ 5	For bildeten, wo read bildeten. Hier,.
Page 495, „ 25	For m t read mit.
Page 500, „ 18	Insert einſame before Menſch.
Page 514, „ 29	Insert inverted commas after entſpringe.
Page 516, „ 4	Substitute a full stop for the comma after treiben.
Page 524, „ 7	For er, ſeinen and umbilde read ſie, ihren and umbilden.

Page 543, ,, 20 Insert a full stop after über.
Page 546, ,, 25 For Wurzel read Wurzelung.
Page 552, ,, 30 Insert reine before exiſtirende.
Page 561, ,, 28 For ignes read eigenes.
Page 564, ,, 29 For Beſtimmtheit read Beſtimmtheiten.
Page 564, ,, 30 For verbreitet read verbreiten.
Page 568, ,, 29 For Fruchtknotens read Fruchtbodens.
Page 571, ,, 29 For verdaute read unverdaute.
Page 575, ,, 10 For Feurigen read Feuers.
Page 578, ,, 6 For über die abſtracte read der abſtracten.
Page 579, ,, 20 For ſind read iſt.
Page 585, ,, 24 For unterbringt read unterbricht.
Page 589, ,, 26 For iſt read ſind. (?)
Page 590, ,, 9 For inneres read Inneres.
Page 593, ,, 8 For ſeiner read feiner.
Page 599, ,, 5 Insert Pulſieren und before Erzittern.
Page 600, ,, 25 For Magen read Mägen.
Page 601, ,, 1 Insert 3 before Endlich.
Page 603, ,, 8 & 12 Delete the quotation marks.
Page 603, ,, 18 For ſogleich read zugleich.
Page 604, ,, 16 For weiß read weich.
Page 604, ,, 17 For Blutlauf read Blutumlauf.
Page 606, ,, 7 For iſt read wird.
Page 612, ,, 30 Insert [1] after geht;.
Page 615, ,, 4 For Auf read auf.
Page 617, ,, 6 For zurücknimmt read zuſammennimmt.
Page 647, ,, 20 For kriegt aus read zeigt in.
Page 647, ,, 21 Delete heraus.
Page 648, ,, 24 Insert als zweckmäßig before das.
Page 666, ,, 4 For befriedigte read beſtimmte.
Page 666, ,, 6 Delete the brackets.
Page 666, ,, 15 For wi read wie.
Page 673, ,, 9 Delete welche,.
Page 673, ,, 12 For iſt: jedoch read iſt,.
Page 673, ,, 16 Delete hiermit.
Page 675, ,, 3 Delete dieß,.
Page 675, ,, 4 For zu unterſcheiden, um read unterſcheidend, und.
Page 675, ,, 5 Delete zu ſeyn.
Page 675, ,, 28 For übrigen read Uebrigen.
Page 680, ,, 2 For ſin read ſind, etc. down the page.
Page 697, ,, 2 Delete vor.
Page 697, ,, 3 For die Gattung read ſie.
Page 706, ,, 24 For Succeßion read Fluß.

Sources

Although several of his Berlin colleagues attended them, Hegel's lectures were designed primarily for *undergraduates*. In his treatment of the natural sciences he was therefore obliged to give some indication of the relevant literature. The greatest difficulty encountered by a modern reader when attempting to follow his expositions originates in the fact that he often gives no indication of his sources once he enters upon matters of *detail*. The present commentary should, to some considerable extent, help to overcome this obstacle to a full appreciation of his work. The main sources of his more *general* views are always mentioned however, and since many modern readers will probably be in the position of his own undergraduates with regard to their general knowledge of the natural sciences of the day, it may be of value to list the works actually referred to in the text.

Where the edition used is known, it has been indicated, where it is not, the first edition has been listed. Works referred to by the writers Hegel is quoting have been included, and where there is a *clear* reference to a specific book or article, although he omits to actually mention it, this has also been identified and listed.

It may be of general interest to note that the works quoted most frequently would not usually be regarded as being in any way 'philosophical', and that most of the philosophical works mentioned are fairly severely criticized for what Hegel regards as their pretentiousness, inaccuracy or incompetence.

I: Mechanics

I. Kant	'Kritik der reinen Vernunft' (Riga, 1781).
S. Clarke	'A collection of papers, which passed between the late learned Mr Leibniz and Dr Clarke' (London, 1717).
J. F. Lorenz	'Euclid's Elemente' (3rd edition ed. Mollweide, Halle, 1809).
Aristotle	'Metaphysics.'
	'Physics.'
I. Newton	'Optice' (2nd ed. London, 1719).
I. Kant	'Metaphysische Anfangsgründe der Naturwissenschaft' (Riga, 1786).
I. Newton	'Philosophiae Naturalis Principia Mathematica' (London, 1687).

R. Descartes	'Principia philosophiae' (Amsterdam, 1644).
L. B. Francoeur	'Traité élémentaire de Mécanique, adopté dans l'instruction publique' (Paris, 1801).
J. L. Lagrange	'Théorie des fonctions analytiques' (Paris, 1797).
G. Galilei	'Discorsi e dimostrazioni matematiche' (Leyden, 1638).
W. Herschel	'Astronomical Observations relating to the Construction of the Heavens' ('Phil. Trans. Roy. Soc.' 1811, pp. 269–336).
I. Kant	'Allgemeine Naturgeschichte des Himmels' (Königsberg and Leipzig, 1755).
W. Herschel	'On the Construction of the Heavens' ('Phil. Trans. Roy. Soc.' vol. 75 p. 213, 1785).
G. M. Sommer	'Ueber den Bau des Himmels' (Königsberg, 1791).
J. Kepler	'Astronomia nova' (Prague, 1609).
J. Kepler	'Harmonica Mundi' (Linz, 1619).
T. Brahe	'Astronomiae Instauratae Progymnasmata' (2 vols. Prague, 1602–1603).
N. Copernicus	'De revolutionibus orbium coelestium' (Nuremberg, 1543).
P. S. Laplace	'Exposition du système du monde' (2 vols. Paris, 1796).
J. F. M. A. Voltaire	Élémens de la Philosophie de Newton mis à la portée de tout le monde' (Amsterdam, 1738). 'Défense du Newtonianisme' (Paris, 1739).
T. Brahe	'De Mundi Aetherei recentioribus Phaenomenis' (Uraniborg, 1588).
A. F. Fourcroy	'Système des Connaissances Chimiques' (10 vols. Paris, 1800).
Plato	'Timaeus' 36.
W. Herschel	'Account of a Comet' ('Phil. Trans. Roy. Soc,' 1781 p. 492).

II: Physics

Light:

J. A. F. Allix	'Théorie de l'univers ou de la cause primitive du mouvement et de ses principaux effets' (Paris, 1818).
I. Newton	'Optice: sive de reflexionibus, refractionibus, inflexionibus et coloribus lucis' (Editio secunda, Londini, 1719).
L. Euler	'Opuscula varii argumenti: Nova Theoria Lucis et Colorum' (Berlin, 1746).

G. M. Sommer	'Ueber den Bau des Himmels' (Königsberg, 1791): cf. 'The Scientific Papers of Sir William Herschel' (ed. Dreyer, 2 vols. London, 1912) vol. I p. 479.
J. W. Goethe	'Zur Naturwissenschaft überhaupt' vol. I (Stuttgart and Tübingen, 1817).
É. T. Malus	'Sur une propriété de la lumière réfléchie par les corps diaphanes' ('Bulletin des Sciences de la Société Philomathique de Paris' Dec. 1808).
É. T. Malus	'Théorie de la Double Refraction de la lumière dans les Substances Cristallisées' (Paris, 1810).

Bodies of the Solar System:

J. L. Heim	'Ueber die Aehnlichkeit der ehemaligen Erd-Oberfläche mit der gegenwärtigen des Mondes' ('Zachs Monatliche Correspondenz zur Beförderung der Erd- und Himmels- Kunde' 1802 pp. 528–542).
P. S. Laplace	'Exposition du système du monde' (2 vols. Paris, 1796).
J. Kepler	'Harmonice Mundi' (Linz, 1619).
I. Newton	'Optice' op. cit.
F. W. J. Schelling	'Betrachtungen über die besondere Bildung und die inneren Verhältnisse unseres Planetensystems' ('Werke' 1st suppl. vol. pp. 502–560).

The Elements:

J. B. Biot	'Traité de physique expérimentale et mathématique' (4 vols. Paris, 1816).

Meteorology:

Aristotle	'The Physics'
F. A. K. Gren	'Grundriss der Naturlehre zum Gebrauch akademischer Vorlesungen' (4th ed. Halle, 1801).
H. B. de Saussure	'Essais sur l'Hygrométrie' (Neuchâtel, 1783).
J. A. Deluc	'Idées sur la météorologie' (2 vols. London, 1786–1787).
J. D. O. Zylius	'Prüfung der Theorie des Herrn Deluc vom Regen' (Berlin, 1795).
G. C. Lichtenberg	'Vertheidigung des Hygrometers und der Luc'schen Theorie vom Regen' (Göttingen, 1800).
J. W. Ritter	'Beyträge zur nähern Kenntniss des Galvanismus' (4 vols. Jena, 1800–1805).

A. von Humboldt and L. J. Gay-Lussac	'Expériences sur les moyens eudiométriques et sur la proportion des principes constituants de l'atmosphère'. ('Gilberts Annalen der Physik' vol. XX pp. 38–95, Halle, 1805).
J. A. F. Allix	'Théorie de l'univers'(Paris, 1818).
W. E. Parry	'Journals of the First, Second and Third Voyages for the discovery of a North-West Passage' (5 vols. London, 1828).
J. W. Goethe	'Zur Naturwissenschaft überhaupt' vol. II (Stuttgart and Tübingen, 1823).
T. Livy	'The History'.
J. B. Biot	'Relation . . . d'un météore observé à l'Aigle' (Paris, 1803).

Specific Gravity:

I. Kant	'Metaphysische Anfangsgründe der Naturwissenschaft' (Riga, 1786).
J. W. Goethe	'Zur Naturwissenschaft überhaupt' vol. II (Stuttgart and Tübingen, 1823).

Cohesion:

F. W. J. Schelling	'System der gesammten Philosophie und der Naturphilosophie insbesondere' (manuscript from 1804, 'Werke' suppl. vol. 2 pp. 252–258).
F. A. K. Gren	'Grundriss der Naturlehre' (4th ed. Halle, 1801).
F. W. J. Schelling	'Darstellung meines Systems der Philosophie' ('Zeitschrift für spekulative Physik' vol. II sect. ii, Jena and Leipzig, 1801).
H. Steffens	'Beiträge zur innern Naturgeschichte der Erde' (pt. I, Freiberg, 1801).

Sound:

E. F. Chladni	'Die Akustik' (Leipzig, 1802).
J. W. Ritter	'Fragmente aus dem Nachlasse eines jungen Physikers' (2 vols. Heidelberg, 1810).
J. B. Biot	'Traité de Physique' (4 vols. Paris, 1816).
G. Tartini	'Trattato di musica secondo la vera scienza dell'armonia' (Padua, 1754).
Pythagoras	Aristotle 'Metaphysics' (Oxford, 1924) vol. I pp. 145–150.
G. J. Vogler	See: H. Spies 'Abt Vogler und die von ihm 1805 simplifizierte Orgel von St. Peter in Salzburg' (Mainz, 1932).

Heat:

J. B. Spix and K. F. P. Martius — 'Reise in Brasilien auf Befehl Sr. Majestät Maximilien Joseph I Königs von Baiern in den Jahren 1817 bis 1820 gemacht' (3 pts. Munich, 1823, 1828, 1831).

B. Thompson — 'An Inquiry concerning the Source of the Heat which is excited by Friction' ('Philosophical Transactions of the Royal Society' 1798 pt. I pp. 80–102).

M. A. Pictet — 'Essais de physique' (Geneva, 1790).

A. Fothergill — 'On the origin and formation of ice islands' ('Memoirs of the American Academy of Arts and Sciences' vol. III pt. i pp. 69–81, Cambridge, Mass., 1809: reviewed in 'Göttingsche gelehrte Anzeigen' vol. III 1817, pp. 1801–1808).

Magnetism:

J. N. Møller — 'Über die Entstehung der Wärme durch Reibung nebst Folgerungen für die Theorie beyder Phänomene' ('Neue Zeitschrift für speculative Physik' Tübingen, 1802 vol. I pt. iii pp. 1–66).

J. B. Richter — 'Ueber die bis jetzt sicherste Reinigungsmethode des Kobalts and Nickels' (Gehlen's 'Neues allgemeines Journal der Chemie' vol. XX, pp. 61–72, Berlin, 1804).

A. von Humboldt — 'On the Magnetic Polarity of a Mountain of Serpentine' (Nicholson's 'Journal of Natural Philosophy' vol. I pp. 97–101, June, 1797).

J. B. Spix and K. F. P. Martius — 'Reise in Brasilien' vol. I (Munich, 1823).

A. Brugmans — 'Tentamina philosophica de materia magnetica ejusque actione in ferrum et magnetem' (Franeker, 1765).

J. H. van Swinden — 'Tentamina Theoriae mathematicae de phaenomenis magneticis' in 'Commentatii de Rebus in Scientia Naturali et Medicina gestis' (44 vols. Leipzig, 1752–1798) vol. XIX p. 458 (1772).

W. E. Parry — 'Journal of a Voyage for the discovery of the north-west Passage' (London, 1821).

P. Erman — 'Umrisse zu den physischen Verhältnissen des von Herrn Professor Ørsted entdeckten elektro-chemischen Magnetismus' (Berlin, 1821).

Crystallography:

A. G. Werner — 'Von den äusserlichen Kennzeichen der Fossilien' (Leipzig, 1774).

R.-J. Hauy	'Essai d'une Théorie sur la Structure des Crystaux' Paris, 1784).

Transparency and Refraction:

C. F. L. Schultz	'Über physiologe Farbenerscheinungen, insbesondere das phosphorische Augenlicht, als Quelle derselben, betreffend' (1821, Goethe's 'Zur Naturwissenschaft' pt. II, 1823).
J. W. Goethe	'Zur Farbenlehre' (2 vols, Tübingen, 1810).
J. B. Biot	'Traité de Physique' (4 vols. Paris, 1816).
R. Descartes	'Discours de la méthode' (Dioptrics) (Leyden, 1637).
F. A. K. Gren	'Grundriss der Naturlehre' (4th ed. Halle, 1801).
J. W. Goethe	'Zur Naturwissenschaft' vol. I (1817).

Colour:

I. Newton	'Optice' (2nd ed. London, 1719).
J. W. Goethe	'Zur Farbenlehre' (2 vols. Tübingen, 1810).
J. T. Mayer	'Commentatio de apparentiis objectorum terrestrium a refractione lucis in atmosphaera nostra pendentibur' 'Commentatio de Polaritate Luminis' ('Commentationes Societatis Regiae Scientarum Gottingensis' vols. I and II, Göttingen, 1811, 1813).
J. B. Biot	'Traité de Physique' (4 vols. Paris, 1816).
L. D. von Henning	'Einleitung zu öffentlichen Vorlesungen über Goethes Farbenlehre, gehalten an der Königlichen Universität zu Berlin' (Berlin, 1822).
T. Pownall	'Inquiries into Coloured Light' (Tilloch's 'Philosophical Magazine' vol. XII pp. 42–49 and 107–112, 1802).
C. F. L. Schultz	Über physiologe Farbenerscheinungen' (1821, Goethe's 'Zur Naturwissenschaft' pt. II, 1823).
F. W. J. Schelling	'Die vier edlen Metalle' (1802): 'Werke' 1st suppl. vol. pp. 565–574.

Electricity:

C. L. Berthollet	'Essai de Statique Chimique' (2 vols. Paris, 1803).
J. B. Biot	'Traité de Physique' (4 vols. Paris, 1816).
R.-J. Hauy	'Traité de mineralogie' (4 vols. Paris, 1801).
G. F. Pohl	Review of Gehler's Dictionary. ('Jahrbücher für wissenschaftliche Kritik' (Stuttgart and Tübingen, 1829).
J. S. T. Gehler	'Physikalisches Wörterbuch' vol. III (Leipzig, 1827).

H. C. Ørsted	'Experimenta circa effectum conflictus electrici in acum magneticam' (Copenhagen, 1820).
F. W. J. Schelling	'Allgemeine Deduction des dynamischen Processes oder der Categorieen der Physik' ('Zeitschrift für spekulative Physik' vol. I, Jena and Leipzig, 1800).
Plato	'Timaeus' $45b^2$–$46a^2$:
Chemistry:	
W. E. Parry	'Journal of a Voyage' (London, 1821).
H. C. Ørsted	'Experimenta circa effectum' etc. (Copenhagen, 1820).
J. W. Ritter	'Galvanische Beobachtungen während der Sonnenfinsterniss vom 11 Februar 1804' ('Voigt's Magazin für den neuesten Zustand der Naturkunde' vol. VII pp. 175–179).
J. J. Winterl	'Prolusiones ad chemiam saeculi decimi noni' (Budae, 1800).
	'Accessiones novae ad prolusionem suam primam et secondam' (Budae, 1803).
Archimedes	See: M. V. Pollio 'De Architectura' (tr. A. Rode, 2 vols. Leipzig, 1796).
J. d'Arcet	'Expériences sur quelques alliages métalliques' ('Journal de Médecine' vol. XLIII pp. 552–561, June, 1775).
J. B. Trommsdorff	'Systematisches Handbuch der gesammten Chemie' (2nd ed. Erfurt, 1805–1820) vol. IV (1812).
L. B. G. de Morveau	'Essai sur l'analyse et la recomposition des deux alcalis fixes' ('Mémoires de L'Institut National' 1802 vol. III pp. 321–336).
H. Steffens	'Grundzüge der philosophischen Naturwissenschaft' (Berlin, 1806).
A. L. Lavoisier	'Sur la Calcination des Métaux dans les vaisseaux fermes' ('Observations sur la Physique' 1774, vol. IV pp. 448–452).
Galvanism:	
G. F. Pohl	'Der Process der galvanischen Kette' (Leipzig, 1826).
J. B. Biot	'Traité de Physique' (4 vols. Paris, 1816).
J. J. Berzelius	'Essai sur la théorie des proportions chimiques' (Paris, 1819).
J. B. Trommsdorff	'Systematisches Handbuch der gesammten Chemie' (2nd ed. 8 vols. Erfurt, 1805–1820).
F. W. J. Schelling	'Die vier edlen Metalle' ('Neue Zeitschrift für speculative Physik' vol. I sect. 3, Tübingen, 1802).
H. Steffens	'Beiträge zur innern Naturgeschichte der Erde' (pt. i Freiberg, 1801).

J. W. Ritter	'Das Elektrische System der Körper' (Leipzig, 1805).
A. von Humboldt	'Versuche über die gereizte Muskel-und Nervenfaser' (2 vols. Posen and Berlin, 1796).
J. S. C. Schweigger	'Galvanische Combinationen' (Gehlen's 'Journal für die Chemie, Physik und Mineralogie' vol. VII pp. 537–578; vol. IX pp. 316–331; pp. 701–706).
W. H. Wollaston	'Experiments on the chemical production and agency of electricity' ('Phil. Trans. Roy. Soc.' 1801 pp. 427–434).
H. Davy	Six papers on galvanism published in 'Nicholson's Journal' 1801–1802: 'Collected Works' (ed. Davy, 9 vols. London, 1838–1840) vol. II pp. 139–181.
L. Galvani	'De Viribus Electricitatis in Motu Musculari Commentarius' ('Comment. Bonon.' VII, 1791).
A. Volta	Letters in Gren's 'Neues Journal der Physik' 1796 vol. III p. 479; 1797 vol. IV pp. 107, 473.
G. Aldini	'Essai Théorique et Expérimental sur le Galvanisme' (2 vols. Paris, 1804).
J. W. Ritter	'Physische-Chemische Abhandlungen' (3 vols. Leipzig, 1806).
J. W. Ritter	'Versuche zum Erweise, dass auch bey der gewöhnlichen Electricität, in chemischer Hinsicht, die positive die oxygenee, die negative die hydrogenee sey' (Gilbert's 'Annalen der Physik' vol. IX pp. 1–17.)

Chemical Processes:

J. Schuster	'System der dualistischen Chemie' (2 vols. Berlin, 1807).
H. Steffens	'Grundzüge der philosophischen Naturwissenschaft' (Berlin, 1806).
C. L. Berthollet	'Essai de Statique Chimique' (2 vols. Paris, 1803).
J. B. Richter	'Anfangsgründe der Stöchyometrie oder Messkunst chymischer Elemente' (3 vols. Breslau and Hirschberg, 1792–1794).
L. B. G. de Morveau	'Affinité' ('Encyclopédie Methodique' vol. I pt. I pp. 535–613, 1786).
W. H. Wollaston	'On the elementary particles of certain crystals' ('Phil. Trans. Roy. Soc.' vol. 104 pp. 51–63, 1813).
J. J. Berzelius	'An attempt to determine the definite and simple proportions, in which the constituent parts of Unorganic Substances are united with each other' ('Philosophical Magazine' vols. 41–43, 1813–1814).

J. Dalton	'A New System of Chemical Philosophy' (pts. I and II, Manchester, 1808, 1810).
J. S. C. Schweigger	'Ueber einige noch unerklärte chemische Erscheinungen' ('Journal für Chemie und Physik' 1812, v, 49; 1814, xiv, 497; 1823, ix, 231).
H. Davy	'On some chemical agencies of electricity' ('Phil. Trans. Roy. Soc.' 1807 pp. 1–56).

III: Organics

Geology:

A. G. Werner	'Von den äusserlichen Kennzeichen der Fossilien' (Leipzig, 1774).
J. Hutton	'Theory of the Earth' (2 vols. Edinburgh, 1795).
J. G. Ebel	'Ueber den Bau der Erde' (2 vols. Zürich, 1808).
J. F. M. A. Voltaire	'Dissertation . . . sur les changemens arrivés dans notre globe' (Boulogne, 1746).
A. von Humboldt	'Personal Narrative of Travels to the Equinoctial Regions of the New Continent' (tr. H. M. Williams, 6 vols. London, 1818–1826).
A. G. Werner	'Classification der Gebirgsarten' (Dresden, 1787).
A. G. Werner	'Neue Theorie von der Entstehung der Gänge' (Freiberg, 1791).
H. Steffens	'Geognostische-geologische Aufsätze' (Hamburg, 1810).
J. L. Heim	'Geologische Beschreibung des Thüringer Waldgebürgs' (3 pts. Meiningen, 1796–1812).
K. G. von Raumer	'Geognostische Versuche' (Berlin, 1815).
F. W. H. von Trebra	'Erfahrungen vom Innern der Gebirge' (Leipzig, 1786).
H. Steffens	'Grundzüge der Philosophischen Naturwissenschaft' (Berlin, 1806).
J. B. Spix and K. F. P. Martius	'Reise in Brasilien' pt. I (Munich, 1823).

Embryology:

A. von Chamisso	'De Salpa' (Berlin, 1819).
C. A. Rudolphi	'Anatomie der Pflanzen' (Berlin, 1807).
A. von Humboldt	'Versuche über die gereizte Muskel-und Nervenfaser' (2 vols. Posen and Berlin, 1796).

Botany:

K. H. Schultz	'Die Natur der lebendigen Pflanze' pt. I (Berlin, 1823).
J. W. Goethe	'Zur Morphologie' vol. I (Stuttgart and Tübingen, 1817).

F. W. J. Schelling	'Ideen zu einer Philosophie der Natur' (Leipzig, 1797),
C. L. Willdenow	'Grundriss der Kräuterkunde' (6th edition ed. Link. Berlin, 1821).
G. R. Treviranus	'Biologie, oder Philosophie der lebenden Natur für Naturforscher und Aerzte' (6 vols. Göttingen, 1802–1822).
C. W. Hufeland	'Ueber die Bewegungen des Hedysarum gyrans' (Voigt's 'Magazin für das Neueste aus der Physik und Naturgeschichte' Gotha, 1790, vol. VI pt. iii pp. 5–27).
A. P. de Candolle	'Expériences relative à l'influence de la lumière sur quelques végétaux' ('Journal de Physique' vol. 52 p. 124).
S. Hermbstädt	'Über die Fähigkeit der lebenden Pflanzen im Winter Wärme zu erzeugen' ('Der Gesellschaft Naturforschender Freunde zu Berlin' vol. II pp. 316–319, Berlin, 1808).
F. Fontana	Letter describing experiments concerning the generation of heat by plants. (Harles and Ritter 'Neues Journal der ausländischen medizinisch-chirurgischen Litteratur' vol. V pt. ii pp. 45–68, Erlangen, 1806).
F. K. Medicus	'Pflanzen-physiologische Abhandlungen' (Leipzig, 1803).
H. F. Link	'Grundlehren der Anatomie und Physiologie der Pflanzen' (Göttingen, 1807).
C. A. Rudolphi	'Anatomie der Pflanzen' (Berlin, 1807).
J. W. Goethe	'Versuch die Metamorphose der Pflanzen zu erklären' (Gotha, 1790).
C. F. B. de Mirbel	'Histoire naturelle, générale et particulière des plantes' vol. I (Paris, 1802).
A. W. Roth	'Catalecta Botanica' (Leipzig, 1797).
L. M. A. Dupetit-Thouars	'Essais sur la Végétation' (Paris, 1809).
G. A. Agricola	'Neu- und nie erhörter . . . Versuch der universal Vermehrung aller Bäume' (Regensburg, 1716).
T. Barnes	'A New Method of propagating fruit-trees and flowering shrubs' (London, 1758).
A. Mandirola	'Manuale di giardinieri' (Vicenza, 1652).
F. J. Schelver	'Kritik der Lehre von den Geschlechtern der Pflanzen' (Heidelberg, 1812: supplements, Karlsruhe, 1814, 1823).
H. F. Autenrieth	'De Discrimine Sexuali' (Tübingen, 1821).
K. Linnaeus	'Fragmenta methodi naturalis' (Halle, 1747).

A. L. de Jussieu 'Genera plantarum' (Paris, 1789).

K. P. J. Sprengel 'Anleitung zur Kenntniss der Gewächse' (Halle, 1802).

L. Oken 'Lehrbuch der Naturphilosophie' (3 vols. Jena, 1809–1811).

K. F. A. von Schreiber Review of two works by Amici: 'Memoria . . . de 'Microscopj catadiottrici' (Modena, 1818), 'Osservazioni sulla circolazioni' (Modena, 1818). ('Jahrbücher der Literature' vol. V pp. 203–215, Vienna, 1819).

B. Corti 'Osservazioni microscopiche sulla Tremella' (Lucca, 1774).
'Lettera sulla circolazione del fluido scoperta in varie piante' (Modena, 1775).

G. A. Amici 'Osservazioni sulla circolazione del succhio nella Chara' ('Memoire della Societa Italiana della Scienza' XIII, Fisica, pp. 183–204, Modena, 1820).

K. F. P. Martius 'Über den Bau und die Natur der Charen' ('Nova Acta Physico Medica Academiae Caesareae Leopoldino-Carolinae naturae curiosorum' vol. IX pp. 181–214, Erlangen, 1818).

L. C. Treviranus 'Beobachtungen über die Bewegung des körnigen Wesens in einigen Conferven und einer Chara' ('Beiträge zur Naturkunde' ed. F. Weber and D. M. H. Mohr, vol. II pp. 126–141, Kiel, 1810).

K. H. Schultz 'Ueber den Kreislauf des Saftes im Schöllkraut und in mehreren andern Pflanzen' (Berlin, 1822).

J. F. C. Meyer 'Naturgetreue Darstellung der Entwikkelung, Ausbildung, und des Wachstums der Pflanzen' (Leipzig, 1808).

N.-T. de Saussure 'Recherches chimiques sur la végétation' (Paris, 1804).

J. B. van Helmont 'Ortus medicinae' (Amsterdam, 1652).

H. L. Duhamel 'De la physique des arbres' (2 vols. Paris, 1758).

J. C. C. Schrader 'Zwei Preisschriften über . . . Getreidearten' (Berlin, 1800).

E. Peine 'Hortulanus, der Bosische Garten in Leipzig' (ed. Wehmann, Leipzig, 1723).

J. G. Kölreuter 'Vorläufige Nachricht von einigen das Geschlecht der Pflanzen betreffenden Versuchen und Beobachtungen' (Leipzig, 1761–1766).

J. G. Gleditsch 'Essai d'une fécondation artificielle fait sur l'espèce de palmier qu'on nomme, Palma Dactylifera folio flabelliformi'. ('Histoire de l'Academie Royale des

	Sciences et Belles Lettres' Berlin, 1749, pub. 1751 pp. 103–108).
L. Spallanzani	'Dissertazioni de fisica animale e vegetabile' (Modena, 1780).
J. Pontedera	'Anthologia sive de floris natura libri tres' (Padua, 1720).
J. Bauhin	'Historia Plantarum Universalis' (Yverdon, 1619, 1650, 1651).
Pliny the Elder	'Naturalis Historia'

Animal and human physiology:

Aristotle	'De Anima'
G. R. Treviranus	'Biologie' (6 vols. Göttingen, 1802–1822).
J. H. Autenreith	'Handbuch der empirischen menschlichen Physiologie' (3 vols. Tübingen, 1801–1802).
J. W. Goethe	'Zur Morphologie' (2 vols. Tübingen, 1817–1823).
L. Oken	'Über die Bedeutung der Schädelknochen' (Jena, 1807).
A.-B. Richerand	'Nouveaux élémens de physiologie' (Paris, 1801).
M. F. X. Bichat	'Recherches physiologiques sur la vie et la mort' (4th ed. ed. Magendie, Paris, 1822).
P. Erman	'Einige Bemerkungen über Muskular-Contraction' ('Gilberts Annalen der Physik' vol. 40 pp. 1–30, Leipzig, 1812).
K. H. Schultz	'Die Natur der lebendigen Pflanze' pt. I (Berlin, 1823).
S. T. von Sömmerring	'Vom Baue des menschlichen Körpers' (5 vols. Frankfurt-on-Main, 1791–1796).
A. Haller	'Elementa physiologiae corporis humani' (8 vols. Lausanne, 1757–1766).
J. J. C. Legallois	'Expériences sur le principe de la vie' (Paris, 1812). 'Le Moniteur Universel' Nov. 8th 1811 pp. 1189–1190.
Dr Wilkinson	'Account of some lizards found in Suffolk' ('Tilloch's Philosophical Magazine' vol. 48 p. 469, Dec. 1816).

Assimilative Processes:

C. F. L. Schultz	'Ueber physiologe Gesichts und Farben Erscheinungen' ('Schweiggers Journal für Chemie und Physik' vol. XVI pp. 121–157, Nuremberg, 1816).
F. W. J. Schelling	'Erster Entwurf eines Systems der Naturphilosophie' (Jena, 1799).

I. P. V. Troxler — 'Ideen der Grundlage zur Nosologie und Therapie' (Jena, 1803)
'Grundriss der Theorie der Medicin' (Vienna, 1805).

L. Oken — 'Lehrbuch der Naturphilosophie' (3 vols. Jena, 1800–1811).

Aristotle — 'The Physics'.

J. R. Forster — 'Observations made during a voyage round the World' (London, 1778).

J. W. Goethe — 'Zur Farbenlehre' (2 vols. Tübingen, 1810).

G. R. Treviranus — 'Biologie' (6 vols. Göttingen, 1802–1822).

M. F. X. Bichat — 'Recherches physiologiques' (4th ed. Paris, 1822).

J. H. Autenrieth — 'Handbuch der . . . Physiologie' (3 vols. Tübingen, 1801–1802).

L. Spallanzani — 'Dissertazioni di fisica animale e vegetabile' (2 vols. Modena, 1780).

W. Bligh — 'A Voyage to the South Sea' (London, 1790).

Pierce Smith — Account of his work in Naples by P. Scheel in 'Nordisches Archiv für Naturkunde, Arzneywissenschaft und Chirurgie' vol. III pt. ii pp. 130–136 (Copenhagen, 1803).

L. Spallanzani — 'Expériences sur la digestion de l'homme et de différentes espèces d'animaux' (Geneva, 1783).

A. F. Fourcroy and L. N. Vauquelin — 'Experiénces sur les excrémens des poules, comparés à la nourriture qu'elles prennent' ('Annales de Chimie' 1779 vol. 29 pp. 1–26). 'Sur le guano' ('Tilloch's Philosophical Journal' 1806 pp. 112–115).
'Analyse du chyle de cheval' (Thomson's 'Annals of Philosophy' II, 1813 pp. 223–225).

J. F. Blumenbach — 'Ueber den Bildungstrieb und das Zeugungsgeschäft' (Göttingen, 1781).

Sex-relationship:

G. H. von Schubert — 'Ahndungen einer allgemeinen Geschichte des Lebens' (3 vols. Leipzig, 1806, 1807, 1821).

J. F. Ackermann — 'Infantis androgyni historia et ichnographia' (Jena, 1805).

Zoology:

Aristotle — 'Historia animalium'.
'De generatione animalium'.
'De partibus animalium'.

G. L. C. F. D. Cuvier — 'Recherches sur les Ossemens Fossiles de Quadrupèdes' (Paris, 1812).

G. R. Treviranus — 'Biologie' (6 vols. Göttingen, 1802–1822).

V. Coiter	Appendix 'De quadrupedum sceletia' to G. Fallopio's 'Lectiones de partibus similaribus corporis humani' (Nuremberg, 1575).
P. Camper	'Naturgeschichte des Orang-Utang' (Amsterdam, 1782, tr. Herbell, Düsseldorf, 1791).
G. L. C. F. D. Cuvier	'Le Règne Animal distribué d'après son Organisation' (4 vols. Paris, 1817).
J. B. Lamarck	'Philosophie zoologique' (2 vols. Paris, 1809).
Medical Science:	
H. A. Goeden	'Critische Bemerkungen ueber Hegel's Begriff vom Wesen der Krankheit und der Heilung' (Oken's 'Isis', Jena, 1819 pp. 1127–1138).
J. Pichler	'Darstellungsversuch der im Markgrafthum Mähren gegen Mitte December 1805 ausgebrochenen und bis halben Juni 1806 gewährten Epidemie' (Brünn, 1807).
J. Brown	'Elementa medicinae' (Edinburgh, 1780).
J. H. Autenrieth	'Handbuch der . . . Physiologie' (3 vols. Tübingen, 1801–1802).

i. TERMINOLOGY

'It is in fact part of the fulfillment of a people's culture that it should be able *to express everything in its own language*. The concepts we denote by means of foreign words seem to be somewhat *alien* to us, to be no immediate part of what is ours.'—Hegel.

With the help of the following publications: Hermann Glockner 'Hegel-Lexikon' (improv. ed. 2 vols. Stuttgart, 1957), Rudolf Eisler 'Wörterbuch der philosophischen Begriffe' (1899, 4th ed. 3 vols. Berlin, 1927–1929) and Johannes Hoffmeister 'Wörterbuch der philosophischen Begriffe' (2nd ed. Hamburg, 1955), it is now possible for the German texts of Hegel's work to be submitted to systematic terminological and linguistic analysis.[1] This is however out of the question with the existing

[1] One of the most striking examples of the value of such analysis is provided by Leonhard von Renthe-Fink, 'Geschichtlichkeit. Ihr terminologischer und begrifflicher Ursprung bei Hegel, Haym, Dilthey und Yorck' ('Abhandlungen der Akademie der Wissenschaften in Göttingen. Philologisch-Historische Klasse. Dritte Folge, Nr. 59 pp. 1–153, Göttingen, 1964), whose historical-philological approach throws a great deal of light upon a concept central to much nineteenth and twentieth century thinking. For more general studies of the significance of language in the development of the Hegelian system see Henri Lauener 'Die Sprache in der Philosophie Hegels, mit besonderer Berücksichtigung der Ästhetik' (Bern, 1962) and Josef Simon 'Das Problem der Sprache bei Hegel' (Kohlhammer Verlag, Stuttgart, 1966). Simon provides a fascinating study of a many-sided problem. He tends however to over emphasize the importance of his central theme, and like Lauener's, his work is curiously devoid of any reference to Hegel's use of the terminology of the natural sciences.

English translations of them, most of which are highly unsatisfactory, and quite inadequate to the purposes of exact scholarship. In this translation, some attempt has been made to reproduce the subtlety and consistency with which Hegel employs his *philosophical* terminology. It has to be admitted however, that a completely satisfactory rendering of this aspect of his language cannot be forthcoming until more of his works have been translated in the light of recent German scholarship, and extensive cross-referencing has become possible.

For the *classical High German* of Hegel's day (Upper-Saxon), J. C. Adelung 'Grammatisch-kritisches Wörterbuch der Hochdeutschen Mundart mit beständiger Vergleichung der übrigen Mundarten, besonders aber der Oberdeutschen' (ed. D. W. Soltau and F. X. Schönberger, 4 pts. Vienna, 1807–1808) is to be highly recommended, and should be on the desk of anyone undertaking Hegel translation. It should be supplemented by reference to J. and W. Grimm 'Deutsches Wörterbuch' (16 vols. Leipzig, 1854–1954) and A. Götze 'Trübners Deutsches Wörterbuch' (ed. W. Mitzka, 8 vols. Berlin, 1939–1956), both of which are firmly based on historical principles and give copious references to their sources. F. Kluge's 'Etymologisches Wörterbuch der Deutschen Sprache' (15th edition ed. W. Mitzka, Berlin, 1963), is by no means exhaustive in range, but is invaluable in that the frequent revisions of it make available up-to-date information on matters of etymological research. Hegel occasionally uses *Swabian* words and expressions, all of which find exhaustive treatment in H. Fischer and W. Pfleiderer 'Schwäbisches Wörterbuch' (6 vols. Tübingen, 1904–1936). The *non-German* words he uses will be found in J. C. A. Heyse 'Allgemeines verdeutschendes und erklärendes Fremdwörterbuch mit Bezeichnung der Aussprache und Betonung der Wörter nebst genauer Angabe ihrer Abstammung und Bildung' (2 pts. Oldenburg, 1804, ed. G. Heyse and W. Wittich, 14th ed. Hanover, 1870).

The most satisfactory *German-English* dictionary for Hegel translation is that by Newton Ivory Lucas, 'A Dictionary of the English and German and German and English Languages adapted to the present state of literature, science, commerce and arts' (4 pts. Bremen and London, 1854–1868). See also J. L. Hilpert's excellent 'Dictionary of the English and German, and the German and English Language' (2 vols. Karlsruhe, 1828). These earlier works should be supplemented by reference to the great late-nineteenth century compilations: 'Muret-Sanders: Enzyklopädisches Englisch-Deutsches und Deutsch-Englisches Wörterbuch' (4 pts. ed. Sanders, Schmidt, Stoffel, Berlin, 1905–1906), and F. Flügel, I. Schmidt, G. Tanger 'A Dictionary of the English and German Languages for home and school' (7th ed. 2 pts. London, 1903). The 'Shorter Oxford English Dictionary' (Ed. C. T. Onions, 3rd ed. Oxford, 1964) is a good companion volume to these works.

The German terminology relating to the subject matter of the '*Mechanics*' and '*Physics*' cannot be handled with any precision and certainty unless there is constant access to the following works: S. Klügel 'Mathematisches Wörterbuch' (7 vols. Leipzig, 1803–1836), J. S. T. Gehler 'Physikalisches Wörterbuch' (ed. Brandes, Muncke etc. 11 vols. Leipzig, 1825–1845), both of which contain exhaustive bibliographies. They should be supplemented by reference to the extensive 'Encyklopädie der Mathematischen Wissenschaften mit Einschluss ihrer Anwendungen' (ed. W. F. Meyer etc. 6 vols. Leipzig, 1898–1934), remembering of course that this work is not primarily historical in purpose. The English works corresponding to these are: C. Hutton 'A Philosophical and Mathematical Dictionary' (2nd ed. 2 vols. London, 1815) and S. Vince 'A Complete System of Astronomy' (2nd ed. 3 vols. London, 1814–1823). They are not so accurate and exhaustive as their German counterparts however, and their bibliographical references are much scantier. They should therefore be supplemented by reference to the general encyclopaedias of the time such as E. Chambers 'Cyclopaedia; or, an Univeral Dictionary of Arts and Sciences' (10th ed. 5 vols. London, 1779–1791), and the 'Encyclopaedia Britannica' (6th ed. 26 vols. Edinburgh, 1823–1824). John Harris's 'Lexicon Technicum: or, an universal English Dictionary of Arts and Sciences: explaining not only the terms of art, but the arts themselves' (5th ed. 2 vols. London, 1736) will be found to be handy and useful in this connection, in that it will often fill in the historical background to a subject or problem. G. Schilling's 'Encyclopädie der gesammten musikalischen Wissenschaften' (6 vols. Stuttgart, 1834–1838) is indispensable if the musical terminology of the time is to be translated correctly.

The *chemists* of Hegel's day had some difficulty in translating current literature satisfactorily. J. R. Partington's definitive 'History of Chemistry' (vols. 3 and 4, London, 1962–1964) is therefore essential to any satisfactory handling of the complicated and inconsistent terminology of the time. The most valuable German work on the subject is by M. H. Klaproth and F. Wolff 'Chemisches Wörterbuch' and 'Supplemente zu dem chemischen Wörterbuche' (9 vols. Berlin, 1807–1819). It may often be profitably supplemented by reference to J. F. John 'Handwörterbuch der allgemeinen Chemie' (4 vols. Leipzig and Altenburg 1817–1819), which has the advantage of being a closely printed and pocketable work. Thomas Thomson's

'A System of Chemistry' (3rd ed. 5 vols. Edinburgh, 1807) was translated into German by F. Wolff, 'System der Chemie' (5 vols. Berlin, 1805–1811), and these two works provide an excellent source for the Anglo-German chemical terminology of the day. See also A. and C. R. Aikin 'A Dictionary of Chemistry and Mineralogy with an account of the processes employed in many of the most important chemical manufactures. To which are added a description of chemical apparatus, and various useful tables of weights and measures, chemical instruments etc. etc.' (2 vols. London, 1807); Andrew Ure 'Dictionary of Chemistry' (2nd ed. London, 1824).

German *geological* terminology was explained on historical principles by H. Veith in his 'Deutsches Bergwörterbuch' (Breslau, 1870). A useful English companion volume to this is D. Page 'Handbook of Geological Terms' (Edinburgh, 1865). These works should be supplemented by reference to H. Steffens 'Handbuch der Oryktognosie' (4 vols. Halle, 1811–1824), which provides a useful survey of the geological literature of the time, and C. Hintze 'Handbuch der Mineralogie' (7 vols. Leipzig, 1897–1933), which provides an exhaustive geographical and to some extent historical survey of the subject matter of mineralogy. J. Challinor's 'A Dictionary of Geology' (Cardiff, 1961) is to be highly recommended for the attempt it makes to relate terms to their historical contexts. The following dictionaries may profitably be consulted, though they have to be used with caution on account of their being either non-historical or not interlingual: A. Cissarz and W. R. Jones 'German-English Geological Terminology' (London, 1931), W. J. Arkell and S. I. Tomkeieff 'English Rock Terms' (Oxford, 1953), C. M. Rice 'Dictionary of Geological Terms' (Michigan, 1955), A. A. G. Schieferdecker 'Geological Nomenclature' (Gorinchem, 1959), J. V. Howell and J. M. Weller 'Glossary of Geology and Related Sciences' (2nd ed. Washington, 1960).

The 'Grundriss der Kräuterkunde' (Berlin, 1792, 7th edition ed. H. F. Link, 4 pts. Berlin, 1831–1833) by C. L. Willdenow is indispensable for an understanding of Hegel's *botanical* terminology. The book was very popular on account of the admirably lucid manner in which its subject-matter is presented, and is especially valuable since a large part of it is devoted to the definition of botanical terms, and it is frequently referred to by Hegel: see the English version of it 'The Principles of Botany, and of vegetable Physiology' (2nd ed. Edinburgh, 1811). Thomas Green's 'The Universal Herbal; or, botanical, medical and agricultural Dictionary' (2nd ed. 2 vols. London, 1824) provides a very useful companion volume to it, since it also includes a section devoted to the definition of terms.

B. D. Jackson's 'A Glossary of Botanic Terms with their derivation and accent' (London, 1960) is not quite so satisfactory on historical matters as might have been wished, but the work is so exhaustive in range and has come to play so important a part in the standardization of English botanical terminology, that its guidance has been heeded throughout the whole of the section on botany. Its inter-linguistics might profitably be supplemented by reference to E. Artschwager 'Dictionary of Botanical Equivalents' (Baltimore, 1925) and W. T. Stearn 'Botanical Latin' (London, 1966), and its historical aspect by reference to Thomas Mawe and John Abercrombie 'The Universal Gardener and Botanist; or, a general dictionary of gardening and botany' (2nd ed. London, 1797).

The *physiological* and *medical* (but not nosological) terminology of Hegel's day cannot be treated with any comprehensiveness or precision unless the student has J. F. Pierer's 'Anatomisches-physiologisches Realwörterbuch' (8 vols. Leipzig and Altenburg, 1816–1829) on his desk. The work has the inestimable merit of having been written for the medical practitioner of the day, and yet of including an historical treatment of its subject matter which carries detailed bibliographies of all the relevant literature published since classical antiquity. Several corresponding *anatomical* works might be mentioned: see J. F. Meckel 'Handbuch der menschlichen Anatomie' (4 vols. Halle and Berlin, 1815–1820), S. T. Sömmerring 'Vom Baue des menschlichen Körpers' (5 pts. Frankfurt-on-Main, 1791–1796, ed. Wagner etc. 8 vols. Leipzig, 1839–1845). Useful British equivalents to these works are: R. Morris and J. Kendrick 'The Edinburgh Medical and Physical Dictionary' (2 vols. Edinburgh, 1807) and G. Motherby 'A New Medical Dictionary; or, general repository of physic. Containing an explanation of the terms relating to anatomy, physiology, physic, surgery, materia medica, chemistry etc. etc. etc.' (3rd ed. London, 1791). I. and W. D. Henderson 'A Dictionary of Biological Terms' (8th edition ed. Kenneth, London, 1966), E. C. Jaeger 'A Source-book of biological names and terms' (Springfield, Illinois, 3rd ed. 1959) and P. Grey 'The Encyclopaedia of the Biological Sciences' (New York, 1960) are works which might profitably be consulted in this connection.

The 'Handbuch der Zoologie' (2 vols. Nuremberg, 1820) by G. A. Goldfuss provides a useful account of contemporary *zoological* knowledge and terminology. The zoological literature of the time is exhaustively surveyed by F. W. Assmann in his 'Quellenkunde der vergleichenden Anatomie' (Brunswick, 1847). Any detailed study of the zoological knowledge and terminology of the period must, of course, involve constant reference to C. D. Sherborn 'Index Animalium sive index nominum quae ab A.D.MDCCLVIII generibus et speciebus animalium imposita sunt' (13 vols. Cambridge and London, 1902–1932), and S. A. Neave 'Nomenclator Zoologicus' (4 vols. London, 1939–1940).

Specialized terminology such as that in the sections on crystallography (§ 315) and colour (§ 320), which can only be mastered by reading the sources on which Hegel is basing his exposition of the subject matter, has been discussed in the commentary. In conclusion, it should perhaps be noted, that Hegel employs the terminology of the natural sciences with what amounts to complete accuracy, precision and consistency. A knowledge of the subject matter of these disciplines is of course essential if there is to be any full appreciation of the significance of his work. The same is also true of his *philosophical* terminology, although as has been noted, the low standard of English translations of his works, and the extent to which his system is misunderstood, have hitherto made it difficult to demonstrate this in the English-speaking world.

Definitions

Hegel was fully aware of the necessity of clarifying the significance of the words he used, and of the difficulties involved in providing truly meaningful definitions of them. Present preoccupation with considerations of this kind might give rise to an interestingly new approach to Hegelian studies once this is more generally realized. Many of the philosophical terms used recurrently throughout the 'Encyclopaedia' are treated as categories in the 'Logic', and this work therefore provides us with a very valuable series of detailed dialectical *definitions*. If its subject matter is to be fully intelligible however, it requires extensive historical and linguistic as well as philosophical analysis. In the following glossary, those terms most likely to cause difficulty to the modern reader have therefore been related to their origins, counterparts and cognate forms in Classical, German and English usage, as well as to the relevant expositions in the first part of the 'Encyclopaedia'.

Actuality: Wirklichkeit (Latin: actualitas). Aristotle's distinction between potentiality and actuality ('Metaphysics' IX 6 ff) accounts for the wide currency of the term in the later Middle Ages. Meister Eckhart (c. 1260–1327) first translated 'actualitas' as 'werkelicheit'. Adelung takes it to signify effectiveness and operativeness as opposed to mere possibility. Hegel defines it ('Encyclopaedia'

§§ 142–159) as, 'the unity, become immediate, of essence with existence, or of inward with outward.'

Cf. H. H. Milman's account of Thomism in the 'History of Latin Christianity' (6 vols. London, 1854–1855, 3rd ed. 9 vols. London, 1864) XIV iii, vol. 9 p. 136, 'Universals are real only in God, and but seemingly, in potentiality rather than actuality; they are subjective in the intelligence of man; they result objectively in things.'

I. 266, 26 'These are lines which should be reserved to mathematical determination, but which have been transformed into physical actualities.'

II. 12, 32 '(The being of light is) actuality as a transparent possibility.'

III. 106, 22 'The vocal faculty comes closest to thought, for in the voice pure subjectivity becomes objective, not as the particular actuality of a condition or sensation, but in the abstract element of space and time.'

Being: Sein (Greek εἶναι, Latin esse). Eisler defines it as, 'the supreme and most general concept, which, taken in its broadest significance, includes everything susceptible, in any manner, of being thought.' Hegel's definition is in substantial agreement with this ('Encyclopaedia' §§ 84–110). Cf. Aristotle 'Metaphysics' VII I, 1028a; St. Thomas 'Summa de veritate' I i, 'Summa theologiae' II qu. 94 a2; E. Coreth S. J. 'Das dialektische Sein in Hegels Logik' (Vienna, 1952), Laszlo Erdei 'Der Anfang der Erkenntnis. Kritische Analyse des ersten Kapitels der Hegelschen Logik' (Budapest, 1964); H. Beck 'Der Akt-Charakter des Seins. Eine spekulative Weiterführung der Seinslehre Thomas v. Aquins aus einer Anregung durch das dialektische Prinzip Hegels' (Munich, 1965).

In English non-Hegelian philosophical writings the term only occurs in connection with the distinction between matter and mind: see Locke 'Human Understanding' 1690, III v 5, 'Species of Actions which were only the Creatures of their own Understandings; Beings that had no other existence but in their own Minds.': Mill 'Logic' I iii 2.62, '*Being* is . . . applied impartially to matter and to mind. . . . A Being is that which excites feelings, and which possesses attributes.'

I. 199, 16 'God is that in which spirit and nature are one, and in which intelligence at the same time has both being and shape.'

II. 85, 23 '(Heat) is a being which is at the same time show, or a show which is still being.

III. 107, 30 'Living existence has *being*, and *preserves itself* only as this reproductiveness, not as mere being.'

Being-in-self: In-sich-sein (Latin, in se esse). This term has its origin in the Aristotelian definition of *substance* as that which, as the sustainer of characteristics, is absolutely independent and cannot be a predicate ('Metaphysics' VII 3, 1029 a 8), and which is therefore to be distinguished from *accidence* ('Metaphysics' V 30). It is therefore to be regarded as the opposite of 'in alio esse.' The terms 'inseity' and 'aseity' might form useful additions to English philosophical terminology: see Joseph Geyser (1869–1948) 'Das philosophische Gottesproblem' (Bonn, 1899).

Hegel never defines the term with any precision, but he deals with closely related categories in §§ 84–98 of the 'Encyclopaedia.'

I. 242, 35 'It can also be said that gravity is the *being-in-self* of matter.'

I. 263, 12 'The *particular* bodies (planets) are however those which simultaneously stand as much in the determination of self-externality, as they do in that of being-in-self.'

II. 81, 22 'The being-in-self which reveals itself in sound, is itself materialized.'

III. 140, 15 'Time is internal quivering, the negativity of being-in-self.'

Body: Körper (Latin corpus). The word first occurred in German in the *medical* literature of the thirteenth century. By the eighteenth century however, it had come to be almost synonymous with 'thing', and Hegel's definition of it is therefore to be found in §§ 125–130 of the 'Encyclopaedia.' Adelung notes that, 'In its widest significance it refers to anything consisting of matter as opposed to anything spiritual. It is in this sense in particular that it is used in the sciences, when things of this kind are simply to be defined as consisting of matter.' Cf. Ralph Cudworth's preface to 'The true intellectual system of the universe' (London, 1678), 'The onely Principles of Bodies, are Magnitude, Figure, Site, Motion, and Rest.'

I. 225, 1 'Relative space is something much higher however, for it is the determinate space of any given material body.'

II. 221, 1 'If one wants to say what a body is, one's description of it will only be complete once the whole cycle of its changes has been presented.'

Coherence: Cohärenz (Latin cohaerentia). The *categories* relating explicitly to coherence are dealt with in §§ 135–141 of the 'Encyclopaedia', the *natural phenomena* in which it is most in evidence in §§ 295–307. Hegel does not refer to coherence in this sense as Zusammenhang or Zusammenhangskraft. See Thomas Hobbes 'Decameron physiologicum: or, ten dialogues of natural philosophy' (London, 1678) IX 108, 'For then not only the points of Contact will be many (which makes the coherence stronger)'.

II. 63, 7 'The coherence of matter *with itself* is (i) purely *quantitative*. It is ordinary cohesion, which is the strength of consistence in resisting weight.'

II. 82, 25 'As the specific and internally coherent body repulses force, it also yields inwardly to it.'

Collaterality: Nebeneinander (Latin col and later-, latus): situated or placed side by side with one another; running side by side, parallel; in geometry and crystallography the term is applied to two faces having a common edge. Eisler (II p. 585) defines it as, 'the concept of a relative positioning (Ordnungsweise), necessary in intuition, and universally construable.' The consideration of continuous and discrete magnitude in § 100 of the 'Encyclopaedia' provides a relevant analysis of the natural phenomena and methods of explanation treated in §§ 254 and 339.

See Berkeley's 'A New Theory of Vision' (Dublin, 1709) § 85, 'In neither of these two ways do microscopes contribute to the improvement of sight; for when we look through a microscope, we neither see more visible points nor are the collateral points more distinct than when we look with the naked eye, at objects placed in a due distance.'

I. 223, 4 'Space constitutes *collaterality* of a completely ideal nature.'

III. 21, 27 'This whole style of explanation is nothing but a transformation of collaterality into temporal succession.

Composition: Zusammensetzung (Latin compositio). Hegel considers this concept in its logical or universal significance in § 135 of the 'Encyclopaedia', and is often critical of the use made of it in the natural sciences. See Charles Hutton 'A course of Mathematics' (2 vols. London, 1807) II p. 137, 'Composition of forces, is the uniting of two or more forces into one.'

I. 237, 29 'It is said of matter that: (a) it is *composite*.'

II. 19, 39 'If one wants to imagine light, one has to discard all determinations relating to composition etc.'

III. 152, 4 'The animal is the absolute self-identity of animation however, it is not a mere composition.'

The word has also been used, on several occasions, to translate 'bestehen'.

II. 35, 19 'The ancients certainly asserted that everything is composed of these four elements.'

II. 187, 4 'They suppose water to be *composed* of oxygen and hydrogen.'

Cf. II. 215, 3 'Categories such as *composition* (Zusammensetzung) and *subsistence* (Bestehen), on the strength of which bodies are supposed to be formed from such substances.'

Condition: Bedingung (Latin conditio). Hegel defines the term in § 146, 'By the Condition of a thing we mean first, an existence, in short an immediate, and secondly the vocation of this immediate to be suspended and subserve the actualizing of something else.' It first occurred in German in *legal* contexts, and first became current in its purely *logical* sense through the writings of Leibniz, and Wolff. The scholastic proposition, 'posita conditione ponitur conditionatum, sublato conditionato tollitur conditio' was well known in Hegel's day, and gave rise to a general recognition of the fact that the condition and the conditioned are correlative. Cf. Mill's 'Logic' I, 388; III, 5, § 3.

III.136, 4 'An inorganic nature to which it is opposed as to its *external* condition and material.'

The word has also been used to translate Zustand (Latin modus). C. A. Crusius (1715–1775) 'Entwurf der notwendigen Vernunft-Wahrheiten' (Leipzig, 1745) § 25 observed that, 'The condition of a thing is its actuality, regarded as occurring together with certain determinations pertaining to it.' Adelung (*IV*. 1775) defines the condition of a thing as, 'the disposition of its essence and of that in it which is variable'. Goethe is certainly not averse to using the word, but in a letter to B. G. Niebuhr dated November 23, 1812, he denounces it as being literally senseless, in that its meaning implies a permanent state, whereas everything is in fact transitory. Hegel uses it to imply transitoriness:

II.49, 16 'Heat and cold are here merely accessory conditions which do not belong to the determination of the process itself.' Cf. T. H. Huxley 'Physiography: an introduction to the study of nature' (1877) p. 104, 'The three conditions of a solid, a liquid and a gas . . . are physical states dependent mainly on Temperature.'

Conditionality: Bedingtheit, i.e. the quality of being conditional. Richard Baxter (1615–1691), in 'Plain scripture-proof of . . . baptism' (1651) p. 92 uses the word, 'Let others plead for its causality; I plead but for its conditionality.' When Hegel used it in German however, it had only recently been coined.

I.256, 4 'Since *fall*, in its freedom, still contains conditionality.'

II.56, 18 'As is the case everywhere in the sphere of finitude and conditionality, this sphere of conditioned individuality is the most difficult to separate from the further context of the concrete object.'

Connection, Connectedness: Zusammenhang (Latin connexio). Hegel uses the word in the usual manner to mean the condition of being related to something else by a bond of interdependence, causality, coherence, or the like. It had been current in German since the seventeenth century. Adelung defines it as, 'that condition in which the separable parts of a thing are bound together with one another'. The general vagueness of its use in scientific contexts is brought out well by Neil Arnott (1788–1874) in his 'Elements of physics or natural philosophy' (1833 ed.) II i, 129, when he speaks of, 'The connexion of temperature with the rise of fevers and other pestilences.'

In the translation, 'connection' has been used for the somewhat less complex phenomena referred to by Hegel.

II. 48, 15 'The Earth would not have a process if it lacked this connection with the Sun.'

III. 128, 7 'The soul is present in the body in a general way, it does not merely conform to the specific connectedness of the corporality.'

III. 128, 30 'The development of the voice together with the coming of puberty . . . is an example of such a connection.'

III. 146, 7 'In so far as need is a connectedness with the *universal* mechanism . . . . , instinct is merely an *internal* stimulation.'

Consistence: Zusammenhalt (Latin con and sistere to stand). Thomas Thomson (1773–1852), in his 'System of Chemistry' (3rd ed. 1807) II 542, uses the word in the same way as Hegel, to mean material coherence and permanence of form, 'It forms cubic crystals without consistence, and resembling a jelly.'

II. 63, 8 'The coherence of matter *with itself* is (i) purely *quantitative*. It is ordinary cohesion, which is the strength of consistence in resisting weight.'

Corporality: Körperliche. The word is not common in German as a noun. Hegel uses it in order to convey *precisely* the same meaning as that attaching to its English equivalent, i.e. 'The quality of consisting of matter; material or corporal existence; materiality.' See J. Chandler's translation of J. B. van Helmont's 'Oriatrike, or Physik refined' (London, 1662) p. 150, 'A Mathematical corporality or bodiliness.'

II. 220, 19 'Corporality which subsists as being indifferent is posited as a mere *moment*.'

III. 128, 7 'The soul is present in the body in a general way, it does not merely conform to the specific connectedness of the corporality.'

Corporeality: Körperlichkeit. The quality or state of being corporeal; bodily form or nature: see Hegel's 'Encyclopaedia' §§ 125–130; Aristotle's 'Metaphysics' VII 2; Robert Southey 'Sir Thomas More' (1831) I 333, 'And assume corporeality as easily as form.'

I. 245, 16 'Inertia, impact, pressure, draw, fall etc., the determinations of ordinary mechanics, belong to the sphere of finite corporeality.'

II. 121, 8 'The primary determination of shaped corporeality is its *self-identical* selfhood.'

Determinate: Bestimmte (Latin determinatus). Luther used the word to mean, 'identifying exactly by giving particulars': see his translation of I Chronicles

VI 65, 'Stedte, die ſie mit namen beſtimpten.' It was not until the eighteenth century however, that this usage became widespread: see Christian Wolff (1679–1754) 'Vernünftige Gedanken von Gott' (1736) § 286, who speaks of 'determining the difference between things'. Natural scientists were said to 'determine' a rock, a plant, an animal, by means of its characteristics: cf. Francis Bacon 'Sylva sylvarum; or a naturall historie' (1626) § 602, 'Plants are all figurate and determinate, which inanimate bodies are not.' In German philosophical usage the word became synonymous with 'defined' and was very popular about the turn of the century: see J. H. Campe 'Wörterbuch der Deutschen Sprache' vol. I (Brunswick, 1807); Schoppe 'Mitteilungen der schlesischen Gesellschaft für Volkskunde' vol. 18 p. 78.

Hegel attaches the usual significance to the word, taking it to mean definitely bounded or limited, in time, space, extent, position, character, or nature; definite, fixed; clearly defined or individualized; distinct, as opposed to vague, undefined, or indefinite.

I. 203, 6 'This contemplated unity is the Notion, which contains the determinate differences simply as an immanent and self-moving unity.'

I. 243, 2 'Where the centre lies is determined by means of the weighted matter of which it is the centre; in so far as it is mass, it is determined, and therefore its tendency, which is consequently a determinate positing of the centre.'

Determinate being: Daſein. Hegel defines this category in §§ 89–95 of the 'Encyclopaedia', where he quotes Spinoza's 'omnis determinatio est negatio' ('Correspondence' letter 59) in support of the proposition that the foundation of all determinateness is negation, an exclusion of other characteristics. He takes it to be quite distinct from existence (op. cit. §§ 123, 124), mainly on account of the latter's presupposing a *ground* and not mere being. In doing so he was probably influenced by Kant, who regarded determinate being as a category of modality, and as such as the opposite of not-being.

The word was first used in philosophical German by Christian Wolff (1679–1754), in order to translate 'existentia': see his 'Vernünftige Gedanken von Gott' (1720) § 226, ‚daher ſind Empfindungen nothwendig, ſowohl in Anſehung ihres Daſeins, als in Anſehung ihrer Beſchaffenheit von Gott.' Cf. 'Zeitschrift für deutsche Wortforschung' 3,338; 8,156; H. Schulz and O. Basler 'Deutsches Fremdwörterbuch' vol. I p. 187 (Strassburg and Berlin, 1913); Adelung I col. 1408.

I. 209, 23 '*Life* is the highest to which nature drives in its determinate being.'

II. 123, 11 'The individual form which has pervaded its matter as a totality, has thereby posited its manifestation however, and so advances to this ideality of determinate being.'

III. 70, 8 'The *stem* comes between leaf and root as the *first* diremption, for here we are considering plants with a developed determinate being.'

Determinateness: Bestimmtheit. The quality of being determinate; definiteness, distinctness, preciseness. Adelung takes it to involve, 'precise definition by the giving of all necessary characteristics.' The word became current in English on account of the translation of German philosophical works: see B. Bosanquet's translation of R. H. Lotze's 'Metaphysic' (1884) p. 31, 'Each of their marks . . . has been limited to a completely individual determinateness.'

II. 134, 4 '(When the crystal) is in fact only active as *immaterial* determinateness.'

III. 197, 6 'These circumstances are of an elemental or climatic nature, they also reside and have their origin in the elemental determinateness of the organism.'

Determination: Bestimmung (Latin determinatio). Hegel uses the word in precisely the same manner as does Kant in his earliest writings (1747–1770), i.e. as the equivalent of 'determinatio', and as signifying any determining characteristic of things and concepts. Cf. Sir Kenelm Digby (1603–1665) 'Two treatisies, in one of which the nature of bodies, in the other the nature of man's soule, is looked into' (1645) I. 87, 'To be a Quality is nothing else but to be the determination or modification of the thing whose quality it is.'

I. 263, 11 'The *particular* bodies (planets) are however those which simultaneously stand as much in the determination of self-externality, as they do in that of being-in-self.'

III. 109, 6 'The developed *determinations* of the *Notion* exist in the subject, and are displayed there by this whole (of shape).'

Determinedness: Bestimmtsein. The German word, like Johnston and Struthers' translation of it, is absent from the standard dictionaries. Hegel uses it in order to refer to the *specific being* of determinateness.

I. 219, 29 'It is this unity of qualitative determinedness and of gravity, which produces itself in life.'

I. 282, 23 'It is in the nature of this sphere (Mechanics) that this externality of determinedness should constitute the peculiar determinateness of matter.'

II. 90, 19 'By starting from the specific determinedness of material being-in-self, we have considered the cohesive aspect of the *generation* of heat.'

II. 92, 39 'As primary subjectivity, (specific gravity) was simple abstract determinedness.'

Difference: Unterschied (Latin differentia). Hegel defines what he understands by difference, and the sub-categories he takes it to involve, in §§ 116–120 of the 'Encyclopaedia.' His use of the word shows that the meaning he attaches to it is entirely orthodox. He employs it to refer to the condition, quality or fact of being different, or not the same in quality or essence; to indicate dissimilarity, distinction or diversity. It may be worth noting that its original and basic meaning in German was, 'that whereby something, such as a room is divided or separated into two different parts or things' (Adelung), and that it was only under the influence of the Latin words 'discernere' and 'distinguere' that it came to take on its modern meaning. Cf. Descartes 'Principia philosophia (1644) I, 60, 'Distinctio triplex est: realis, modalis et rationis': Kant 'Die falsche Spitzfindigkeit der vier syllogistichen Figuren' (1762) § 6, ,Es ist ganz was anderes, Dinge voneinander unterscheiden, und den Unterschied der Dinge erkennen. Das letztere ist nur durch Urteilen möglich.'

II. 17, 29 'Weighted matter is *divisible* into *masses*, since it is concrete, quantitative being-for-self; but in the quite *abstract* ideality of light there is no such difference.'

III. 59, 5 '(The simple basic life of the plant) is spiritual, a fleeting breath of forms, which does not attain to qualitative and fundamental difference.'

Differentiation: Differenz (Greek διαφορά Latin differentia). The action of differentiating, or condition of being differentiated; any state in which like things are also unlike or something homogeneous is also heterogeneous. See Herbert Spencer 'Principles of Psychology' 1855 (1870) I i, iii 49, 'In the rudimentary nervous system, there is no such structural differentiation.'

I. 217, 28 'The Idea, as nature, has . . . the determination of *particularity*, in which reality is posited with an immanent determinateness of form and its own existent differentiation.'

II. 204, 25 'It is however acid and alkali which constitutes the specific differentiation, as opposition.'

III. 93, 15 'With regard to *sexual difference*, it has to be pointed out that the differentiation reached by the plant . . . is only present as a determination analogous to that of the sexual relationship.'

Hegel occasionally coins words which would appear to be almost entirely synonymous, e.g.

I. 243, 33 'This finitude of matter is the differentiated being of motion and of matter as such.' (Unterschiedensein).

I. 258, 4 'The other moment, which is the differentiation of place within itself.' (Differentsein).

The different units involved in differentiation are referred to by Hegel not as ‚Differentiale' (differentials) but as ‚Differenter'.

II. 109, 28 'It has been said that all electrical activity is magnetism, and that magnetism is the force which is fundamental to the differentials.'

II. 114, 29 'As shape is the equilibrium of differentials, it also has to display these differentiations within itself.'

III. 174, 12 'As the *different sexes* constitute the sex-drive as differentials, there must be a *difference* in their formation.'

Existence: Existenz (Latin exsistere to stand out). In his treatment of this category in the 'Encyclopaedia', Hegel shows that he recognizes the significance of its etymological origins, 'The phrase "Existence" (derived from existere) suggests the fact of having proceeded from something. Existence is Being which has proceeded from the ground, and been reinstated by annulling its intermediation.' (§ 123 Addition).

The word was introduced into German by V. L. von Seckendorf (1626–1692), see 'Der Christenstaat' (1685) 2. 11. For its subsequent history see the article 'Determinate being'. There is little evidence of its having been employed self-consciously in its literal meaning in English. When it is used to mean 'having place in the domain of reality, having objective being' however, this does at least carry the vague implication of an ideality or subjectivity which might be regarded as a rough approximation to Hegel's related category of 'ground.' See Robert South (1634–1716) 'Sermons Preached on Several Occasions' (1737 ed.) I ii 45, 'To conceive the world . . . to have existed from eternity.'

I. 266, 18 'Bodies which have a semi-independent existence, with their centre partly in themselves, and partly in another.'

II. 71, 24 'A phenomenon such as this (sound), in which a being-in-self assumes physical existence, holds no surprises for us.'

III. 92, 28 'If this negation of the plant's coming out of itself is now to attain *existence* . . . this idea matrix of the plant becomes *isolated*.'

Extrinsicality: Außereinander (Latin extrinsecus, on the outside). The etymology of the Latin word does not quite coincide with the origin of Hegel's coinage. The word itself may be regarded as capturing his meaning quite well however, and is more convenient that an Anglo-Saxon monstrosity such as 'outside-one-anotherness'. See Thomas Blundeville (fl. 1561) 'Exercises' (1594) III, ix 292, 'These two circles having respect to a materiall Spheare, are said to be extrinsicall or outward.'

I. 223, 4 'It is on account of its being self-externality, that space constitutes *collaterality* of a completely ideal nature; as this extrinsicality is still completely *abstract*, space is simply *continuous*, and is devoid of any determinate difference.'

II. 69, 2 'The negating of the extrinsic subsistence of the material parts is itself negated as the reinstating of their juxtaposition and their cohesion.'

II. 100, 4 'Nature is the Idea in the element of extrinsicality, and like the understanding, it holds fast to the *dispersed* moments of the Notion and so expresses their reality.'

III. 151, 30 'The soul is omnipresent within the body however, and the extrinsicality of bones, nerves and veins is of no significance to its ideality.'

Figuration, Formation: Gestaltung (Latin figuratio). Hegel assesses the categories closely related to figuration in §§ 127–128 of the 'Encyclopaedia.' He uses the word in a fairly orthodox manner, to refer to the action or process of forming into a figure, the determining of a certain form, the resulting form or shape, contour or outline. He fails to distinguish between its relevance to inorganic and organic phenomena however. English usage often demands that it should be rendered by 'formation' in organic contexts. On the complex problems relating to the word at the beginning of the last century see F. Weinhandl 'Zum Gestaltproblem bei Aristoteles, Kant und Goethe' ('Beiträge zur Philosophie des deutschen Idealismus' vol. IV sect. 2, 1927). Cf. Henry Pemberton (1694–1771) 'View of Sir Isaac Newton's Philosophy' (1728) 8, 'The figuration and the motion of bodies strike our sense more immediately than most of their other properties.'

II. 92, 22 'Whereas the figurations of space, the point, line and surface, were merely the negations of space however, they are now described by form within a matter which it alone determines.'

II. 113, 21 'All figuration contains magnetism, for it is a complete limitation in space posited by the immanent drive of its *overseer*, which is form.'

III. 47, 15 'It is in this way that the process of formation, and of the reproduction of the *single* individual, coincides with the process of the genus.'

III. 131, 17 '*The process of formation.*'

For itself: Für sich. This term has its origin in everyday German usage, in which it occurs in such phrases as 'to live by oneself' (für sich leben), 'to remain single' (für sich bleiben) 'to speak to oneself' (für sich sprechen), i.e. with the meaning of alone, without relationships, withdrawn from company: see Adelung II col. 359. In general German philosophical usage it is used to refer to ipseity as opposed to being-for-other, and to the inwardness or subjectivity of essence as opposed to its objectivation: see Eisler I p. 451. It is of more general significance in Hegel's system, since it also refers to the second stage in the dialectical interpretation of a sphere: see 'Encyclopaedia' § 95.

II. 27, 22 'The independence of this being-for-self is rigid in so far as it is still immobile.'

II. 101, 35 'Each pole (of the magnet) posits the other and excludes it from itself; the terms of the syllogism can only exist in the connection, they cannot exist for themselves.'

III. 210, 20 'In that its activities become universal, animation endows itself with a universality which is for itself.'

Form: Form (Greek μορφή, Latin forma). Cf. the definition of 'Shape'. Hegel defines form, in conjunction with content, in §§ 133–134 of the 'Encyclopaedia', where it is presented as a sub-category of appearance. The distinction between matter and form, as employed by the scholastics, was very largely determined by Aristotle's 'Metaphysics' (Bk. VII 7–10), in which form is presented as the essential determinant principle of a thing, that which makes matter into a determinate species or kind of being. It was in this Aristotelian and scholastic sense that the word was first used in German by Konrad von Würzburg (d. 1287). A detailed investigation of contemporary usage merely tends to blur the distinction between form and shape (Gestalt): see F. Schiller 'On the Aesthetic Education of Man' (tr. and ed. Wilkinson and Willoughby, Oxford, 1967) pp. 308–309. Hegel distinguishes sharply and consistently between the two, and in the main accepts Adelung's definition (II 246), according to which a form may be regarded as that by means of which a body acquires its shape.

II. 34, 33 'As crystallization, this third term (a salt) also has shape however, so that it is not just a simple abstract unity of chemical elements, but individual unity of form.'

II. 121, 25 'Shape, as the pure form, by which matter is completely determined and pervaded, is merely self-identical in matter, and dominates it throughout.'

III. 113, 12 'Now although each system is the developed whole, and as such contains moments of the other systems, the single form of the Notion remains predominant in each of them.'

Formation: Gebild (Latin formatio). This is an old word in German, which was revived during the eighteenth century by Klopstock, Herder and Voss. It often implied somewhat less substantiality than form (Form) or shape (Gestalt): see Schiller 'Das Lied von der Glocke' (1799) line 63:

> 'Wie ein Gebild aus Himmelshöhn . . .
> Sieht er die Jungfrau vor sich stehn.'

Goethe 'Faust' II line 6277,

> 'Entfliehe dem Entstandnen
> In der Gebilde losgebundne Reiche!'

'Productive of some disgusting formation in their children.' ('The Medical and Physical Journal' vol. III p. 501, 1800) provides an example of a corresponding contemporary English usage.

I. 215, 10 'This contingency is particularly prevalent in the realm of concrete individual formations.'

I. 216, 10 'Nature never fails to blur essential limits with intermediate and defective formations.'

II. 123, 23 'In so far as the punctiform self of individuality is unhindered in its internal formativeness (Bildner), it has nothing further within this dark material being which is alien to it.'

Ideality: Idealität (from Greek *ἰδέα*). The Greek word is derived from *ἰδεῖν*, to see. In philosophical contexts it is used to refer to a state of being which is in conformity with the character of an ideal, i.e. which is typical, which serves as a *pattern*, or which is regarded as *perfect*. Its literal meaning therefore carries the important implication that *comparison* is not only essential to exact definition, but also an integral part of all *cognition*. Hegel develops the more general significance of this in §§ 213–215 of the 'Encyclopaedia.' His redefinition of the category was evidently needed. At the beginning of the eighteenth century the word was usually employed with precision: see John Norris (1657–1711) 'Practical discourses upon several divine subjects' 1691–1698 (1711) III p. 153; 'The natural existence of things is founded upon their Ideal existence; if things had not first existed in Idea, they could never have existed in Nature'; C. F. Nicolai (1733–1811) 'Briefe, die neueste Literatur betreffend' IX p. 56 (1761), ‚Homer vermeidet mit aller Sorgfalt das sittliche Ideal.' Once it had been introduced into *aesthetics* however, it tended to lose this general clarity of meaning: see C. M. Wieland (1733–1813), 'Teutscher Merkur' IV p. 62 (1772), who criticizes the extreme looseness of the contemporary usage.

III. 102, 1 'Organic individuality exists as *subjectivity* in so far as the externality proper to shape is *idealized* into members.'

III. 104, 4 'The animal's *vocal faculty* is bound up with this, for as the *actual* ideality of soul, animal *subjectivity* dominates the abstract ideality of time and space.'

Immediate: unmittelbar (Latin, immediatus). This word first occurred in German in *juridical* contexts. Certain political units within the Empire, such as the free Imperial cities, were *immediately* subject to the Emperor, others were only subject to him through the *mediation* of, for example, the Electors. In the eighteenth century this was still one of its best-known uses: see J. L. Frisch 'Teutsch-Lateinisches Wörterbuch' (2 pts. Berlin, 1741) 666b. During the sixteenth century it was first widely employed in *religious* contexts (e.g. ‚die unmittelbare Hülfe Gottes'), and it is with regard to these and closely related *philosophical* matters, that Hegel gives it its most extensive treatment in the 'Encyclopaedia' (§§ 61–78). In these lectures however, he uses it in a perfectly general manner to refer to *anything* devoid of an intermediary or intervening medium. It is therefore usually the phenomena selected to illustrate the initial level of a sphere, which are said to be 'immediate', or to exhibit 'immediacy'.

I. 211, 26 'Immediacy is the other form of otherness, and consists of what is different subsisting abstractly by itself.'

II. 15, 14 'This body (the sun) is the primordial and uncreated light, it is immediate, and does not arise from the conditions of finite existence.'

II. 81, 15 'In its own immediacy however, this alternation (of sound) is consequently the negation of materially specific subsistence.'

II. 92, 4 'The real *dissolution* of *immediacy* is accompanied by the reciprocal indifference of specified material beings, and it is this moment which is posited in heat.'

Implicit: an sich (Greek καθ' αὑτό, Latin in se). The precise meaning given to this phrase by Hegel should not be confused with the various senses in which it is used by other writers: cf. Aristotle 'Metaphysics' Bk. V, 18, 1022a; Kant 'Critique of Pure Reason' 1st ed. p. 386; Grimm 'Deutsches Wörterbuch' I col. 287; H. Eggers 'Deutscher Wortschatz' (12th ed. Stuttgart, 1961) 1 and 10. Christian Wolff (1679–1754) was the first to introduce it into German as a translation of the Greek.

Hegel attempts to present the initial level of each sphere as being 'implicit', and so as containing the 'potential' of the being-for-self of its second level, and of the 'being-in-and-for-self' of its third level. The progression in *complexity* involved in this pattern is open to criticism through an understanding of the *subject matter* he is dealing with. The *triadicity* in which the concept of implicitness plays such a basic part, is only open to valid criticism through an examination of the Hegelian system as a *whole*.

I. 221, 5 'Mechanics treats of . . . *matter* in the freedom of its implicit Notion, i.e. the *absolute* mechanics of *free motion*.'

II. 221, 23 'Iron is always implicitly iron, but it is also only implicitly so, for its mode of existence changes.'

III. 173, 6 'This is not merely implicit sentience, but a sentience which is existent and animated.'

Independent: selbständig. The meaning of the German word is occasionally coloured by the fact that in the sixteenth century ‚Selbstand' was used to render the Latin 'persona': L. Diefenbach 'Glossarium latino-germanicum' (Frankfurt-on-Main, 1857) 430. There seems to be no peculiarity in Hegel's use of it however. In accordance with the ordinary philosophical usage of his day (cf.

Adelung), he employs it simply to refer to states in which something does not depend upon something else for its existence, validity, efficiency, operation, or some other attribute; to anything which is not contingent on or conditioned by anything else. John Playfair (1748–1819) 'Outlines of Natural Philosophy' 1816 vol. II p. 323, 'This is quite independent of the figure of the Earth, and would be the same though the Earth were truly spherical.'

I. 266, 36 'It is in the so-called *explanation* of uniformly accelerated and retarded motion by means of an *alternating decrease* and *increase* in the magnitude of the centripetal and centrifugal forces, that the *confusion* caused by the postulation of such independent forces is greatest.'

II. 72, 18 'In this case, the tremor is forced by each on the other, rather than being independent.'

III. 103, 10 'In so far as the animal's members are simply moments of its form, and are perpetually negating their independence, and withdrawing into a unity which is the reality of the Notion, and is for the Notion, the animal is the existent Idea.'

Indifference: Gleichgültigkeit. Hegel does use this word simply to mean the fact of making no difference:

III. 140, 18 'The arrangement is more or less a matter of indifference, the main point being that the senses in their rationality constitute a totality.' More often than not however, he employs it to convey further shades of meaning, some of which were better understood in eighteenth century English and German than they are today. In the following context for example, its adjectival form is synonymous with 'neutral'.

II. 34, 5 'Rigidity, which is the lunar principle, is no longer indifferent being-for-self, but as an element entering into relation with something other than itself, i.e. individuality, it is the full process of active and restless being-for-self, and is therefore liberated negativity, or fire.'

The most misleading examples of his use of it are however those in which it might appear to mean the indetermination of a body to rest or motion: Henry Pemberton (1694–1771) 'View of Sir Isaac Newton's Philosophy' (1728) p. 29, 'All bodies have such an indifference to rest, or motion, that if once at rest they remain so.' Cf. D. Lardner (1793–1859) 'Pneumatics' (1831) Hydrostatics VII p. 124. When reading Hegel, it has often to be remembered that various currencies circulating within the Empire were said to ‚gleich gelten', i.e. be in a state of *parity*, and that this gave the German word a further meaning, which he frequently has in mind, but which is absent from its English equivalent.

I. 244, 21 'In accordance with the temporal determination in which indifferent spatial subsistence is sublated, (the body) is *transitory*.'

See Adelung's strictures on the looseness of contemporary usage (II, 714–715), and the Berlin joke recorded by H. Schrader in 'Bilderschmuck der deutschen Sprache' (Berlin, 1901) p. 482.

Intro-reflection: Reflexion-in-sich. This term is not to be related too closely to the 'reflection' involved in psychological phenomena and epistemological problems. When employing it, Hegel evidently has in mind the standard usage of his day (Adelung III, 1018), according to which reflection is, 'The action by which one body is thrown back by another, especially in catoptrics, when light-rays are thrown back from a smooth surface.' He might therefore have defined intro-reflection as, 'the reciprocal activity by means of which distinguishable factors constitute a unity.'

I. 261, 11 'In the syllogism which contains the *Idea* of gravity, this Idea is the Notion disclosing itself in external reality in the particularity of bodies, and at the same time, in the ideality and intro-reflection of these bodies, displaying its *integration into itself* in motion.'

II. 160, 11 'Physical being has withdrawn into itself from touch and from determinate being lacking all quality; it is intro-reflected, and is in its otherness.'

III. 107, 9 'As an intro-reflected unity of various singularities, the animal exists as a spontaneously self-producing end, and is a movement which returns into its *particular* individuality.'

III. 137, 2 'In this external relation, the animal organism is *immediately* intro-reflected.'

Intuition: Anschauung (Latin intuitio). Throughout the whole exposition of his system, Hegel makes an *implicit* acknowledgement of the fact that it is intuition which provides the *subject matter* of knowledge. He distinguishes sharply between intuition and dialectical thinking however ('Encyclopaedia' § 246). The part played by intuition in the development of his system needs a more thoroughgoing analysis than it has received hitherto. In many respects his attitude toward intuited knowledge bears a much closer resemblance to that of the empiricists than is often realized. Cf. John Locke 'An Essay Concerning Human Understanding' Bk. IV ch. 2 § i ('Works' 10 vols. London, 1823 II p. 320), 'For if we will reflect on our ways of thinking, we shall find that sometimes the mind perceives the agreement or disagreement of two ideas immediately by themselves, without the intervention of any other: and this, I think, we may call intuitive knowledge. . . . Thus the mind perceives, that white is not black, that a circle is not a triangle, that three are more than two, and equal to one and two.'

I. 203, 1 'Intuition has therefore been reinstated in the philosophy of nature, and set above reflection, but this gets us nowhere, because one cannot philosophize on the basis of intuition.'

III. 27, 26 'Even for the intuition, the variety of the species occurs in precise accordance with Notional distinction.'

Juxtaposition: Außereinandersein. The categories involving this state most explicitly are assessed in §§ 86–111 of the 'Encyclopaedia'. The condition of '*being outside one another*' is not described with perfect accuracy by 'juxtaposition', which usually implies that two or more things are *side by side*, but no other English word enables one to maintain Hegel's distinctions between this condition, *collaterality* and *extrinsicality*. Cf. Joseph Glanvill (1636–1680) 'Scepsis scientifica, or confest ignorance the way to science' (1665) vii 37, 'Parts that are united by a meer juxta-position.'

I. 223, 19 'Space is merely the possibility, not the *positedness* of juxtaposition and what is negative, and is therefore simply continuous.'

II. 64, 23 'Qualitative coherence is therefore a specific mode of juxtaposition, i.e. a determination of space.'

Material being: Materielle (Latin materialitas). Hegel uses this word to refer to that which constitutes the 'matter' of something as opposed to its formality. The meaning he attaches to it is therefore *precisely* the same as one of the meanings covered by the English word 'materiality' (German Materialität). Cf. Jeremy Taylor (1613–1667) 'Ductor dubitantium' (1660) II ii Rule 2, 'If blood be taken in its own materiality when the beast is dead . . .'

II. 92. 10 'Selfhood . . . maintains itself in the externality which is subject to it, and as the freely determining *totality* of this material being, constitutes *free individuality*.'

II. 119, 36 'Consequently, the sense of hearing coincides with this specialization, in which infinite form is related to material being.'

II. 123, 23 'In so far as the punctiform self of individuality is unhindered in its internal formativeness, it has nothing further within this dark material being which is alien to it.'

Mediation: Vermittelung (Latin mediatio). The wider significance of this term is discussed in §§ 65 et seq. of the 'Encyclopaedia'. Cf. H. Niel 'De la médiation dans la philosophie de Hegel' (Paris, 1945). In this treatment of the natural sciences Hegel uses it in a great variety of contexts, not all of which have a predominantly philosophical as well as a scientific significance. Cf. Richard Kirwan (1733–1812) 'Elements of Mineralogy' (2nd ed. 1794–1796) II p. 269, 'By the mediation of nickel it will unite to Bismuth.'

II. 185, 1 'The bodies which enter into (the real process) are mediated by a third term which is not identical with them.'

III. 68, 10 'In plants, and especially in the lower forms, there is no mediation by means of opposition; opposition gives rise to no conjunction, nutrition is a transformation which is devoid of process.'

III. 173, 2 'The genus is present in the individual . . . as an urge to . . . integrate itself through union with this other, and by means of this mediation to bring the genus into existence by linking itself into it.'

Multiplicity: Mannigfaltigkeit (Latin multiplicitas). Adelung (III 61–62) defines it as 'that condition in which things exhibit difference in plurality: multiplicity of flowers, colours, animals etc.' In Biblical contexts the English equivalents of the German word are 'manifoldness' or 'many things': Ephesians III. 10; James III. 2. Cf. 'Encyclopaedia' §§ 116–120.

I. 219, 9 'We see gravity revealed for the first time as the being-for-self which submits multiplicity to its rule.'

II. 72, 9 'Vibration is also present in friction, for while it lasts, a multiplicity is posited in unity.'

III. 47, 33 'All organic being differentiates itself within itself, and maintains the unity of multiplicity.'

Hegel sometimes emphasizes the *unity* of a plurality by using the word ‚Mannigfaltige'. This might have been rendered by 'manifoldness'. Since the contexts usually make his meaning clear however, it has been thought advisable to avoid the use of this clumsy synonym.

I. 210, 23 'The organic body is still a whole composed of a multiplicity of mutually external members.'

II. 101, 6 'Sensuous comprehension merely binds together multiplicity in an external manner.'

The English word has occasionally been used to cover further shades of meaning:

II. 61, 24 'The determination of the form is still a specific mode of the spatial interrelation of its elemental multiplicity.' (‚ihres Vielfachen auseinander').

II. 92, 20 'The shape . . . is absolute centrality, which unlike gravity, no longer has multiplicity merely external to it.' (‚die Vielen').

Object: Gegenstand (Latin objectum). This term first appeared in German as a translation of the Latin in 1625, although it was not widely used in philosophical contexts until the early eighteenth century: see J. C. Gottsched (1700–1766) 'Erste Gründe der gesammten Weltweisheit' (1734) Theoretischer Theil § 320,

,Jede wirkende Ursache muß etwas vor sich haben, darein sie wirket . . . dieses nennet man das Object oder den Gegenstand.' Henry Home (1696–1782) 'Elements of Criticism' (1762) 'Everything we perceive or are conscious of, whether a being or a quality, . . . is with respect to the percipient termed an object.'

Towards the close of the seventeenth century the word was used in devotional contexts to mean *trust* and *support* in dealing with inner temptation and external affliction: see Q. Kuhlmann (1651–1689) 'Kühlpsalter' (1684/5) nos. 70, 79. In the Swabian dialect of Hegel's day it was also synonymous with *impediment*, *opposition*, *obstacle*, *resistance* (H. Fischer 'Schwäbisches Wörterbuch' (1911) vol. III. 180). At that time, this meaning had almost fallen out of use in High German however, and its survival was deplored by lexicographers, since it tended to give rise to misunderstandings (Adelung II 486).

For Hegel's most extensive *treatment* of the term see the 'Encyclopaedia' §§ 193–212. The bearing of its various meanings upon his contextural *use* of it might, perhaps, be profitably investigated.

I. 204, 38 'If subjective truth is the correspondence between sensuous representation and the object, objective truth is the correspondence of the object, of the fact, with itself, so that its reality is in conformity with its Notion.'

III. 104, 28 'Although this awareness is punctiform, it is infinitely determinable, and as it has itself as its object, the subject of which is the ego=ego of sentience, it maintains the lucidity of its simplicity.'

Of an ideal nature: ideell: *Of a real nature*: reell. Hegel's use of either of these terms implies reference to the other.

Between 1741 and 1796 there were many instances in German of ,ideal' being used to mean 'mental, conceived solely through thought': see Hans Schulz 'Deutsches Fremdwörterbuch' (Strassburg, 1913) vol. I p. 280. Schelling seems to have coined the word ,ideell' to cover this meaning, and his mintage is now common currency (Trübner vol. IV). He did so in the course of grappling with the Fichtean problem of the relationship between the ego and the non-ego: see 'System des transcendentalen Idealismus' (1800) p. 76 ('Werke' vol. II p. 385), '*Now the bounds* (dividing the ego from the non-ego) *must however be both of a real and of an ideal nature*. They are *of a real nature* in that they are independent of the ego, since the ego is not actually limited in any other way: they are *of an ideal nature* in that they are dependent upon the ego, since the ego only posits itself through perception as that which is limited. Both statements, that the bounds are of a real nature and that they are simply of an ideal nature, may be deduced from self-consciousness.'

Hegel evidently found this Schellingian terminology convenient. He did not however, confine his use of it to contexts relating to epistemological and psychological problems ('Encyclopaedia' § 96). By saying that a phenomenon is 'of an ideal nature' he usually means that it is to be regarded as *homogeneously unified.*

I. 223, 5 'It is on account of its being self-externality, that space constitutes *collaterality* of a completely ideal nature.'

II. 81,29 'This internal disturbance of the body within itself contains not only the ideal nature of a sublation of matter, but also the real sublation of it by heat.'

III. 212, 12 'It is in this way that the Idea exists in the independent subject, which as an organ of the Notion, finds everything to be fluid and of an ideal nature, i.e. it *thinks*, appropriates to itself all that is spatial and temporal, and so contains universality, i.e. itself.'

By saying that it is of a real nature, he implies that a phenomenon, on account of its reality, is distinct from and yet an *aspect of* a *homogeneous unity.*

I. 238, 29 'Even this thought implies vaguely that the *effect* of force is a sensuous event of a real nature however, that there is no difference between the *content* and expression of force, and that precisely *this force* has the *real nature* of its *expression* in the relationship between the ideal nature of the moments of space and time.'

II. 99, 32 'It is true that all shape of a real nature which is not merely brittle involves this principle of determination' (magnetism).

III. 148, 16 'The real nature of the process is primarily a process with the elements, for in the first instance external being itself is universal.'

Opposition: Gegensatz (Greek ἀντίθεσις, Latin oppositio). The *general* significance of opposition is discussed in § 119 of the 'Encyclopaedia' (cf. Aristotle 'Metaphysics' V, 18). Like Aristotle ('Physics' I, 5), Hegel also recognizes that it occurs in natural phenomena in a philosophically unimportant manner. Cf. Sir Balthazar Gerbier (1591?–1667) 'Counsel and Advise to all Builders' (London, 1663) p. 10, 'The Nature of Aire being to ascend, and when it meets with a sudden opposition it spreads.' The German word was probably coined by the natural scientists and lawyers of the later Middle Ages. It is first *recorded*, as a translation of the Latin, by Johannes Frisius (1505–1565): see 'Dictionarium Latino-germanicum' (Zürich, 1541) 614b.

I. 192, 12 'The initial opposition we encounter is to be regarded as accidental and superficial.'

II. 157, 39 'It is in this way that this universal element becomes a particular moment, separated from the whole; and the other moment is the antithesis.'

II. 161, 26 'The metallicism . . . is a base or extremity which may only be brought into active opposition by an external agent.'

III. 11, 3 'Life is not merely the resolution of the opposition between the Notion and reality, but of oppositions in general.'

Otherness: Anderssein (Latin alteritas). Eisler (vol. I p. 48) distinguishes between alterity (Anderheit) and otherness (Anderssein), but we have Coleridge's authority for regarding them as synonymous in English: 'Blackwood's Magazine' vol. X p. 249 (1821), '*Outness* is but the feeling of *otherness* (alterity), redered intuitive, or alterity visually represented.' Cf. the 'Encyclopaedia' § 91.

The distinction out of which Hegel's use of this word arises bears a very close resemblance to that motivating his use of 'of an ideal nature' and 'of a real nature' (cf.). In its most *general* form it involves the recognition of the comprehensive difference between the universals of the 'Logic' and the particularities of 'Nature'.

I. 205, 7 'Nature has yielded itself as the Idea in the form of *otherness.*'

Cf. Alexander Gill (1597–1642) 'The Sacred Philosophie of the Holy Scripture' (1635) I. 83, 'Absolute perfection, . . . without othernesse or change.' Henry More (1614–1687) 'A Platonicall Song of the Soul' (1642) I i;

'Psyche! from thee they spring,
O life of Time, and all Alterity.'

He does not confine its use solely to this context however.

II. 160, 12 'Physical being has withdrawn into itself from touch and from determinate being lacking all quality; it is intro-reflected, and is in its otherness.'

III. 132, 22 'The otherness or externality of the organism is the untrammelled being of shape, the quiescence opposed to the process.' Cf. Thomas Stanley (1625–1678) 'The History of Philosophy' (4 vols. 1655–1662) 1701 ed. 377.2, 'The Maker of all things took union, and Division, and Identity, and Alterity, and Station, and Motion to compleat the soul.'

Particularity: Besonderheit (Latin particularitas). On the three moments of the Notion (universality, particularity, singularity) see the 'Encyclopaedia' §§ 163–165. Hegel does use ,Particularität':

II. 144, 27 'Another Englishman has in fact maintained that black is composed of all the colours. This obliterates the particularity of colour.' In cases such as this he simply has in mind 'The quality of being particular as opposed to general.' Cf. Isaac Watts (1674–1748) 'Logick' (1725) I iv § 4, 'Any common name whatever is made proper by terms of particularity added to it.'

Adelung refers to Besonderheit as, 'a word which some have recently dared' to put into currency. Hegel evidently made use of it in order to emphasize the strict technicality of the meaning it derives from the structure of the 'Notion'.

I. 217, 26 'The Idea, as nature, has . . . the determination of *particularity*, in which reality is posited with an immanent determinateness of form and its own existent differentiation.'

I. 277, 26 'It is the dependent heavenly bodies which constitute the aspect of particularity; this is why they fall apart and differentiate themselves, for in nature particularity exists as duality, and not as unity, as it does in spirit.'

Plurality: Vielheit (Latin pluralitas). The wider significance of this category is analyzed in § 98 of the 'Encyclopaedia'. A consideration of this assessment and treatment of it might possibly open up an enlightening dialogue with those intimately acquainted with the original inspiration of the pluralism and logical atomism etc. which flourished during the first half of this century: see Eisler II p. 469, III p. 422; G. J. Warnock 'English Philosophy since 1900' (London, 1958).

In everyday German usage, as in English, 'plurality' is distinguished from 'multitude' (Menge) in that it is more abstract, and in that it tends to imply slightly more of an emphasis upon its *component* entities; unlike 'multiplicity' (Mannigfaltigkeit) however, it does not have the further connotation of an emphasis upon *difference*. Cf. Adelung IV 1203; J. R. Illingworth 'Divine Immanence' (1904) vii 86/2, 'The fact that there is plurality, triune plurality in God.'

I. 261, 23 'Difference is posited therefore, and plurality is no longer indeterminate as with the stars.'

III. 9, 26 'In nature, animation certainly disperses into the indeterminate plurality of living beings.'

Posit: setzen (Greek τιθέναι). Despite the use Fichte and Schelling made of it in dealing with epistemological problems, Hegel does not usually employ this word to mean 'postulate'. The meaning he attaches to it is closely related to its significance in those contexts where it is employed in the sense of bringing something into a specific place (Adelung IV. 65), see Genesis I. 17. ‚Und Gott setzte (Lichter) an die Feste des Himmels', or of *setting* a goal or boundaries, see Deuteronomy XXXII. 8, ‚Da der Allerhöchste (sie) zerteilte . . . setzte er die Grenzen der Völker.' The whole structure of the 'Encyclopaedia' has therefore to be borne in mind if the junctures at which he uses the word are to be interpreted correctly.

I. 216, 23 'Nature is *implicitly* a living whole; more closely considered, the movement through its series of stages consists of the Idea *positing* itself as what it is *implicitly*.'

II. 25, 6 'Light is active identity, and posits the identification of everything.'

III. 105, 26 'This positing of itself as the pure and proper negativity of *various specific* places etc., is an extremely important distinguishing faculty (of the animal).'

The assessment of *space* as being the initial level of nature, and as having logical considerations as a whole as its immediate *presupposition*, throws light upon the exact meaning Hegel attaches to 'positedness' (Gesetztsein).

I. 209, 8 'Its (nature's) distinctive characteristic is its *positedness*, its negativity.'

I. 223, 19 'On account of its lack of difference, space is merely the possibility, not the *positedness* of juxtaposition.'

Presupposition: Voraussetzung (Latin praesuppositio). Hegel's system might profitably be regarded as a thoroughgoing and consistent analysis of *all* presuppositions. The *progressions* in complexity basic to the arrangement of its subject matter, when regarded retrogressively, are seen to involve the attempt to establish the precise interrelatedness of the presuppositions made in specialized thought, research and activity: see Theodor Litt 'Hegel. Versuch einer kritischen Erneuerung' (Heidelberg, 1953); cf. E. Husserl 'Logische Untersuchungen' (1900–1901) vol. II p. 19; A. Meinong 'Über Möglichkeit und Wahrscheinlichkeit' (1915) p. 450 et seq.

II. 188, 13 'Consequently, the real totality of this course becomes a cycle of *particular processes*, each of which has the other as its presupposition.'

III. 15, 6 'The first moment of *particularization* is that the organism converts itself into its own *presupposition*, and so assumes the mode of *immediacy*, in which it *confronts* itself with its condition and outer subsistence.'

Purpose: Zweck (Greek τέλος, Latin finis, causa finalis). This category is dealt with in some detail in §§ 204–212 of the 'Encyclopaedia'. In the 'Philosophy of Nature' Hegel calls attention to it in various contexts, none of which presents any great difficulty in respect of interpretation.

I. 212, 28 'The view that natural things are useful is true in that it denies that they are absolute purpose in and for themselves.'

II. 114, 6 'This in the first instance of the purposiveness of nature itself.'

III. 145, 20 'Instinct is supposed to be shrouded in mystery and difficult to grasp, but the root of this difficulty is merely that purpose can only be grasped as the inner *Notion*.'

Reality: Realität (Latin realitas). This category is assessed in § 91 of the 'Encyclopaedia', and a distinction is drawn between two occurrences of it:

(i) 'We speak, for example, of the reality of a plan or a purpose, meaning thereby that they are no longer inner and subjective, but have passed into being-there-and-then.' Cf. 'Encyclopaedia Britannica' (3rd ed., 1797) vol. XVIII 79/1, 'Numberless absurdities, such as, that . . . forms or sensible qualities are real things independent of their subject and the sentient beings who perceive them.'

I. 217, 26 'The Idea, as nature, has . . . the determination of *particularity*, in which reality is posited with an immanent determinateness.'

I. 258, 16 'The self-positing of matter within the determinations of its moments is necessary to material reality.'

II. 25, 7 'Light is active identity, and posits the identification of everything. As this identity is still entirely abstract however, there is as yet no real identity of things.'

(ii) 'The word "reality" is however used in another acceptation to mean that something behaves conformably to its essential characteristic or notion.' Cf. Locke 'Essay on Human Understanding' II XXX § 2, 'Our simple ideas are all real, all agree to the Reality of things.'

II. 14, 40 'After having developed the Notion of light, the question of its *reality* naturally presents itself.'

II. 215, 33 'On being abandoned as a middle term, they (water and air) become the means by which the real extremes of the syllogism assume the *existence* of their original differentiation.'

III. 166, 12 'The *mechanical drive*, as an instinct, constitutes the third moment; it is the unity of the ideal nature of the theoretical process, and of the real process of digestion.'

Relatedness: Verhalten. The German word can mean behaviour, deportment, conduct, demeanour, bearing. In its verbal form it has been used in mathematical contexts since the seventeenth century. Hegel's use of it in mechanics, physics and the organic sciences, though not unique, is unusual. He employs it to refer to a relationship, *one* factor of which tends to be predominant or to take the initiative. His practice therefore provides an interesting adaption of the accepted usage of his day: see Adelung IV 1056–1057, who takes the word to signify, 'The free determination of our own activity in relation to the things external to us, the aggregate of numerous concurrent actions of this kind, isolated actions being unable to constitute a relatedness.'

II. 62, 11 'We have seen that pressure and impact constitute a purely mechanical relatedness.'

III. 51, 1 'As the plant has not yet attained to this selfhood however, it lacks the inwardness which would be free of external relatedness.'

III. 104, 36 'The animal, like the plant, treats externality as something which is of an ideal nature, . . . (this) is a relatedness which makes no demands.'

Relation: Beziehung (Latin relatio). This word first appeared in German chancery jargon in 1671. Its origin was evidently still well-known in Hegel's day, for in 1813 J. H. Campe (1746–1818) noted that a recently coined adjectival form of it (bezüglich—relative to), ' smells very strongly of chancery': 'Wörterbuch' (Brunswick, 1813).

Hegel uses it in a perfectly straightforward manner to refer to any connection, correspondence, or association, which can be conceived as naturally existing between things. In accordance with normal usage, he takes a relation to be less complex than a relationship. Cf. Robert Jameson (1774–1854) 'Treatise on the external characters of minerals' (3rd ed. 1817) p. 173, 'The nucleus increases on its part, always preserving the same relation with the entire crystal.'

I. 221, 11 'When this is not an external relation, it gives rise to self-motivated matter, i.e. to the absolute unity of matter and motion.'

II. 33, 24 'Here (in the Earth) the subjective principle of individuality, which is an infinite self-relation, is still exterior to the universal individuality which is not yet reflected into itself, i.e. to the stimulating and animating principle of light.'

III. 30, 34 'Some lodes yield precious metals, others base metals, and here there are significant relations which are indicative of a higher connection.'

Relationship: Verhältniß (Latin proportio, relatio). Hegel uses the word to refer to connections more complex than 'relations'. In German, as in English, it is widely used with reference to *human* affairs. Adelung carefully notes its various shades of meaning and adds, 'often however, it is also nothing more than the factotum of the classroom philosophers, who employ it in the purveyance of turgid and confused concepts.'

I. 238, 18 'Velocity . . . is a quantitative relationship, simply between space and time'.

II. 68, 32 'In form, every particle has its particular place, and is the preserver of this particular relationship.'

III. 193, 8 'In the two relationships considered above, the self-mediation of the genus with itself is the process of its diremption into individuals.'

Self: Selbst. The ultimate German origin of this word, as used by Hegel, was the *pietistic* literature of the late seventeenth century, in which it tended to carry the connotation of selfishness and egocentricity. During the eighteenth century it entered German *philosophical* writing as a synonym for 'ego'. Hegel's use of it with reference to inanimate phenomena was probably influenced by its forming a constituent element in the structure of ‚selbständig' (independent), and by his intense awareness of the complexity relationships implicit in all natural *entities*. This usage appears to be peculiar to him.

The German pietists borrowed the word from *English*, in which its early philosophical usage shows the influence of Cartesianism and Hobbism. See Locke 'Human Understanding' (1690) II xxvii § 17, 'Self is that conscious thinking thing, whatever Substance, made up of Spiritual, or Material, Simple, or Compounded, it matters not, which is sensible, or conscious of Pleasure and Pain . . . and so is concern'd for it self, as far as that consciousness extends.'

I. 245, 14 'The positing of this sublation begins already in the selfless body'.

II. 68, 17 'Elasticity is retreat into self for the subsequently immediate re-establishment of self.'

III. 104, 17 'The animal's self is of an ideal nature, it is not effused and immersed in materiality, but is merely active and present within it.'

Selfhood (Selbstischkeit) made its appearance in English through John Ellistone's translations of Boehme's works: see 'The epistles of Jacob Behmen' (1649) X 8, 'A child's naturall understanding of selfehood' (Selbheit). Hegel simply uses the word to generalize the concept of 'self'.

II. 25, 13 'Light is still entirely abstract selfhood, and is therefore the not-self, the free self-identity which is devoid of all opposition within itself.'

II. 165, 3 'Nevertheless, although this selfhood is at the same time an abstract reality, it is an intrinsically *differentiated* light,—*electrical* relationship.'

III. 48, 3 'The plant has not yet advanced to this internal difference however; if it had, the unifying point of selfhood and the organic crystal would already constitute the two aspects of its life.'

Self-externality: Außersichsein. The categories predominating in this condition are dealt with in §§ 137–141 of the 'Encyclopaedia'. If the treatment of a phenomenon demands a distinction between its internal and external characteristics, and yet the appearance of it, 'shows nothing that is not in the essence, and in the essence there is nothing but what is manifested', it may be said to be self-external.

I. 224, 11 'The further requirement is that the intuition of space shall correspond to the thought of pure self-externality.'

II. 88, 24 'Heat . . . as an existent negative . . . , is its self-externality and self-positedness within another.'

III. 211, 7 'The last *self-externality* of nature is sublated, so that the Notion, which in nature merely has *implicit* being, has become *for itself*.'

Shape: Gestalt. Cf. the definition of ‚Form'. Hegel takes shape to be the *external* form or contour of things, i.e. that quality of a material object or geometrical figure which depends on constant relations of position and proportionate distance among all the points composing its *outline* or its *external surface*. Cf. Adelung II 633–634, who observes that the word has its origin in ‚stellen' (to place), and so derives its literal meaning from the manner in which the parts of anything are *disposed*. The shades of meaning current in early nineteenth century usage are extremely complicated. Schiller, for example, gives the following account of the relationship between form and shape as he understood it, 'The word *shape* is used in both a figurative and literal sense to express, in a general concept, the object of that which has a tendency to take form. It is a concept which includes all the formal qualities of things, as well as their relations to the faculties of thinking.' ('On the Aesthetic Education of Man' letter xv, 2.)

II. 92, 13 'The *transition* now has to be made to real individuality or shape, the moments of which have been seen in that which preceded.'

II. 121, 25 'Shape, as the pure form, by which matter is completely determined and pervaded, is merely self-identical in matter, and dominates it throughout.'

III. 46, 9 'On the other hand, living being is also the shape which has substantial form dwelling within it.'

Singularity: Einzelnheit (Latin singularitas). Cf. J. H. Campe 'Wörterbuch der Deutschen Sprache' (1807) I. 887. On the three moments of the Notion (universality, particularity, singularity) see the 'Encyclopaedia' §§ 163–165. Since Hegel makes the attempt to present the most complex levels of each sphere as singularities, he is perpetually attempting to show that singularity as such *includes* the less complex levels of universality and particularity, 'The third (moment of the Notion) is *singularity*—meaning the reflection-into-self of the specific characters of universality and particularity; which negative self-unity has *complete and original determinateness*, without any loss to its self-identity or universality.' (op. cit. § 163). Cf. Theophilus Gale (1628–1678) 'The Court of the Gentiles' (1669–1676) I i p. 4, 'His Universal Ideas . . . he makes to be the . . . great Exemplar and image of all singulars.'

I. 237, 4 'Place is spatial and therefore indifferent *singularity*.'

III. 42, 25 'The first has the form of singularity, the second that of universality.'

Sublate: aufheben (Latin tollere). The double sense in which Hegel uses this word is explained in § 96 of the 'Encyclopaedia', 'We mean by it (i) to clear away, or annul: thus, we say, a law or a regulation is set aside: (ii) to keep or preserve: in which sense we use it when we say: something is well put by.' The Latin equivalent has the same double meaning as the German word.

Prior to the publication of J. H. Stirling's 'The Secret of Hegel' in 1865, sublation was used in English simply to mean *removal* or *denial*: Michael Hawke 'Killing is murder and no murder' (1657) p. 46, 'Tiberius was sublated by poison'; Sir William Hamilton (1805–1865) 'Lectures on Logic 1837–1838' (1866) xvii, I 331, 'When of two opposite predicates the one is posited or affirmed, the other is sublated or denied.'

I. 242, 9 'It is essential to distinguish *gravity* from mere *attraction*, which is simply the general sublation of juxtaposition, and yields nothing but continuity.'

II. 163, 16 'Taste is the third particularity of the body, and as the result of its neutrality, it has sublated this relationship to the element once again, and drawn itself away from it.'

III. 212, 3 'The other side, which is death, constitutes the sublation of the singular, and is therefore the proceeding forth of the genus, of spirit.'

Subsistence: Bestehen (Latin subsistentia). The condition or quality of inhering or residing in something: see Thomas Spencer 'The art of logick' (1628) p. 50, 'The forme is not the difference it selfe: for, a forme is a subsistence in an unitie.' This meaning was part of the normal German usage of Hegel's day. Adelung (I, 926b) defines the word as meaning, 'Having its essence in something, as when the happiness of the soul is said to subsist in activity.' That which subsists was usually regarded as being more permanent than that constituted by it. Cf. ‚Schönheit vergeht, Tugend besteht.' In its verbal form the word is usually most *conveniently* translated into English by means of 'consist'.

The second major sphere of the 'Logic' ('Encyclopaedia' §§ 112–159), i.e. that concerned with 'Essence' or the hierarchy of categories exhibiting pairs of correlatives, may be regarded as constituting an extended analysis of subsistence in general.

I. 242, 15 'In the sphere of the primary *immediacy* of nature, the self-external being of continuity is still posited as *subsistent* however.'

II. 67, 1 'That which is material has its *indifferent* and specific *subsistence* as its place.'

III. 137, 27 'The theoretical process is the free disinterested process of sensation, which also allows for the subsistence of the external being.'

Substance: Substanz (Greek ὑποκίεμενον, ὑπόστασις, Latin substantia). Since scientific research is continually revising our interpretations of complexity relationships, no precise philosophical definition of substance is of any permanent interest, and Hegel never attempts to give one. He sometimes appears to emphasize the necessary revisability of all definitions of it by taking the word to be synonymous with ‚Stoff', which can mean 'stuff' as well as matter, substance, element etc.

He is aware of its convenience as a heuristic concept however: see 'Encyclopaedia', §§ 126–128. Cf. Locke 'Human Understanding' II xxiii § 2, 'The idea . . . to which we give the general name Substance, being nothing, but the supposed . . . support of those Qualities . . . which we imagine cannot subsist, sine re substante, without something to support them.' Cf. Henry Home (1696–1782) 'Elements of Criticism' (1774) II app. 507, 'A being with respect to its properties or attributes is termed a subject, or substratum. Every substratum of visible qualities, is termed substance.'

II. 11,25 'In the first sphere the determinations are still distinguished from the substance, they are not material determinations; substance as such is still shut up within itself and unmanifest.'

II. 214, 32 '*Animal* and *vegetable* substances belong moreover to quite another natural order.'

II. 215, 22 'In this connection it is most surprising to find the four chemical elements of oxygen etc., regarded *substances*.' (Stoffe).

III. 121, 21 'As the substance which is common to all the parts, the blood is the irritable principle uniting them all in an inner unity.'

Thing: Ding (Greek χρῆμα, πρᾶγμα; Latin res, ens). In the 'Logic' ('Encyclopaedia' §§ 123–130) Hegel defines thing as presupposing existence and as the immediate antecedent of matter and form. His conception of it therefore corresponds fairly closely to that prevailing in normal English usage, according to which it is, 'that which has separate or individual existence, as distinct on the one hand from the totality of being, on the other from attributes or qualities'. See Coleridge 'Biographia Literaria' (1817) xii I 267, 'An infinite independent thing is no less a contradiction than an infinite circle or a sideless triangle.'

I. 196, 31 '*Aristotle* had already noticed this notion of purpose in nature, and he called the activity the *nature of a thing*.'

I. 200, 17 'Theoretical consciousness, because of its onesided assumption that the natural things over against us are persistent and impenetrable, creates a difficulty which is refuted point-blank by the practical approach, which displays the absolutely idealistic belief that individual things are nothing in themselves.'

Totality: Totalität (Latin totalitas). It becomes evident from the contexts in which Hegel uses this word, that he regards the *plurality* so immediately apparent in all knowledge and experience, as deriving various degrees of *unity* from *qualitative* differences and similarities. He was therefore evidently of the opinion, that it is only the appreciation of the *interdependence* of this plurality and unity which can give rise to meaningful definitions of totalities. Any complete understanding of the overall totality he claimed for his system must therefore be founded upon an analysis of §§ 84–86 of the 'Encyclopaedia'. W. van Dooren 'Het Totaliteitsbegrip bij Hegel en zijn Voorgangers' (Assen, 1965). Cf. the definition of *being*; C. M. Ingleby (1823–1886) 'Introduction to Metaphysics' (1869) II ii 171, 'I remark, obiter, that Totality is plurality in unity.'

I. 206, 25 'God is subjectivity, activity, infinite actuosity, within which the other is only momentary, and remains implicit within the unity of the Idea, because it is itself this totality of the Idea.'

I. 219, 22 'Organic being, which is an individuality existing for itself and developing itself into its differences within itself, constitutes totality as found in nature. It determinations are at the same time concrete totalities, not merely specific properties, and remain qualitatively determined with regard to one another.'

II. 181, 7 'Philosophically systematic consideration differs from an empirical approach in that it presents the stages of determinations, and not the stages of the concrete existences of nature as totalities.'

II. 190, 35 '(In the *philosophical* consideration of chemistry) we have to regard the process in its totality, and the way in which it divides bodies into classes, and defines them as the potentially fixed stages of its course.''

Undifferentiation: Indifferenz. Cf. the definition of 'differentiation'. Herbert Spencer 'First Principles' (1862) I iv 26, 'That undifferentiated substance of consciousness which is conditioned anew in every thought.'

II. 39, 2 'Air is already the negativity of particularity, although this is not apparent because it is still posited in the shape of undifferentiated sameness.' (ununterschiedenen).

II. 124, 9 'Powdered glass for example, and water whipped into foam, are opaque. Their mechanical undifferentiation and homogeneity are removed and interrupted, and brought into the form of individualized being-for-self, while they were formerly a mechanical continuum.'

II. 157, 40 'Transparent being is also undifferentiated, although as it has this characteristic on account of its form, this lack of differentiation is opposed to the dead and dark undifferentiation we have here.'

III. 142, 29 'The cause of this aberration lay in the fundamental error of first defining the Absolute as the absolute undifferentiation of subjective and objective being, and then supposing that all determination is merely *quantitative* difference.'

Unity: Einheit (Greek *μονάς*, Latin unitas). Hegel's insistence upon the importance of including both unity and plurality in any meaningful definition of a *totality* (cf.) probably accounts for the fact that he rarely refers to anything but a relative unity: see Aristotle 'Metaphysics' Bk. V ch. vi. Although he recognizes that the *unit* (die Eins) basic to arithmetic is in some respects no ordinary unity (§ 259 Rem.), he would therefore have disagreed with Locke's statement ('Human Understanding' II vi § I) that, 'Amongst all the Ideas we have . . . there is none more simple than that of Unity, or One.' Cf. the 'Encyclopaedia' §§ 96–97.

I. 210, 31 'One should not allow oneself to be deceived by the appearance of extrinsicality; one should remember that the mutual externality constitutes only a single unity.'

I. 229, 31 'Time, as the negative unity of self-externality, is also purely abstract and of an ideal nature.'

II. 170, 39 'Through form, the crystal has certainly brought back the difference of material being-for-self into a unity.'

III. 103, 14 'The unity which is produced has being for the implicit unity of the animal. This implicit unity is the soul or Notion, which is present in the body in so far as the body constitutes the process of idealization.'

Universality: Allgemeinheit (Latin universalitas). On the three moments of the Notion (universality, particularity, singularity) see the 'Encyclopaedia' §§ 163–165. Hegel emphasizes their *interdependence*, 'But the universal of the notion is not a mere sum of features common to several things, confronted by a particular which enjoys an existence of its own. It is, on the contrary, self-particularizing or self-specifying, and with undimmed clearness finds itself at home in its antithesis.' Cf. Theodor Litt 'Das Allgemeine im Aufbau der geisteswissenschaftlichen Erkenntnis' (1941): Thomas Hobbes 'Human nature' (1650) V. 50, 'The appellations that be universal, and common to many things, are not always given to all the particulars.' Logic, in that its subject matter is involved in but not confined to natural and spiritual phenomena, exhibits the characteristic of universality in its purest form.

I. 197, 1 'Physics . . . does aim at comprehending that which is *universal* in nature as it presents itself in a *determinate* form, i.e. forces, laws, genera.'

I. 201, 4 'The empirical view of nature has this category of universality in common with the philosophy of nature.'

III. 42, 7 'The universal is existent, and the organic unit is the power which controls and consumes this negation of itself, this external being.'

Variety: Verschiedenheit (Greek ἑτερότης, Latin varietas, diversitas). In German, this word is first recorded, in its adjectival form, in 1678, and Lessing was the first to use it as a noun. Hegel defines it as follows ('Encyclopaedia' § 117), 'In variety the different things are each individually what they are, and unaffected by the relation in which they stand to each other. This relation is therefore external to them.' Adelung (IV. 117) confirms the orthodoxy of this definition, 'the property by which a certain thing differs from others', and Trübner notes that the word implies 'opposition, difference and multiplicity'.

II. 25, 24 'Dark matter . . . has material reality, and within itself falls apart into a *duality* of . . . corporeal *variety* . . . , and the *opposition* as such.'

II. 43, 8 'Consideration of this field (of the elements) suffers from a basic defect, which has its origin in the fixed conception of a substantial and unalterable *variety* of elements.'

III. 27, 26 'Nature . . . does not . . . indicate necessity through the transition of various stratifications into one another . . . merely by means of a gradual diminution however, for even for the intuition, the variety of the species occurs in precise accordance with Notional distinction.'

Whole: Ganze (Greek ὅλον, Latin totum). In § 135 of the 'Encyclopaedia', Hegel emphasizes the *interdependence* of the whole and the parts, 'The notion of the whole is to contain parts: but if the whole is taken and made what its notion implies, i.e. if it is divided, it at once ceases to be a whole. Things there are, no doubt, which correspond to this relation: but for that very reason they are low and untrue existences.' Cf. Aristotle 'Metaphysics' Bk. V. 26; Leibnitz 'Die philosophischen Schriften' (ed. C. J. Gerhardt, 7 vols. 1875–1890) vol. VII p. 544; Christian Wolff 'Philosophia prima sive ontologia' (1736) § 341; Isaac Watts 'Logick' (1725) I vi § 7, 'All Parts have a Reference to some Whole.'

I. 270, 37 'This is the origin of the mathematical conception of the parallelogram of forces in finite mechanics, in which the space traversed is presented as the diagonal, which is therefore posited as part of a whole or function, and so susceptible to mathematical treatment.'

II. 181, 36 'This is the position of the chemical process within the whole.'

III. 41, 3 'Although it is a life of parts, it is ceaselessly dissolving itself within itself, and brings forth nothing but the whole.'

FOREWORD

by

+ KARL LUDWIG MICHELET

+ 'To philosophize about nature is to create nature.' As I now finish the task allotted me by the Hegel Society of editing this priceless relic from the wealth of material Hegel has left us, it is only fitting that I should begin by quoting the man who really planned the revival of the philo-
5 sophy of nature. It is with the consummate energy of enthusiasm, and the supreme confidence of thinking cognition, that this sentence expresses the point of view which the divine twins of modern science held four decades ago, and which they defended triumphantly against the philosophy of reflection and everything associated with it. Their friendship developed
10 in early youth, and gathered strength in their public activity at Jena,
+ and the publication of the 'Critical Journal of Philosophy'. It was this friendship which won the ground on which *Hegel* was able to erect the sciences into a structure which is unsurpassable in its comprehensiveness, and which has its like only in the writings of *Aristotle*. If the sunny day of
15 victorious truth now rises into the heavens of science after that bright and glorious dawn with which the century began, we shall enjoy in these lectures on the *philosophy of nature* one of the choicest fruits to have ripened from the garland of blossoms then in bud.

One could regard this statement of *Schelling's* as presumptuous, and
20 take it as evidence of the self-deification with which philosophy is so often charged at present. The poet says that it is the concern of philosophy 'to think again the great thoughts of the creation' however, and if we express the thought in this way, it seems to be less outrageous. What in fact can be our object in philosophizing about nature, if it is not to re-
25 produce its intelligible essence or generative ideas by thinking them forth from our spiritual inwardness? In this connection I should like to draw attention to the end of these lectures, where *Hegel* brings out the creative activity of spirit in nature in a similar way.

It is generally asserted however, that as experience is the only basis of
30 scientific cognition, and most certainly the only basis of natural science,

the whole business of a philosophy of nature, which is the comprehension of nature through thoughts, is idle and utopian. One cannot deny of course that the philosophy of nature would never be able to think about nature unless it could draw upon experience, but experiences are in no way conducive to the discovery of ideas, unless these ideas flow from an inner source. It can be seen only too often, that the continuous and unorderly accumulation of empirical *data*, instead of furthering our *knowledge* of nature, merely gives rise to further confusions and contradictions. Consequently, when the attempt is made to introduce a systematic consistency into natural science, this is said to be a useless and impossible task, and even the empirical scientists themselves will admit that it is doomed to failure. Yet this continual hoarding of fresh discoveries must be motivated by the fundamental assumption that there is a final result to be reached, and that at some time or another there will be a breakthrough from the phenomena to the essence of nature. As an excuse for the perpetual postponement of this, it is always pointed out that everything has not yet been discovered, —as if the goal which research of this kind has before it were not being continually shifted into the distance, for there is no end to what may be discovered. It is not surprising therefore, that when a philosophy of nature also enters the field, and attempts, as it must, to present the idea of the whole, it is passed by with a shrug of the shoulders, and a commiserating smile.

We can say therefore, that natural science still finds itself with the following difficulty: 'If we concern ourselves with understanding, noting particularities, exact observation, and distinguishing one thing from another, we shall tend to regard whatever arises from an idea and leads back into it, as to some extent a burden to us. We shall be at home in our labyrinths in our own way, and will not feel the need for a line of enquiry that might lead us more rapidly throughout the whole. If we are able to survey wider areas of science however, the danger is that we shall be tempted to despise detail, and to force that which depends for its life upon separation, into a stifling universality.' If we now enquire into the attempts + that have hitherto been made to break out of this difficult situation, a balanced and all-round understanding will seem to be even more of an impossibility.

The so-called philosophers of nature have certainly attempted to think over a great deal of empirical material. They have however been only too ready to apply the rigidly worked out schemata which were given currency by *Eschenmayer* under the name of potencies, in order to ravage and + obliterate the bright abundance and infinite multifariousness of nature, and transform it into the drabbest of uniformities. Their turbid mixture of thought and empiricism was all the rage forty years ago, and one can hardly blame the empirical physicists for the forthright way in which they + have rejected it. Our worthy friend *Link* passed judgement upon it, and 5 we quote him with approbation, 'There is very little research to be done if one is prepared to accept the pronouncements of certain physiophilosophers. They tell us for example that a plant is the product of light, earth, and attraction. According to *Kieser*, the plant in its integrity is the + organic magnet, and shows this both in its entirety and in its parts. One 10 runs across the holy triad of undifferentiation in differentiation everywhere. Nature has never been so abused. Speculation of this kind can offer us nothing but vague relationships and superficialities; it never touches the inexhaustible profusion of actuality, and instead of interpreting the actual world, offers us hieroglyphics.' This philosophy of nature 15 certainly applied the principle of creating nature through thought in a most unfortunate manner, for the figments of cognition it dealt with were merely the products of an eccentric imagination.

Can we say however that empiricism has helped to close the gap which divides it from philosophy? If we note some of the views now being 20 expressed by natural scientists, we shall have good reason to believe that *Hegel's* polemic against the atomistic and materialistic interpretations of + nature is beginning to take effect. '*Resonant matter*' has already been discarded, and even *Newton's* theory of colour has not remained unquestioned, although the wave-theory which is replacing it seems to be even + more materialistic. It has even been said quite recently that electricity is merely a *direction*, which sounds idealistic enough. These developments should not be overrated however, for if atoms are transformed in a cheap way into molecules, physicists will still swear by them, as they will by pores, caloric and its latency, magnetic fluid and many of the other odd 30 names given to artificial concepts of the understanding. These names are also figments of cognition, and are in no way superior to the schemata of the philosophers of nature.

I have heard it objected that *Hegel* was tilting at windmills. Physics itself is said to be capable of accepting the proposition that heat, electri-35 city, atoms, and magnetic fluidity etc., are merely modifications of matter and not independent essences, without the help of philosophy. It is added moreover, that these expressions are essential to communication and the discovery of further phenomena; physics is said to make use of them as heuristic concepts, which it then attempts to confirm by means of ex-40 periment. One might reply to this as follows.

Philosophy should be grateful for the concession implicit in the point about the windmills, for as it was behind these windmills that the giant of empiricism had hidden himself, the fact that *Hegel* was knighted for combat of this kind should not detract in any way from his reputation. With regard to the second point, it should be remembered that even if this metaphysic of forces, matter, substances, and atoms etc. is only accepted as an hypothesis, it will still distort our initial assessment of experiments. It is impossible to interpret experiments soundly if fixed preconceptions of this kind are read into them, and one then deludes oneself into thinking that they confirm these preconceptions. The way in which we speak is never a matter of indifference, for thoughts cleave to expressions. Philosophy and physics have hitherto spoken different languages, and I am convinced that this is the root cause of their being unable to understand one another.

I can see no reason why we should regard this as an insuperable obstacle however, and by offering this book to the general public, I believe that we shall be helping to overcome it, for it is here that the divine language of Hegel's rational dialectic already approximates to many of the modes of human speech used by the understanding. The French and English are mainly to blame for the labyrinths of complicated theory that have been introduced into physics, and *Hegel* was only too justified when he blamed our physicists for relying too heavily upon the ways of thinking which predominate beyond the Rhine and the Channel (II. 212). It is surely not unreasonable to expect our physicists to draw upon their German cultural resources, or at least to show that they are willing to negotiate with German philosophy, and to correct it should it fall into error. A state of mutual understanding is one of the essential conditions of any future peace treaty however. Each side will have to be aware of the other's method of comprehension, for it is only by mastering an opposing point of view that one is fully qualified to refute or accept it. It cannot be denied that *Hegel's* attacks were strongly tinged with bitterness, and as he improvised upon his notes in the lecture room, the sharpness of his remarks was often involuntarily heightened. I beg the physicists to remember the noble passion for truth which characterized the deceased however, and to take into consideration the conscientiousness with which I have attempted to given an account of what was communicated. Whatever has gone wrong among the living has either been put right already or is still open to rectification however; and here we are striving for reconciliation, not fresh dissensions.

We cannot hope to succeed without this understanding, but no matter how earnestly we attempt to create it, we shall achieve nothing unless we have the objective support of a mediating principle, and both empiricism and the philosophy of nature are unable to provide this. If this medius terminus is to be a true middle term, it will have to display two aspects, 5 so that both extremes occur within it. I should now like to suggest that Goethe's sense of nature in its bearing upon experience, and this work of Hegel's in its bearing upon philosophy, constitute the mediating principle required.

Although *Goethe* takes experience as his starting point, he does so in 10 a different way from the natural scientists, for instead of concentrating upon an investigation of the remotest and subtlest relationships, in which phenomena are obscured and distorted by their multifarious connections, he concentrates upon the purest, simplest, and most basic form of a phenomenon, analyses this basic datum of experience, and without 15 making use of any preconceived terminology, merely describes it. He therefore presents the distinct and basic aspects of a phenomenon, or the thought of their relationship. We may say therefore that *Goethe's archetypal phenomena* constitute the immediately intuited ideas of experience, and that they may only be readily discovered in experience by those in 20 command of the sure procedure of an instinctively rational genius. *Goethe's* fine sense of nature enabled him to discover the archetypal phenomena of colours, plants, and bones etc. He was proud of a presentation from Alexander *von Humboldt* which confirmed this, and which was accompanied by, 'a flattering characterization, in which he suggested that 25 poetry might also be able to lift the veil of nature'. . . . 'If von Humboldt + acknowledges this, who will deny it?'

Goethe's archetypal phenomenon is the idea which constitutes the factual nature of an appearance. If this idea is not discovered by any kind of obscure drive, but is grasped consciously by the precise procedure of the 30 self-motivating progression of dialectical thought, it constitutes the Hegelian method, which develops the Idea of space, time, motion, and matter etc., out of the logical Idea. Although these entities are only discovered because the philosopher has prior experience of them, they are quite independent of this experience, and are in no way determined by its 35 content. Philosophy certainly does not make an immediate deduction of the shapes of nature as such, it merely deduces certain of the thought-relationships characteristic of nature, and then discovers the intuitions which correspond to them in the sphere of natural phenomena. In this second a posteriori procedure, it places space at the apex, for it is the intui-40 tion we call space which corresponds most exactly to the simplest form of the Idea of nature to issue forth from logical development. However, philosophy does not anticipate this placing of space by means of a priori deduction. When we make the transition from the Idea of space to the second Idea of nature, we find that this has its closest corresponding intuition in time, so that this *recognition* of our concept in an intuition repeats itself, as it does throughout the philosophy of nature. It cannot be said of this procedure that the Idea is extracted from the intuition, for if the individual deduction had allowed the Idea of space to be followed by the subjective thought-determination that the second Idea of nature corresponded more exactly to the intuition of motion or even of the plant, then the philosopher would have rejected time, and placed this intuition next to space in the series of natural forms.

Consequently, before he enters upon metaphysical determinations of this kind, the philosopher will have to make a preliminary survey of natural phenomena, in order to assess their relative worth and comparative development. Only the dialectical development of the Ideas themselves can decide where intuitions such as space and time should be placed however, and therefore what general order should be adopted; for it would be preposterous to assert that the graded series of forms had also been created out of nature, as it is certain that they are all in nature together. If an Idea is derived a priori, and no corresponding intuition is forthcoming, we may proceed in either of two ways. To a certain extent we may be justified in assuming that the empty place contains a phenomenon which has not yet been discovered empirically, but although *Oken* frequently made use of this expedient, it is not to be recommended. The other procedure open to us is to throw the thought back into the melting-pot of the dialectic, and then to raise it once more from the productive mine of reason into the daylight of consciousness, for there is every possibility that despite the universally creative thought which slumbers in every breast, and which can guide us only along the correct path, our idiosyncrasies will have caused us to go astray in our thinking.

It is literally true therefore, that *Hegel's* philosophy of nature creates the entire system of nature's productive Ideas out of its own freedom. *Schelling* says *in effect* that *Hegel's* logical Idea *precipitates itself* into nature. As the logical Idea remains a matter of thought, it is difficult to see what he means by this. The logical Idea has no need 'to take the first difficult step into actuality', because its thought coincides with the true actuality of nature. How can it be said then that philosophy is '*limited*' because it can '*only produce thoughts*', and not '*a single blade of grass*'? Are we to regard it as limited because it produces the universal, the abiding, and the exclusively valuable, instead of the individual, the sensuous, and the transitory? If the limitation of philosophy is supposed to consist not only of its being unable to *constitute* individuality, but also of its being *unaware* of *how* individual things are constituted, one has to reply that this 'how' is *inferior* to knowledge, not *superior* to it, and that knowledge cannot therefore be circumscribed by it. Consequently, knowledge goes by the board when we ask '*How this transformation of the Idea into reality*' etc., the precise reason being that nature is the unconscious Idea, and that knowledge is unnecessary to the growth of a blade of grass. The true creation is that of the universal, which remains securely within philosophic cognition itself.

Hegel's philosophy of nature also does full justice to experience however, by which the speculative course of its Ideas must always be *regulated.* I am therefore convinced that in its purest speculative development, thought will coincide most completely with the results of experience, and on the other hand, that the full capabilities of a mature sense of nature based on experience will yield nothing to supersede an insight into the embodiments of Ideas. It seems to me therefore, that *Goethe* and *Hegel* are the two geniuses destined to direct the course of the *speculative physics* of the future, for it is these two men who have pointed the way towards the reconciliation of speculation with experience.

This work displays a wide range of empirical knowledge, and it is probably for this reason that it will first attract attention, for it was in these lectures that *Hegel's* speculations underwent their severest test. I have made every possible effort to avoid the introduction of errors, by carefully consulting sources, and by making use of the expert advice of my colleagues, which has always been given willingly, and for which I should now like to thank them. I am certain therefore that if any errors remain, they are not important enough to have a disturbing effect upon the Ideas which sought their corresponding intuitions in experience. It can always be said of course that Hegel was unaware of certain discoveries, but as his Ideas are rooted in their own validity, this has no bearing upon their soundness, and when they undergo a further inner development, there is always a corresponding increase in the room available for the new intuitions which might present themselves from without. If one attacks Hegel by saying, '*that is it impossible to approach actuality with that which is purely rational*', it has to be replied that although that which is rational in the actual phenomena of nature is stunted and distorted in various ways by the form of externality, it is always present there in a purer form than it is in the extremely sketchy systems of those who want to draw a sharp dividing line between that which is purely rational, and that which is actual.

It now remains for me to indicate the procedure I have employed in editing these lectures, and to give an account of the sources I have drawn upon, which consist of Hegel's own lecture notes, and of notes taken down by those who attended his courses. Hegel lectured on the philosophy of nature eight times in all: once at Jena between 1804 and 1806, once at Heidelberg in the summer of 1818, and six times at Berlin in 1819–1820, 1821–1822, 1823–1824, 1825–1826, 1828 and 1830. From the Jena period we have a complete note-book of Hegel's in quarto. The first edition of his 'Encyclopaedia' (1817) was the basis of his lectures at Heidelberg, and he interleaved it with notes he had written down on sheets of paper. At Berlin, the first two series of lectures were based upon yet another complete note-book in quarto. He prepared a new introduction for the lectures of 1823–1824, and added a new supplementary note-book, both of which were in folio. For these and the later lectures he also made use of his earlier note-books however, even the one from Jena. The second edition of his 'Encyclopaedia' appeared in 1827, and was also used for the last two series of lectures. The third edition only appeared towards the end of 1830. The autographic sources I have used also include the numerous and copious notes he interpolated from time to time as the lectures were repeated. I have also made use of the following sources: (1) notes which I took during the winter course of 1821–1822; (2) three sets of notes from the winter course of 1823–1824, taken down by Captain *von Griesheim*, my worthy colleague Professor *Hotho*, and myself; (3) notes taken by Vice-principal *Geyer* in the summer of 1830.

There is no need for me to describe the method I have employed in making use of these sources, because it is essentially the same as that I used in editing Hegel's 'History of Philosophy', and I have explained it in detail in the preamble to that work. I should add however, that when lectures are brought out in book form, many obvious alterations have to be made. As I have had to present the reader with material from all periods of Hegel's activity as a writer, I feel that I should give some account of Hegel's own note-books, and of the printed versions of them which appeared in the various editions of the 'Encyclopaedia'.

The general arrangement of the material in Hegel's Berlin note-books differs very little from that of the second edition of the 'Encyclopaedia' and the third edition introduced no changes. In the note-books, part of the theory of colours is placed differently however, and attention has been drawn to this in a note (II. 378). These note-books, and the lectures delivered from them, were still based upon the first edition of the 'Encyclopaedia', where much of the material was arranged differently. Hegel became aware of the shortcomings in the ordering of its material soon after he had published this book, but its arrangement approximates 5 to that of his later work more than it does to that of the Jena notes, and it is therefore an important link in the history of his development. The main fault in the first edition was that the higher relationships of a sphere were regarded as the premises of the lower relationships. In mechanics for example, universal gravitation is said to give rise to pressure, fall, 10 impact, and inertia. In physics, the individual physics of shape has the more finite relationships of specific gravity, cohesion, sound, and heat worked into it. Thus the mathematics of space and time constitute section one of the whole; in section two, physics is subdivided into the triad of absolute and finite mechanics, elementary physics, and individual physics; 15 and section three deals with organics. In the second edition however, for the first time, the abstract moments of a whole such as shape are no longer introduced in the sphere of their totality, but are allowed to precede in logical progression as the stages of its becoming, though shape is also the true prius of these stages (II. 92–93).

20 The Jena note-book still takes the basic division of objectivity in the 'Logic' as its point of departure, and the philosophy of nature is therefore divided into mechanics, chemism, and life as teleology. Its mechanics include space, time, place, motion, mass, and the celestial sphere. The first sub-division of chemism is 'figuration', and presents light, inertia, fall, 25 projection, pendulum, pressure, elasticity, impact, sound, cohesion, magnetism, the crystal, and electricity. The second sub-division is 'The chemical process', which begins with heat, passes to the four physical and the four chemical elements, then to the meteorological process, and concludes with odour, taste, and colour as the particular characteristics of 30 bodies, together with their particular existence as metal, sulphur and salt. The third sub-division is 'The chemism of physically individual bodies', and covers the actual chemical processes of fire and water, and galvanism. In this note-book, the only essential change in the arrangement of the 'Organics' occurs in the unique and somewhat clumsy ordering of 35 the three universal organic processes (III. 41–44), the first two divisions + of which cover the processes of nutrition and formation.

This note-book has many passages which bear the marks of *Hegel's* struggle to complete the dissolution of empirical material into logical thought, and in particular to maintain the strictness of the dialectical 40 transitions from one matter to another. I could draw attention to several passages illustrating this, and despite the efforts I have made to round off their phrases and clarify their thought, the reader will still be aware of the laboured awkwardness with which their profundity was first expressed. Other passages are still brightly coloured with the full poetry of the philosophy of nature, and even its method of drawing ingenious parallels has not completely disappeared. The pervasive thoughtfulness of mature Hegelianism already shines through this glitter however, for even at the beginning of his career, *Hegel's* mastery in dialectic goes hand in hand with the whole breadth of empirical knowledge, and it is this combination which breaks forth into his weighty and illuminating thoughts. I did not want to suppress these passages, their style distinguishes them clearly enough from the rest of the writing, and the reader will have no difficulty in picking them out by the genuine poetry with which they touch the true nature of the subject matter.

I should also like to draw attention to the fact that in this early notebook, *Hegel* began the philosophy of nature with *ether*. This principle has recently found great favour with physicists, and if I now have to dampen the enthusiasm with which they have accepted it, this is merely because I do not wish to lay *Hegel* open to the censure of having regarded it in the same way as they do. The words he uses when discussing it indicate a philosophy of nature which is still closely related to the striving Fichtean idealism which *Schelling* built into his first sketch of a systematic philosophy of nature. Hegel begins in the following way: this is in fact the first transition he made from the logical Idea to nature, 'As the determinate being which has gone back into its Notion, the Idea may now be called *absolute matter* or *ether*. It is evident that this has the same significance as pure spirit, for this absolute matter is in no way sensuous, but is the Notion as pure Notion in itself. As such this is existent spirit. It is called ether in so far as spirit is not being thought of, the one name replacing the other for the same reason. Ether in its simplicity and self-equality is therefore the indeterminate soul of spirit; it is motionless quiescence or the essence which is perpetually returning into itself from otherness. It is the substance and being of all things, as well as the infinite *elasticity* which has rejected and dissolved every form and determinateness within it, but which for that very reason constitutes the absolute *pliability* and potentiality of all form. Ether is therefore *being*, and although it is not ubiquitous in its penetration, it *constitutes* everything. It has nothing external to it, and does not change, for it is the dissolution of everything, the simple purity of negativity, the fluidity of undisturbable transparency. By having returned into the self-equality of *being*, this pure essence has eradicated and left behind *difference as such*, and has become opposed to it. Ether is therefore the implicitness which has not displayed its becoming, in difference, as this essence. It is merely the teeming matter which is in itself the absolute motion of the fermentation which is certain of itself as the whole truth, and which remains in itself and equal to itself in this free independence of the moments which have preserved the truth within it. In so far as it is said to be ether or absolute matter, it is *in itself*, or pure self-consciousness, and is this as general *being*, not as *determinate* being nor as being of a determinately real nature. This determinateness of non-determinate being passes over into *determinate being* however, and the element of reality is the universal determinateness in which spirit has its being as nature. The inner essence or ether is not present *there*, and one might say that the inwardness of its being-in-*self* is not its truth; it is in precisely the same way that the determination of *implicit* being expresses the essence of ether, which is opposed to form'.

This philosophic encyclopaedia of the natural sciences now awaits the judgement of philosophers and scientists. The considerable range of empirical material it covers is not taken for granted, and is often presented with a certain predilection. This is by no means out of place in academic discourses of this kind however, for although the professionals are sufficiently aware of the facts, *Hegel* was not always able to assume that this basic knowledge was already present in the minds of his students, and as it was indispensable for the understanding of his ideas, he was forced to present it to them.

History is rich in the decrees of fate, and the appearance of this work together with the arrival of *Schelling* at *Berlin*, is certainly one of them. The man who planned the philosophy of nature, but was unable to do more than lay its foundations, will find the building completed in this work. In this book he may hail the genius of one who 'later became' his friend, for he is the father of the science developed here, and he of all men living is most to be honoured for it. Yet if he believes it to be his mission, 'to lead philosophy out of the undeniably difficult position in which it finds itself at present', and to save if from, a 'terrible shipwreck, and the destruction of all noble convictions', in order to, 'really break through into the promised land of philosophy'; he will have to undertake a scientific refutation of these legitimate children of his own philosophizing, for without this he cannot hope to return from his long exile, and to grasp again the sceptre of philosophy. The 'page in the history of philosophy' which be began to write forty years ago has been 'finished' by his followers, and it is some years now since it was turned, and its conclusions drawn and generally acknowledged. The history of philosophy has not yet failed to find expression because Schelling has kept quiet.

Philosophy is not without 'a free, untroubled, and completely unhindered movement', merely because *Schelling's* 'inner nature' causes him to feel constrained and embarrassed by the strictly scientific procedure of a dialectical method. 'It is in this metropolis that the fate of German philosophy will have to be decided,' but if Schelling merely repeats the 5 promises he has made for forty years; if the whole world is still said to have misunderstood him, and his first philosophy merely to have contained the injunction '*to avoid absence of thought*', while his second philosophy is attempting to draw all its positive content from beyond rationality; then despite the most solemn assurances that this is not the case, he 10 will have shown that he has abandoned the true freedom of a scientific philosophy, and will most certainly come to grief in the shadow of the giant he is trying to overreach. In any case, we now await him here on this field of battle, where many of the heroes of modern German philosophy are still to be found. He is by no means 'a burden' to us, nor are we unable 15 to 'accommodate' him, for we welcome the opportunity of accounting for the necessity of his relapse into a philosophy of revelation, and we shall therefore give careful consideration to his reasons for having found it impossible to keep to the giddy height which formed the intellectual intuition of his youth. 20

Berlin,
December 10, 1841.

Michelet.

THE PHILOSOPHY OF NATURE

The second part of the Encyclopaedia of the Philosophical Sciences in outline

INTRODUCTION

Addition. It can *perhaps* be said that philosophy, in our time, enjoys no particular favour or affection; it is at least no longer recognized as the foundation which must constitute the indispensable introduction to all
\+ further scientific and vocational education. It may certainly be accepted as
5 *indisputably* true however, that the *philosophy of nature* in particular is suffering from a very considerable lack of favour. I shall not concern myself very fully with the extent to which this particular prejudice is justified, although I cannot of course entirely overlook this question. Intense stimulation has had the effect that one might have expected, and
10 looking at the way in which the *Idea of the philosophy of nature* has exhibited itself in recent times, one might say that in the first gratification which its discovery has afforded, it has been grasped by fumbling hands instead of being wooed by active reason, and that it is by its suitors rather than by its detractors that it has been done to death. For the most part it
15 has been variously transformed into an external formalism, and perverted into a notionless instrument for superficiality of thought and unbridled powers of imagination. The details of the extravaganzas into which death-struck forms of the Idea have been perverted do not concern me here. Some years ago I expressed myself more fully on this subject in the
\+ preface to 'The Phenomenology of Spirit'. It need cause no surprise that the more thoughtful view of nature, in which perception has been guided by the Idea, as well as the crass empiricism of the external abstract understanding, should have shunned such a procedure, which is as grotesque as it is pretentious. Crude empiricism and travestied thought-forms, capri-
25 ciousness of fancy and the flattest methods of proceeding according to superficial analogy, have been mixed into a complete chaos, and this stew has been served up as the Idea, reason, science, divine perception. A complete lack of system and scientific method has been hailed as the very peak of scientific accomplishment. It is charlatanry such as this, and

Schelling's philosophy is a prime example of it, that has brought the philosophy of nature into disrepute. +

To reject the philosophy of nature outright because of such bungling and misrepresentation of the Idea, is quite another matter however. Those possessed by a hatred of philosophy have often welcomed its misuse and 5 perversion, which they have used in order to bring the science itself into discredit, and out of their established rejection of what is bogus, to fabricate nebulous evidence of their having called philosophy itself in question.

Bearing in mind the present *prejudices and* the widespread *misunder-* 10 *standings* of the philosophy of nature, it might seem appropriate to begin by evincing the *true* Notion of this science. The initial opposition we encounter is to be regarded as accidental and superficial however, and all that it entails may be left on one side without more ado. Dealing with it would tend to involve polemics, and would not be gratifying. What 15 might be learnt is partly subsumed under the science itself, and would not be so instructive as to justify reducing still further the already limited space available for the wealth of material to be dealt with in an encyclopaedia. We shall therefore content ourselves with what has already been said; it can serve as a kind of protest against this manner of thinking, and 20 as an assurance that such philosophizing about nature, which often glitters and entertains, which will always thrill and astonish, and which may well satisfy those daring enough to follow the brilliance of a flare dropped into the philosophy of nature if it obviates the need for thought, is not to be expected from this presentation. What we are engaged on here is not a 25 matter of imagination and phantasy; it is the matter of the Notion, and of reason.

This standpoint does not justify our discussing the Notion, determination, manner and method of the philosophy of nature at this juncture. It is fitting however that the treatment of a science should be preceded by the 30 determination of its position, purpose, and content, and the way in which the content is to be regarded. It is unnecessary to counter a perversion of the philosophy of nature once we have defined the Notion of the science more precisely. The science of philosophy is a sphere, and each member of the sphere has its antecedent and sequel, so that the philosophy of nature 35 appears as only one sphere within the whole of the encyclopaedia. Nature's proceeding forth from the eternal Idea, its creation, the proof indeed that there necessarily is a nature, lies in that which precedes it (§ 244). Here we have to presuppose this as known. In order to determine what the philosophy of nature is, it is convenient that we should separate it from 40

that which determines it; for all determining requires two terms. In the first place we find it standing in a peculiar relationship to natural science in general, that is to say, to physics, natural history, and physiology. It is indeed physics, but *rational physics*, and it is at this point of rationality
5 that we have to grasp it, and in particular to determine its relationship to physics. This procedure might appear to rest upon a novel distinction. At first the philosophy of nature will tend to be regarded as new science, and there is no doubt that in one sense it is. In another sense it is not, for it is as old as all observation of nature. It does not differ from this observa-
10 tion, and thus has traditions more ancient than those of physics, which in Aristotle for example, is much closer to a philosophy of nature than it is
+ today. It is only in recent times that the two have become separated. The separation is already apparent in *Wolff's* philosophy, where the science of cosmology, which is supposed to be a metaphysic of the world or nature,
15 but which confines itself to completely abstract determinations of the
+ understanding, is distinguished from physics. This metaphysics was certainly further removed from physics than what we now know as the philosophy of nature. The first thing to be noticed about this distinction between physics and the philosophy of nature and the mutual determination
20 which exists between them, is that they are not so widely separated as they might seem to be at first. Physics and natural history are regarded as eminently empirical sciences, as belonging exclusively to observation and experience, and as therefore opposed to the philosophy of nature, the cognition of nature by means of thought. It has in the first instance to be
25 pointed out however, that empirical physics contains much more thought than it will either realize or admit; that it is in fact better than it supposes, or if thought is considered to be a bad thing for it, that it is worse than it supposes. Physics and the philosophy of nature are therefore to be distinguished, not as perception and thought, but merely *by the nature and*
30 *manner of their thought*. Both are a thinking cognition of nature.

We shall *first* consider the place of thought in physics; this will lead us on to observe what nature is; and our *third* concern will be the division of the philosophy of nature.

A

Ways of regarding nature

Addition. In order to find the *Notion of the philosophy of nature*, we have
35 *first* to indicate the Notion of the knowledge of nature in general, and *then* to develop the *distinction between physics and the philosophy of nature*.

What is nature? It is through the knowledge and the philosophy of nature that we propose to find the answer to this general question. We find nature before us as an enigma and a problem, the solution of which seems to both attract and repel us; it attracts us in that spirit has a presentiment of itself in nature; it repulses us in that nature is an alienation in 5 which spirit does not find itself. From this arose Aristotle's dictum that philosophy has its origin in wonder. We begin to observe, and we collect + data from the multifarious formations and laws of nature, which may be pursued for their own sake into endless detail in all directions; and because we can see no end to this procedure, it leaves us unsatisfied. What is more, 10 despite all this wealth of knowledge, the question, 'What is nature?' can always be asked and never completely answered. It remains a problem. + When we see nature's processes and transmutations, we want to grasp its simple essence, and force this Proteus to relinquish his transformations, to reveal himself to us, and to speak out; not so that he merely dupes us with 15 an everchanging variety of new forms, but so that he renders himself to consciousness in a more simple way, through language. This quest for + *being* has a multiple meaning. It is merely the matter of a name if we ask, 'What sort of plant *is* this? If we know the name, it may be a matter of perception. If for example I do not know what a box-compass is, I merely 20 have to get someone to show me the instrument, and then I can say that I know. In the question, 'What is this man?', '*is*' refers to his status, but this is not its meaning if we ask, 'What is nature?' The meaning of this question, when we ask it because we want to know what the philosophy of nature is, is the object of this investigation. 25

We could resort immediately to the philosophical Idea, and say that the philosophy of nature should provide us with the Idea of nature. To begin in this way might however be confusing. Our task is to grasp the Idea itself in its concreteness; and so to apprehend and bring together its different determinations; in order to take possession of the Idea, we therefore 30 have to work through a series of determinations, by means of which the Idea first comes into being for us. Now if we take these determinations in forms known to us, and say that we wish to relate ourselves thinkingly to nature, we are immediately presented with still further ways in which to relate ourselves to it. I shall introduce these here not in the interest of com- 35 pleteness, but so that we may find in them the raw material or moments which necessarily belong to the cognition of the Idea, and which we are aware of earlier, particularized as the various *ways of regarding nature*. In this way we shall reach the point at which the characteristic feature of our undertaking becomes apparent. We relate ourselves to nature partly in 40 practice and partly in theory. A contradiction in the theoretical view will become apparent and will, in the third instance, open the way to our standpoint; in order to resolve the contradiction we must incorporate what is peculiar to the practical relationship, and in this way both the practical and theoretical approaches will be united and integrated into totality.

§ 245

In the *practical* relationship which man establishes between himself and nature, he treats it as something immediate and external; he is himself an immediately external, and therefore sensuous individual, who is nevertheless also justified in acting as *purpose* in the face of natural situations. Nature, viewed in the light of the relationship thus established, is seen from the finite-*teleological* standpoint (§ 205) which is based on the correct supposition, that nature does not itself contain the absolute and ultimate end (§ 207–211). Nevertheless, if this view is based on particular *finite* ends, it transforms them partly into presuppositions, the contingent content of which can, by itself, be insignificant and trivial. However, for itself, the teleological relationship demands a deeper manner of comprehension than that appropriate to external and finite relationships. It thus opens the way for the Notional point of view, which is universally immanent, and therefore also immanent within nature.

Addition. In general, the practical approach to nature is determined by the self-seeking of appetite; need impels us to turn nature to our advantage, to exploit and harness and in short to annihilate it. Two further determinations are immediately apparent here. (*a*) The practical approach is only concerned with the individual products of nature, or with certain aspects of these products. Need and ingenuity have enabled man to discover endlessly varied ways of mastering and making use of nature. As Sophocles says:

οὐδὲν ἀνθρώπου δεινότερον πέλει, —
ἄπορος ἐπ' οὐδὲν ἔρχεται.

Whatever powers nature develops and releases against him, cold, wild beasts, flood and fire, man knows how to counter them. He uses nature as a means to defeating nature; the nimbleness of his reason enables him to protect and preserve himself by pitting the objects of nature against the natural forces which threaten him and so nullifying them. Nature itself, as it is in its universality, cannot be mastered in this manner however, nor bent to the purposes of man. (*b*) The other aspect of the practical approach is that our purpose overrides the objects of nature, so that they become means, the determination of which lies not in themselves but in us, as for example when we turn food into blood. (*c*) The outcome is our satisfaction and self-assertion, which had been disturbed by some kind of deficiency. The negation of myself, which is within me when I am hungry, is present at the same time as something to be consumed; I cancel this opposition by acting so as to make this other identical with myself; I sacrifice this something in order to restore my unity with myself.

The teleological interpretation, which was formerly so popular, was certainly based on the relation to spirit; it limited itself to external functionalism however, and so confined the significance of spirit to finite and natural purposes: it has become descredited as a way of indicating the wisdom of God on account of the triviality of the finite purposes cited as evidence of the usefulness of natural objects. The notion of purpose is not merely external to nature, as it is when I say that sheep bear wool only in order that I may clothe myself. Silly remarks of this kind are often made, as for example in the Xenia, where the wisdom of God is admired because He causes cork trees to grow that we might have bottlestoppers, herbs that we might cure disordered stomachs, and cinnabar that we might make ourselves up. To see purpose as inherent within natural objects, is to grasp nature in its simple determinateness, e.g. the seed of a plant, which contains the real potential of everything pertaining to the tree, and which as purposeful activity is therefore orientated solely towards self-preservation. *Aristotle* had already noticed this notion of purpose in nature, and he called the activity the *nature of a thing*. This is the true teleological view, for it regards nature in its proper animation as free, and is therefore the highest view of nature.

§ 246

What is now called physics, was formerly called natural philosophy. It is, what is more, a theoretical and thinking consideration of nature, and while on the one hand it does not concern itself with determinations such as these purposes, which are external to nature, on the other hand it does aim at comprehending

that which is *universal* in nature as it presents itself in a *determinate* form, i.e. forces, laws, genera. Here the content is not a simple aggregate, but is distributed through orders and classes, and must be regarded as an organic whole. In that the philosophy of nature is a comprehending consideration, its object is the same *universal*; it is however the universal *for itself*, which it regards in its *own immanent necessity*, according to the self-determination of the Notion.

Remark

The relationship of philosophy to what is empirical was discussed in the general introduction. It is not only that philosophy must accord with the experience nature gives rise to; in its *formation* and in its *development*, philosophic science presupposes and is conditioned by empirical physics. The procedure involved in the formation and preliminaries of a science is not the same as the science itself however, for in this latter case it is no longer experience, but rather the necessity of the Notion, which must emerge as the foundation. It has already been pointed out that in the procedure of philosophic cognition, the object has not only to be presented in its *Notional determination*, the *empirical* appearance corresponding to this determination also has to be specified, and it has to be shown that the appearance does in fact correspond to its Notion. This is not however an appeal to experience in regard to the necessity of the content, and an appeal to what has been called *intuition*, which was usually nothing more than a purveyance of random concepts by means of fanciful and even fantastic *analogies*, is even less admissable here. These analogies may have a certain value, but they can only impose determinations and schemata on the objects in an external manner. (§ 231 Rem.)

Addition. In the theoretical approach (*a*) the initial factor is our withdrawing from natural things, leaving them as they are, and adjusting to them. In doing this we start from our sense-knowledge of nature. If physics were based only on perceptions however, and perceptions were nothing but the evidence of the senses, the activity of a natural scientist would consist only of seeing, smelling, hearing etc., so that animals would also be physicists. It is however a spirit, a thinking entity, which sees and hears etc. If we say that in the theoretical approach things are left as they are, we shall be referring only partly to the external senses, for these are themselves partly theoretical and partly practical (§ 358); only ideation or intelligence has this free relation to things. We can of course also look at them through the medium of the senses, but cognition will then be merely a means, not an end in itself. (*b*) In the second relation of things to us, they either acquire the determination of universality for us, or we transform them into something universal. The more thought predominates in ordinary perceptiveness, so much the more does the naturalness, individuality, and immediacy of things vanish away. As thoughts invade the limitless multiformity of nature, its richness is impoverished, its springtimes die, and there is a fading in the play of its colours. That which in nature was noisy with life, falls silent in the quietude of thought; its warm abundance, which shaped itself into a thousand intriguing wonders, withers into arid forms and shapeless generalities, which resemble a dull northern fog. (*c*) Both these determinations are opposed to both practical ones, and we also find that the theoretical approach is inwardly self-contradictory, for it appears to bring about the precise opposite of what it intends. We want to know the nature that really is, not something which is not, but instead of leaving it alone and accepting it as it is in truth, instead of taking it as given, we make something completely different out of it. By thinking things, we transform them into something universal; things are singularities however, and the lion in general does not exist. We make them into something subjective, produced by us, belonging to us, and of course peculiar to us as men; for the things of nature do not think, and are neither representations nor thought. In the second determination which we have just considered, it is precisely this inversion which takes place; and consequently, what we have started upon may well seem to be impossible from the start. The theoretical approach begins by checking appetite, it is disinterested, it leaves things to subsist in their own way, and thus immediately displays two aspects, subject and object, the separation of which is fixed as this side and that. Our aim is rather to grasp and comprehend nature however, to make it ours, so that it is not something beyond and alien to us. This is where the difficulty comes in. How are we as subjects to get over into the object? If we venture the leap over this gap, and, while failing to find our footing, think that we have found nature, we shall turn that which is something other than we are into something other than what it is. Both theoretical relationships are also the precise opposites of one another: we turn things into universals or make them our own, yet as natural things they should be free for themselves. This is the crux of the issue concerning the nature of cognition, and is the concern of philosophy.

The philosophy of nature is in such a perilous condition however, that it has to demonstrate its existence, and in order to justify it, we shall have 5 to trace it back to what is familiar. In the dissolution of the subject-object opposition a specific shape may be noticed, which has been made known partly by science, and partly by religion, in which it is however a past, and which readily overcomes the whole difficulty. The unification of both determinations is what is called the *primal state of innocence*, in which spirit 10 is identical with nature, and the spiritual eye stands immediately in the centre of nature. The standpoint of the division of consciousness is the fall of man from the eternal and divine unity. This unity is represented as a primal intuition, a ratiocination, which is at the same time a vision, forming and so rationalizing sensuous shapes. This intuitive reason is the divine 15 reason, for we may say that God is that in which spirit and nature are one, and in which intelligence at the same time has both being and shape. The eccentricities of the philosophy of nature have their basis partly in this idea, which implies that although people nowadays no longer find themselves in a state of paradise, there are still some on the sunny side of the 20 hedge to whom God imparts the verities of cognition and science while they sleep, and that even if a man is not on that side of the hedge, he can transport himself thither merely by believing in the moments in which the secret of nature automatically becomes apparent to him, and allowing himself to have brainwaves, so that by giving rein to his imagination, he + may give prophetic utterance to truth. Such a performance, which offers no further credentials, has been generally regarded as the consummation of scientific ability. What is more, it is also asserted that such a state of consummate science preceded the present history of the world, and that since our fall from this unity some remnants and distant glimmerings of 30 that state of spiritual light have remained with us in myths, tradition, and other fragments, on to which the subsequent religious culture of the human race has fastened, and from which all scientific cognition has proceeded. If it were no more difficult than this for consciousness to know truth, but one only had to sit on a tripod and utter oracles, much of the + labour of thought would certainly be spared.

Nevertheless, in order to state clearly where the failing of such a general conception lies, it must be admitted that there is something lofty in it, which at first sight seems highly promising. This unity of intelligence and intuition, of the being-in-self of spirit and its relation to externality, must 40 however be the goal not the beginning; it must be a unity which is brought forth, not one which is immediate. The natural unity of thought and intuition found in a child or an animal is no more than feeling, it is not spirituality. Man must have eaten of the tree of the knowledge of good and evil, he must have gone through the labour and activity of thought in order to be what he is, i.e. the subjugator of the separation of what is his, 5 from nature. That immediate unity is therefore merely abstract, it is the being-in-self of truth, not the actuality of it; not only the content, but also the form must be true. The healing of the schism must have the shape of the form of the knowing Idea, and the moments of the healing must be sought in consciousness itself. It is not a matter of resorting to abstraction 10 and vacuity and deserting knowledge; consciousness must preserve itself, so that ordinary consciousness may itself overcome the assumptions out of which the contradiction arose.

Theoretical consciousness, because of its onesided assumption that the natural things over against us are persistent and impenetrable, creates a 15 difficulty which is refuted point-blank by the practical approach, which displays the absolutely idealistic belief that individual things are nothing in themselves. In its relationship to things, appetite is defective not because its attitude towards them is realistic, but because it is all too idealistic. Philosophically valid idealism consists in nothing other than the determi- 20 nation that the truth of things lies in their immediate particularity or sensuousness, that they are in fact mere show or appearance. According to a metaphysics prevalent at the moment, we cannot know things because they are uncompromisingly exterior to us. It might be worth noticing that + even the animals, which go out after things, grab, maul, and consume them, 25 are not so stupid as these metaphysicians. The same determination, i.e. that we think natural objects, occurs in the second aspect of the theoretical approach already indicated. Intelligence does not of course familiarize itself with things in their material existence. In that it thinks them, it sets their content within itself, and to practical ideality, which for itself is mere 30 negativity, it adds form, universality so to speak, and so gives affirmative determination to the negative of particularity. This universality of things is not something subjective and belonging to us; it is, rather, the noumenon as opposed to the transient phenomenon, the truth, objectivity, and actual being of the things themselves. It resembles the platonic ideas, 35 which do not have their being somewhere in the beyond, but which exist in individual things as substantial genera. Proteus will only be compelled + into telling the truth if he is roughly handled, and we are not content with sensuous appearance. The inscription on the veil of Isis, 'I am what was, is, and shall be, and my veil has been lifted by no mortal', melts before +

thought. *Hamann* is therefore right when he says, 'Nature is a Hebrew word, written only with consonants; it is left to the understanding to add the points'.

The empirical view of nature has this category of universality in common with the philosophy of nature, but it oscillates between regarding it as subjective, and regarding it as objective, and one often hears that these classes and orders are only formulated for the convenience of cognition. This uncertainty is even more apparent when distinguishing features are looked for not because it is thought that they are the essential objective determinations of things, but because they are a convenient way for us to distinguish things. If there were nothing more to it than this, one could for example select the earlobe as a distinctive feature of humanity, for no animal has it. One feels immediately however that such a determination is inadequate to the cognition of the essential nature of man. If the universal is determined as law, force or matter however, it will not be asserted that this is an external form, a subjective trimming; objective reality is attributed to laws, forces are said to be immanent, and matter is taken to be the true nature of the fact. Something similar is also asserted of the genera, i.e. that they are not such a ranging together of that which is similar, an abstraction made by us, that they not only have something in common, but that they are the peculiar inner essence of objects themselves: what is more, that the orders are not merely our mental vision, but form a graduated scale in nature itself. The distinguishing features are claimed to be the universal, the substantial element of the genus. Physics regards these universals as its triumph, and it is unfortunately true to say that too much of its activity is concerned with such universalization. The current philosophy is called the philosophy of identity. It might be much more appropriate to apply this name to this kind of physics, which simply dispenses with determinateness. Contemporary electro-chemistry, in which magnetism electricity and chemism are regarded as one and the same thing, is a good example. It is a fault in physics that it should involve so much identity, for identity is the basic category of the understanding.

The material prepared out of experience by physics, is taken by the philosophy of nature at the point to which physics has brought it, and reconstituted without any further reference to experience as the basis of verification. Physics must therefore work together with philosophy so that the universalized understanding which it provides may be translated into the Notion by showing how this universal, as an intrinsically necessary whole, proceeds out of the Notion. The philosophic manner of presentation is not arbitrary, it does not stand on its head for a while because it has got tired of using its legs, nor does it paint up its every-day face just for a change; the ways of physics are not adequate to the Notion, and for that reason advances have to be made.

The philosophy of nature distinguishes itself from physics on account of the metaphysical procedure it employs, for metaphysics is nothing but the range of universal thought-determinations, and is as it were the diamond-net into which we bring everything in order to make it intelligible. Every cultured consciousness has its metaphysics, its instinctive way of thinking. This is the absolute power within us, and we shall only master it if we make it the object of our knowledge. Philosophy in general, as philosophy, has different categories from those of ordinary consciousness. All cultural change reduces itself to a difference of categories. All revolutions, whether in the sciences or world history, occur merely because spirit has changed its categories in order to understand and examine what belongs to it, in order to possess and grasp itself in a truer, deeper, more intimate and unified manner. The inadequacy of the thought determinations used in physics may be traced to two very closely connected points. (*a*) The universal of physics is abstract or simply formal; its determination is not immanent within it, and does not pass over into particularity. (*b*) This is precisely the reason why its determinate content is external to the universal, and is therefore split up, dismembered, particularized, separated and lacking in any necessary connection within itself; why it is in fact merely finite. Take a flower for example. The understanding can note its particular qualities, and chemistry can break it down and analyse it. Its colour, the shape of its leaves, citric acid, volatile oil, carbon, hydrogen etc., can be distinguished; and we then say that the flower is made up of all these parts.

> *'Εγχείρησιν* naturae chemistry calls it,
> Mocks itself, knows not what befalls it,
> Holds the parts within its hand,
> But lacks, alas, the spiritual band,

as *Goethe* says. Spirit cannot be confined to this procedure of the reflective understanding. There are two possible ways out. (*a*) When nature is viewed by an alive and open mind, as it is in the apt and effectual manner we find so often in Goethe, this mind feels the life and the universal relatedness within nature; it has a presentiment of the universe as an organic whole, a rational totality, just as it experiences an inner unity with itself through the living individual. We can assemble all the separate constituents of the flower, but this will not make the flower. Intuition has therefore been reinstated in the philosophy of nature, and set above reflection, but this gets us nowhere, because one cannot philosophize on the basis of intuition. (*b*) Intuition has to be submitted to thought, so that what has been dismembered may be restored to simple universality through thought. This contemplated unity is the Notion, which contains the determinate differences simply as an immanent and self-moving unity. Philosophic universality is not indifferent to the determinations; it is the self-fulfilling universality, the diamantine identity, which at the same time holds difference within itself.

True infinity is the unity of itself and the finite; it is the category of philosophy, and also therefore of the philosophy of nature. If the genera and forces constitute the inwardness of nature, and as opposed to this universal what is outward and particular is ephemeral, a third stage is required, the inwardness of this inwardness. This, according to what has been said, would be the unity of the universal and the particular.

> 'Into nature's inwardness'—
> Oh! you philistine!—
> 'No created spirits steal.'
> I ask you never to remind
> Me and mine
> Of sayings of this kind.
> We think: and here and there
> We find the centre everywhere.
> 'The sweet of mortal blessedness
> Is to taste the outer peel!'
> For sixty years they've told it me,
> I've learnt to curse them silently;
> But tell me till the shadows fall:
> All riches from its bounty pour,
> Nature has neither rind
> Nor core,
> But everything is found in all.
> Look to yourself, and only find
> Whether you are core or rind.

When this inwardness is grasped, the onesidedness of the theoretical and practical approaches is transcended, and at the same time justice is done to both determinations. The one contains a universality without determinateness, the other a particularity without universality. Notional apprehension stands between the two, where universality is not personal and so opposed to the particularity of objects, but relates itself negatively to things and assimilates them, and while eliciting their particularity, leaves them alone, and allows them to determine themselves freely within it. Notional comprehension is therefore the unity of the theoretical and practical approaches; the negation of particularity, as negation of the negative, is affirmative universality, which gives subsistence to the determinations, for true particularity is at the same time universality in itself.

Objections may be raised of course to this standpoint. One might ask how the universal comes to determine itself, or how the infinite issues forth into finitude. In concrete terms this is the question of the creation of the world by God, in which God is imagined to be a subject, an actuality for Himself, and divorced from the world. If such abstract infinitude and universality were external to singularity however, it would itself be only one side of the matter, and therefore finite and singular. The insensibility of the understanding consists in its precise cancellation of the determination which it establishes, and so in its doing the opposite of what it intends. The singular is supposed to be separated from the universal, but it is precisely on account of this separateness that it is posited within the universal, so that what is present is merely the unity of the universal and the particular. God has two relevations, as nature and as spirit, and both manifestations are temples which He fills, and in which He is present. God as an abstraction is not the true God; His truth is the positing of his other, the living process, the world, which is His Son when it is comprehended in its divine form. God is subject only in unity with His other in spirit. The determination and the purpose of the philosophy of nature is therefore that spirit should find its own essence, its counterpart, i.e. the Notion, within nature. The study of nature is therefore the liberation of what belongs to spirit within nature, for spirit is in nature in so far as it relates itself not to another, but to itself. This is likewise the liberation of nature, which in itself is reason; it is only through spirit however, that reason as such comes forth from nature into existence. Spirit has the certainty which Adam had when he beheld Eve, 'This is flesh of my flesh, this is bone of my bones.' Nature is, so to speak, the bride espoused by spirit. Is this + certainty also truth however? The inwardness of nature is nothing but the universal, and we enter it of our own accord if we have thoughts. If subjective truth is the correspondence between sensuous representation and the object, objective truth is the correspondence of the object, of the fact, with itself, so that its reality is in conformity with its Notion. The essential ego is the self-equality of the Notion, which pervades everything, and which through maintaining its control over particular differences, constitutes the universal returning into itself. This Notion is, on this account, the true Idea of the universe, the sole actuality. Thus God alone is truth, according to Plato, He is that which is immortally alive, and his body and soul are by nature one. The first question to arise is therefore, 'Why has God determined himself in order to create nature?'

B

The Notion of nature

§ 247

Nature has yielded itself as the Idea in the form of *otherness*. Since the *Idea* is **therefore** the negative of itself, or *external to itself*, nature is not merely external relative to this Idea (**and to the subjective existence of the same, spirit**), but is embodied as nature is the determination of *externality*.

Addition. If God is all sufficient and lacks nothing, how does He come to release Himself into something so clearly unequal to Him? The divine Idea is just this self-release, the expulsion of this other out of itself, and the acceptance of it again, in order to constitute subjectivity and spirit. The philosophy of nature itself belongs to this pathway of return, for it is the philosophy of nature which overcomes the division of nature and spirit, and renders to spirit the recognition of its essence in nature. This then is the position of nature within the whole; its determinateness lies in the self-determination of the Idea, by which it posits difference, another, within itself, whole maintaining infinite good in its indivisibility, and imparting its entire content in what it provides for this otherness. God disposes therefore, while remaining equal to Himself; each of these moments is itself the whole Idea, and must be posited as the divine totality. Distinctiveness can be grasped in three forms; the universal, the particular, and the singular; firstly it is preserved in the eternal unity of the Idea, i.e. the λόγος, the eternal son of God as it was to *Philo*. The other of this extreme is singularity, the form of finite spirit. Singularity, as return into self, is certainly spirit, but as otherness to the exclusion of everything else, it is finite or human spirit, for we are not concerned with finite spirits other than men. In so far as the individual man is at the same time received into the unity of the divine essence, he is the object of the Christian religion, which is the most tremendous demand that may be made upon him. Nature is the third form with which we are concerned here, and as the Idea in particularity, it stands between both extremes. This form is the most congenial to the understanding. Spirit is posited as contradiction existing for itself, for there is an objective contradiction between the Idea in its infinite freedom and in the form of singularity, which occurs in nature only as an implicit contradiction, or as a contradiction which has being for us in that otherness appears in the Idea as a stable form. In Christ the contradiction is posited and overcome as life, passion and resurrection. Nature is the Son of God, not as the Son however, but as abiding in otherness, in which the divine Idea is alienated from love and held fast for a moment. Nature is self-alienated spirit; spirit, a bacchantic god innocent of restraint and reflection has merely been *let loose* into it; in nature, the unity of the Notion conceals itself.

The thinking view of nature must note the implicit process by which nature sublates its otherness to become spirit, and the way in which the Idea is present in each stage of nature itself. Estranged from the Idea, nature is merely the corpse of the understanding. Nature is the Idea, but only implicitly. That was why *Schelling* called it a petrified intelligence, which others have even said is frozen. God does not remain petrified and moribund however, the stones cry out and lift themselves up to spirit. God is subjectivity, activity, infinite actuosity, within which the other is only momentary, and remains implicit within the unity of the Idea, because it is itself this totality of the Idea. Since nature is the Idea in the form of otherness, according to the Notion of the Idea, the Idea is not within it as it is in and for itself, although nature is nevertheless one of the modes in which the Idea manifests itself, and in which it must come forth. Secondly, it has to be established and demonstrated that this mode of the Idea is nature. In order to do this, a comparison will subsequently have to be made, to see if the definition corresponds to ordinary thinking about nature. In other respects however, philosophy need not concern itself with ordinary thinking, nor undertake the tasks it carries out with respect to nature; although such thinking is conformable however, there must, in general, be an agreement between these two aspects.

The relation between the metaphysical aspect and this basic determination of nature has now to be indicated, and presents itself as the question of the *eternity of the world*. It might well seem as though we could leave metaphysics alone in this connection, but as they may be dealt with succinctly and efficiently at this point, we should not hesitate to bring them forward. The metaphysics of nature, the essential thought-determinateness of its distinctiveness, is that it is the Idea in its otherness. It is therefore essentially of an ideal nature, and determinate only through its being relative to a first principle. The question of the eternity of the world (which is confused with nature, since it is a collection of what is spiritual and natural), is primarily concerned with a time-image, an eternity as it is called, an infinitely long period of time, involving the world's having had no beginning in time. Its secondary content is the image of nature as something uncreated, eternal, and inherently independent of God. This secondary content is removed and completely disposed of by the determinateness of nature, its constituting the otherness of the Idea. With regard to its primary meaning therefore, after the absoluteness of the world has been removed from the argument, the question is merely concerned with the relation between eternity and the time-image employed.

At this point certain observations may be made. (*a*) Eternity is not before or after time, it is not prior to the creation of the world, nor is it the sequel to its disappearance; it is absolute present, the now, and has no before or after. The world is created, is now being created, and always has been created; this becomes apparent in the conservation of the world. The activity of the absolute Idea is created; like the Idea as such, the Idea of nature is eternal. (*b*) If one asks whether the world, nature, in its finitude, has a beginning in time or not, one has the world or nature in general before one's mind, i.e. the universal; and it has already been shown that the true universal is the Idea, which is eternal. That which is finite is temporal however, and has a before and after; and if one has the finite as one's object, one is within time. That which is finite has a beginning, but not an absolute beginning; its time begins with it, and there is no time without finitude. Philosophy is the timeless comprehension of everything in general according to its eternal determination, and including time. Having removed the concept of the absolute beginning of time, the opposite concept of an infinite time occurs; but infinite time, if it is still regarded as time, and not as transcended time, is still to be distinguished from eternity, and if thought cannot resolve the finite into the eternal, it can never be this time; it is perhaps another time, or another, and always another (§ 258). Matter presents a parallel example, for in that it is infinitely divisible, its nature is such, that what is posited as a whole, as a one, is completcly external to itself, while within itself it constitutes a plurality. Matter is not in fact divided in this way however, and does not consist of atoms; its divisibility is a possibility and nothing but a possibility, so that this infinite division is not something positive and actual, but only a subjective idea. Infinite time is similar in that it also is merely an idea, a postulated beyond which remains negatived. It is a necessary conception so long as one continues to regard what is finite, but if one passes to the universal, to that which is not finite, then one has left the standpoint at which there is an occurrence of individuality and its variability. To ordinary thinking, 5 the world is merely a collection of finitudes; but if it is grasped as universal, as totality, the question of its beginning becomes meaningless. It is then not clear where the beginning is to be made; a beginning has to be made, but only a relative beginning. One goes beyond it, but not into infinity, merely to another beginning, which is of course also only a con- 10 ditioned one. In short this beginning simply expresses the nature of that which is relative, because we are dealing with finitude.

Here we have a metaphysics moving indiscriminately between abstract determinations which it takes to be absolute. If we ask whether or not the world has a beginning in time, it is impossible that we should receive a 15 plain and straightforward answer to the question. It is assumed that a plain answer would assure us of *one* or the *other* of these alternatives, but the plain answer is that the either-or assumed by the question is unwarranted. Being finite, one's beginning is also not a beginning, and the conflict between these opposed determinations, as it is involved in finitude, 20 is devoid of resolution and reconciliation. It is because the finite is this contradiction that it perishes. The finite is preceded by another, and its antecedents have to be sought, in the history of the earth or of mankind for example, when its context is being traced. There is no end to such an enquiry, just as there is an end to be found in all that is finite, time having 25 power over the plurality of the finite. The finite has a beginning, but this beginning is not the first; it is independent, but this immediacy is limited in the same way. When ordinary thinking leaves this determinate finitude, which has a before or after, and passes on to the empty concept of time, or of the world in general, it flounders about in the empty ideas of 30 merely abstract thoughts.

§ 248

In this externality, the determinations of the Notion have the appearance of an *indifferent subsistence* and *isolation* with regard to one another; the Notion is therefore internal, and nature in its determinate being displays *necessity* 35 and *contingency*, not freedom.

Remark

Nature is what it is through its determinate existence, and it should not therefore be deified. It is wrong to regard and treat the sun, the moon, animals, plants etc. as works of God superior to the deeds and events of humanity. Nature
5 is *implicitly* divine in that it is in the Idea; but in *reality* its being does not correspond to its Notion, **and it is rather the unresolved contradiction. Its distinctive characteristic is its positedness,** its negativity. The ancients grasped
\+ *matter* in general as non-ens, and nature has also been **regard-**
10 **ed** as the Idea's *falling short* of itself, **for in this** external shape **the Idea is** inadequate to itself. **It is only to the external and immediate stage of sensuous consciousness that nature appears as that which is primary, immediate, as mere being.** Even in such an element of externality, nature is, nevertheless,
15 the representation of *the Idea*, and consequently one may and should admire the wisdom of God within it. *Vanini* said that a piece of straw was enough to prove the being of
\+ God, but every product of the spirit, the very worst of its imaginings, the capriciousness of its most arbitrary moods,
20 a mere word, are all better evidence of God's being than any single object. It is not only that in nature the play of forms has unbounded and unbridled contingency, but that each shape by itself is devoid of its Notion. *Life* is the highest to which nature drives in its determinate being, but
25 as merely natural Idea, life is submerged in the irrationality of externality, and the living individual is bound with another individuality in every moment of its existence, while spiritual manifestation contains the moment of a free and universal relation of spirit to itself.

30 It is by a similar misunderstanding that **we are led to regard that which is spiritual as generally less important than the things of nature.** *Works of art* are sometimes prized less highly than natural things because material has to be brought to them from without, and they do not live. This is to talk as if the
35 spiritual form did not contain a higher animation, and spirit were not superior to natural form, as if form in general were not superior to matter, and as if that which may be called the matter of moral activity were not purely and

simply the product of spirit; as if that which is higher and **more animated in nature did not also take its material from without. The superiority of its conforming to its eternal laws** through all its contingency **is attributed** to nature, but that is also the case in the realm of self-consciousness. Even faith acknowledges that a providence guides human events. Should we regard the determinations of this providence in the field of human events as merely contingent and irrational? If spiritual contingency or *caprice* goes forth into *evil*, that which goes astray is still infinitely superior to the regular **movement** of stars, or the innocent life of the plant, **because that which errs is still spirit.**

Addition. The infinite divisibility of matter simply means that it is external to itself. It is precisely this externality which we first wonder at in the immeasurability of nature. Thoughts are not co-ordinated in nature, for Notionlessness holds sway here, and each material point appears to be entirely independent of all the others. The sun, planets, comets, elements, plants, animals, all exist as self-contained particulars. The sun is not one and the same individual as the earth, and is only bound to the planets by gravity. Subjectivity is first encountered in life, which is the opposite of extrinsicality. The heart, liver, eye are not independent individualities on their own account; the hand, severed from the body, decays. The organic body is still a whole composed of a multiplicity of mutually external members, but each individual organ subsists only in the subject, and the Notion exists as the power which unites them. In this way the Notion, which is something merely inward in Notionlessness, first comes into existence in life, as soul. The spatiality of the organism is completely devoid of truth for the soul; if this were not so, we should have as many souls as points, for the soul feels at every point. One should not allow oneself to be deceived by the appearance of extrinsicality; one should remember that the mutual externality constitutes only a single unity. Although they appear to be independent, the celestial bodies have to patrol a single field. Since unity in nature is a relation between apparently self-subsistent entities however, nature is not free, but merely necessary and contingent. Necessity is the inseparability of terms which are different, and yet appear to be indifferent. The abstraction of self-externality also receives its due there however, hence the contingency or external necessity, contrasting with the inner necessity of the Notion. In physics a lot has been said about *polarity*, and this concept has marked a great advance in the meta-

physics of physics, for as a concept it is nothing more nor less than the determination of the necessary relationship between two different terms, which, in so far as the positing of one is also the positing of the other, constitute a unity. Polarity of this kind limits itself only to the opposi-
5 tion; it is by means of the opposition however that there is also a positing of the return out of the opposition into unity, and it is this third term which constitutes the necessity of the Notion, a necessity which is not found in polarity. In nature taken as otherness, the square or tetrad also belongs to the whole form of necessity, as in the four elements, the four
10 colours etc.; the pentad may also be found, in the five fingers and the five senses for example; but in spirit the fundamental form of necessity is the triad. The totality of the disjunction of the Notion exists in nature as a tetrad, the first of which is universality as such. The second term is difference, and appears in nature as a duality, for in nature the other must
15 exist for itself as an otherness. Consequently, the subjective unity of universality and particularity is the fourth term, which has a further existence as against the other three. In themselves the monad and the dyad constitute the entire particularity, and the totality of the Notion itself can therefore proceed to the pentad.

20 Nature is the negative because it negates the Idea. *Jacob Boehme* says that God's first birth is Lucifer, this creature of light having centred his imagination upon himself and become evil; this is the moment of difference, of otherness held firm in opposition to the Son, who is otherness
\+ held in love. Representations such as this, which have a free rein in
25 orientalized taste, have their ground and significance in the negative nature of nature. Immediacy is the other form of otherness, and consists of what is different subsisting abstractly by itself. This subsisting is only momentary however, it is not true subsistence; only the Idea, because it has returned into itself and is therefore being in and for self, subsists
30 eternally. In time nature comes first, but the absolute prius is the Idea.
\+ This absolute prius is the finis, the true beginning, alpha is omega. Men often consider that which is immediate to be superior to that which is mediated, because the latter seems to imply dependence. The Notion has both aspects however, it is mediation through the sublation of mediation,
35 and therefore immediacy. An immediate belief in God is often spoken of. This is the more degraded, and not the higher mode however, and the
\+ original or primitive nature-religions were an expression of it. Affirmation in nature is the shining through of the Notion, which soon displays its power through the mutability of this externality. All existences are in fact
40 one body, in which the soul has its dwelling. Although the Notion

displays itself in these gigantic members, it does so imperfectly, and it is only in spirit that it exists as it is.

§ 249

Nature is to be regarded as a *system of stages*, the one proceeding of necessity out of the other, and being the proximate truth of that from which it results. This is not to be thought of as a *natural* engendering of one out of the other however, but as an engendering within the inner Idea which constitutes the ground of nature. **Metamorphosis accrues only to the Notion as such, for development is nothing but the alteration of the same. In nature the Notion is however partly a mere inner principle, and partly an existence which is simply a living individuality; existent metamorphosis is therefore limited solely to this individuality.**

Remark

The inept conception in which the progression and transition of one natural form and sphere into a higher is regarded as an outwardly actual production somewhat *clarified* by being relegated into the *murkiness* of the past, may be found in both ancient and modern philosophies of nature. It is precisely the externality which allows differences to fall apart and appear as indifferent existence, which is characteristic of nature; it is the dialectical Notion which is the inner principle of the same, and guides its *stages* forward. **Thinking consideration must reject such nebulous and basically sensuous conceptions as for example the so-called emergence of plants and animals out of water, and of the more highly developed animal organizations out of the lower etc.** +

Addition. The view that natural things are useful is true in that it denies that they are absolute purpose in and for themselves. This negativity is not however external to them, but is the immanent moment of their Idea, which brings about their mutability and transition into another existence, but at the same time their transition into a higher Notion. As the Notion posits all particularity within existence at once, it does so in a universal manner. To think of the genera as gradually evolving themselves out of one another in time is to make use of a completely empty concept; the time-difference is quite devoid of interest for thought. If it is merely a matter of enumerating the genera in order to show in a convenient way how the series of living being divides itself into general 5 classes, from the simplest to those richer in determinations and content, or the other way about, this will always be of general interest. It is a way of + ordering things, as is the division of nature into the three kingdoms, and is better than mixing everything up, which tends to repel the intuitive Notion in general intelligence. But one must not think one makes such a 10 dry series dynamic, philosophical, more comprehensible, or what you will, merely be using the concept of emergence. The animal world is the truth of the vegetable world, which in its turn is the truth of the mineralogical world; the earth is the truth of the solar system. In a system, the most abstract term is the first, and the truth of each sphere is the last; it is 15 at the same time only the first term of a higher stage however. The completion of one stage out of the other constitutes the necessity of the Idea, and the variety of forms has to be grasped as necessary and determinate. A land animal has not proceeded by a natural process out of an aquatic animal, and then flown into the air, neither has the bird returned to the 20 earth again. If we want to compare the stages of nature with one another we are perfectly justified in observing that this animal has one ventricle, while that has two; but we cannot go on to say that parts have been added, as if this had actually taken place. Nor should we use the category of an earlier stage in order to explain a later one; it would be a formal howler to + say that the plant constituted the carbon, and the animal the nitrogen pole.

Evolution and *emanation* are the two forms in which the progressive stages of nature have been grasped. The course of evolution begins with what is imperfect and formless, such as humidity and aquatic formations, leads on to what emerged from water, such as plants, polyps, mollusca, 30 and fishes, progresses to land animals, and arrives finally at man, as he emerges out of animals. This gradual alteration is said to be an explanation and comprehension of nature. The doctrine is derived from the philosophy of nature, and is still widely prevalent. Although quantitative difference is easy enough to understand however, it explains nothing. The 35 course of emanation is peculiar to the oriental world, where it is regarded as a series of degradations, beginning with the perfection and absolute totality of God. God has created, and fulgurations, flashes, and likenesses have proceeded from Him, so that the first likeness most resembles Him. The first production is supposed, in its turn, to have given birth to something less perfect than itself, and so on down the scale, so that each thing begotten is in its turn procreative down as far as the negative, which is matter, or the acme of evil. In this way emanation ends in the complete absence of form. Both these progressions are onesided and superficial, and + postulate an indeterminate goal, but the progress from the more to the less perfect has the advantage of holding up the prototype of a perfect organ- 5 ism, which is the picture that must be in our mind's eye if we are to understand stunted organizations. That which appears to be subordinate within them, such as organs with no functions, may only be clearly understood by means of the higher organizations in which one recognizes the functions they perform. If that which is perfect is to have the advantage over that 10 which is imperfect it must exist in reality, and not only in the imagination.

In the concept of metamorphosis there is also a fundamental idea which persists throughout all the various genera as well as the individual organs, so that they are merely transfigurations of the form of one and the same prototype. One speaks for example of the metamorphosis of an insect, in 15 which the caterpillar, the chrysalis and the butterfly are one and the same individual. In individuals it is certainly true that the development takes place in time, but this is not so in the genus. If the genus exists in a particular way, the other modes of its existence are also posited. If water is posited, air and fire are also etc. It is important to maintain 20 identity, but not less important to maintain difference, which is pushed into the background if only quantitative change is considered. It is here that the simple concept of metamorphosis shows itself to be insufficient.

This leads on to the concept of a *series* of natural things, and in parti- 25 cular, of living things. The desire to understand the necessity of such a development makes us look for a law governing the series, or a basic determination which, while positing variety, recapitulates itself within it, and so simultaneously engenders a new variety. But to augment a term by the successive addition of uniformly determined elements, and only to 30 see the same relationship between all the members of the series, is not the way in which the Notion determines. It is in fact precisely this conception of a series of stages and so on, which has hindered advances in the recognition of the necessity of formations. It turns out to be a hopeless task to attempt to arrange the planets, metals or chemical bodies in general, 35 plants, and animals, into a series, and to look for a law governing such a series, because nature does not distribute its formations into series and member, and the Notion distinguishes according to qualitative determinateness, making leaps in the process. The old saying, or law as it is called, 'non datur saltus in natura' is by no means adequate to the diremp- +

tion of the Notion. The continuity of the Notion with itself is of an entirely different nature.

§ 250

In so far as the contradiction of the Idea is external to itself as nature, one side of it is formed by the Notionally generated necessity of its formations and their rational determination within the organic totality, and the other by their indifferent contingency and indeterminable irregularity. In the sphere of nature, contingency and determinability from without come into their own. This contingency is particularly prevalent in the realm of concrete individual formations, which are at the same time only immediately concrete as things of nature. That which is immediately concrete is in fact an ensemble of juxtaposed properties, external and more or less indifferent to one another, to which simple subjective being-for-self is therefore equally indifferent, and which it consequently abandons to external contingent determination. The impotence of nature is to be attributed to its only being able to maintain the determinations of the Notion in an abstract manner, and to its exposing the foundation of the particular to determination from without.

Remark

The infinite wealth and variety of forms, and the utterly irrational contingency which mixes with the external order of natural formations, have been praised as the sublime freedom and divinity of nature, or at least as the divinity within it. It is to be expected that ordinary ways of thinking should mistake contingency, caprice and lack of order, for freedom and rationality. This impotence on the part of nature sets limits to philosophy, and it is the height of pointlessness to demand of the Notion that it should explain, and as it is said, construe or deduce these contingent products of nature, although the more isolated and trifling they are the easier the task appears to be. Traces of Notional determination will certainly survive in the most particularized product, although they will not exhaust its nature. The traces of this transmission and inner connection will often surprise the investigator, but will be

particularly astonishing or even incredible to those accustomed only to seeing the same contingency in the history of nature as they see in that of humanity. Here one has to guard against accepting + **such traces as the determinate totality of formations, for it is this that gives rise to the analogies mentioned above.** 5

The difficulty, and in many cases the impossibility of finding clear distinctions for classes and orders on the basis of empirical observation, has its root in the inability of nature to hold fast to the realization of the Notion. Nature never fails to blur essential limits with intermediate and defective formations, and so to provide 10 **instances which qualify every firm distinction. Even within a specific genus such as mankind, monsters occur, which have to be included within the genus, although they lack some of the characteristic determinations which would have been regarded as essential to it. In order to classify such formations as defective,** 15 **imperfect, or deformed, an invariable prototype has to be assumed, with the help of which we are able to recognize these so-called monsters' deformities, and borderline cases. This prototype cannot be drawn from experience, but has as its presupposition the independence and worth of Notional determination.** 20

§ 251

Nature is *implicitly* a living whole; more closely considered, the movement through its series of stages consists of the Idea *positing* itself as what it is *implicitly*, i.e. the Idea passes *into itself* by proceeding out of its immediacy and externality, which is *death*. It does this primarily in order 25 to take on *living* being, but also in order to transcend this determinateness, in which it is merely life, and to **bring itself forth** into **the existence of spirit,** which constitutes **the** truth **and ultimate purpose of nature, and the true actuality of the Idea.** 30

Addition. It is as a positing of that which it is implicitly, that the development of the Notion in accordance with its determination is to be grasped. This determination might be regarded as its goal or purpose. In the development, these determinations of its content come into existence and are manifested, not however as independent self-sufficient being, but 35 as posited moments of an ideal nature, which remain within its unity.

This positedness can therefore be grasped as an expression, protrusion, exposition, or self-externalization in so far as the subjectivity of the Notion loses itself in the juxtaposition of its determinations. It preserves itself within them as their unity and ideality however; and seen from the 5 opposite side therefore, this outward movement of the centre towards the periphery is just as much an internal resumption of that which is outward; it is a reminder that it is the Notion which exists in what is expressed. Beginning with the externality in which it is first contained, the progress of the Notion is therefore a turning into itself in the centre, i.e. 10 the assimilation into subjective unity or being-within-self of what is, to the Notion, the inadequate existence of immediacy or externality; not so that the Notion withdraws from this existence and leaves it as an empty shell, but so that existence as such is immanent within itself, or adequate to the Notion, and so that being-within-self, which is life, itself exists. The 15 Notion wants to break the rind of externality in order to become itself. Life is the Notion which has reached its manifestation and stands displayed in its clarity; at the same time however it is the most difficult for the understanding to come to terms with, because the understanding finds it easiest to grasp whatever is simplest, abstract, and dead.

C

Division

(*The division of the philosophy of nature*)

§ 252

20 The Idea, as nature, has:

I. the determination of extrinsicality and of infinite individuation. Unity of form, as it is external to this, is of an ideal nature, and as it is simply implicit, is merely sought after. This constitutes matter and the ideal nature of the system of matter, 25 i.e. mechanics.

II. the determination of particularity, in which reality is posited with an immanent determinateness of form and its own existent differentiation. This is a relationship of reflection, the being-in-self of which constitutes natural individuality, i.e. physics.

30 III. the determination of subjectivity, in which the real differences of form are also brought back into a unity of an ideal nature, + which has found itself and has being for itself, i.e. organics.

Addition. This division follows from the standpoint of the Notion as it is grasped in its totality, and displays the diremption of the Notion in its determinations. As it exhibits its determinations in this diremption and yet only allows them independence as moments, it realizes itself in this, and so posits itself as Idea. The Notion not only exhibits its moments and expresses itself in its differences however, but also leads these apparently independent stages back into their ideality and unity. By leading them back into itself, it in fact turns them for the first time into the concrete Notion, the Idea, and truth. There seem therefore to be two ways of formulating this division and so proceeding scientifically. The one begins with the concrete Notion, which in nature is life regarded for itself, and from this it is led to the expressions which the Notion throws out of itself as independent spheres of nature, and to which it relates itself as to another in the more abstract aspects of its existence, ending with the complete extinction of life. The other is the opposite one. It begins with the last self-externality of the merely immediate manner in which the Notion first exists, and ends with its true determinate being, the truth of its whole exposition. The first way may be compared to the progression in the conception of emanation, the second to the progression implied in the conception of evolution (§ 249 Addition). Each of these two forms taken by itself is onesided, for they take place simultaneously, and the eternal divine process is a unified flow in two antithetical directions, which simply meet and completely permeate each other. The first, even when it is given the highest names and regarded as being concrete, is merely an immediacy. When matter negates itself as untrue existence for example, a higher existence emerges, and in one respect the earlier stage is sublated by means of an evolution; on the other hand however, it remains in the background, and is reproduced by emanation. Matter involves itself into life, and evolution is therefore also involution. As the result of the drive of the Idea towards being for itself, independent moments such as the senses of the animal, come into objective existence as the sun, and the lunar and cometary bodies. Despite some changes, these bodies retain their shape but lose their independence even in the physical sphere, where they are the elements. Projected outwards, subjective sight is the sun, taste is water, and smell is air. As it is necessary to posit determinations of the Notion here, we must begin with the most abstract, not with the most concrete sphere. +

Initially, matter is the form in which the self-externality of nature attains its first being-in-self. It is the abstract being-for-self which, in that it is exclusive, is a plurality which has its unity within itself and at the same time outside itself, as the plural being-for-self included within universal being-for-self. It is in fact gravity. In mechanics, being-for-self is still not an individual stable unity having the power to subordinate plurality to itself. Weighted matter does not yet possess the individuality which preserves its determinations, and since the determinations of the 5 Notion in it are still external to one another, difference is indifferent or merely quantitative, not qualitative, and matter as simple mass has no form. It is in physics that the individual bodies acquire form, and at the same time it is there that we see gravity revealed for the first time as the being-for-self which submits multiplicity to its rule, and which is no 10 longer a nisus, but which has at least the superficial appearance of being at rest. Each atom of gold for example contains all the determinations or properties of gold, so that matter is immanently specified and particularized. The second determination is that specification as qualitative determinateness, and being-for-self as the point of individuality, still unite 15 in one and the same term, so that the body is finitely determined. Individuality is still bound to definite, exclusive and specific properties, and is not yet present in its complete and general form. If a body of this kind is brought into the process, it ceases to be what it is if it loses these properties. In this way qualitative determinateness is posited affirmatively, 20 but not at the same time negatively. Organic being, which is an individuality existing for itself and developing itself into its differences within itself, constitutes totality as found in nature. Its determinations are at the same time concrete totalities, not merely specific properties, and remain qualitatively determined with regard to one another. Life expresses itself 25 within the process of these members, and also posits them as finite elements of an ideal nature. We thus have a number of beings-for-self, which are however brought back to the being-for-self which is for itself, and which, as its own end, subjugates the members and reduces them to means. It is unity of qualitative determinedness and of gravity, which 30 produces itself in life.

Each of these stages constitutes a characteristic realm of nature, and all of them appear to be separately self-subsistent. Each subsequent stage contains those prior to it however, so that the last is the concrete unity of all that have preceded it, and presupposes them as constituting its inorganic 35 nature. One stage is the power of the other, but this is a mutual relation, and within it one finds the true meaning of *potencies*. That which is inorganic constitutes the potencies opposed to that which is individual and subjective, that is to say that whatever is inorganic subverts that which is organic. In its turn organic being is the power opposed to its universal 40 forces such as air and water, which although they are perpetually being released, are also being ceaselessly appropriated and assimilated by it. The eternal life of nature consists firstly in the Idea displaying itself in each sphere to whatever extent finitude makes possible, just as every drop of water yields an image of the sun. Secondly, it consists in the dialectic of the Notion, which breaks through the limitation of this sphere, and since 5 it only finds partial satisfaction in such an inadequate element, necessarily passes over into a higher stage.

SECTION ONE

Mechanics

§ 253

Mechanics treats of:

A. The completely abstract extrinsicality of space and time.

B. Individualized extrinsicality and its relation within this abstraction, i.e. the finite mechanics of matter and motion.

5 **C. Matter in the freedom of its implicit Notion, i.e. the absolute mechanics of free motion.**

Addition. Self-externality immediately breaks down into two forms: as a positive form it is space, and then as a negative form it is time. Matter is the first concrete unity and negation of these abstract moments, and in that it 10 is related to these moments, the moments are related to one another in motion. When this is not an external relation, it gives rise to self-motivated + matter, i.e. to the absolute unity of matter and motion.

CHAPTER ONE

Space and time

(*Mathematical mechanics*)

A

Space

§ 254

The primary or immediate determination of nature is the abstract *universality of its self-externality*, **its** unmediated indifference, i.e. *space*. It is on account of its being self-externality, that space constitutes *collaterality* of a comple-
5 tely ideal nature; as this extrinsicality is still completely *abstract*, space is simply *continuous*, and is devoid of any determinate difference.

Remark

\+ The nature of space has given rise to many theories. I shall only make mention of the *Kantian* determination of it
\+ as a *form* of *sensuous intuition* like time. It is now generally accepted that space must be regarded as a merely subjective element of the representative faculty. If we disregard the determinations of the Kantian Notion and subjective ideal-ism in this theory, we are left with the correct determina-
15 tion of space as a simple form, i.e. an *abstraction*, the form of immediate *externality*. It is inadmissible to speak of *spatial points* as if they constituted the positive element in space, because on account of its lack of difference, space is merely the possibility, not the *positedness* **of juxtaposition and**
20 what is negative, and is therefore simply continuous. The point, **which is being-for-self,** is therefore rather the *negation* of space, **a negation which is posited within space.** This also
\+ resolves the question of the infinitude of space (§ 100 Obs.).

Space is, in general, pure *quantity*, no longer in its merely logical determination, but as an immediate and external being. Consequently, nature begins with **quantity and not with quality,** because its determination is not a primary **abstract** and immediate state like logical Being. Essentially, **it is already internally** *mediated* externality and otherness.

Addition. As it is our procedure to ask how the thought which has been established as a necessity by means of the Notion looks in our sensuous intuition, the further requirement is that the intuition of space shall correspond to the thought of pure self-externality. Even if we should deceive ourselves in this respect, this would in no way effect the truth of our thought. In the empirical sciences on the other hand, the opposite procedure is adopted; the empirical intuition of space comes first, and is then followed by the thought of space. In order to prove that space accords with our thought, we have to compare the image of space with the determination of our Notion. The content of space has nothing to do with space itself, in which various heres are juxtaposed without impinging upon one another. Here is not yet place, it is merely the possibility of place. The heres are completely identical, and this abstract plurality, which has no true interruption and limit, is the precise constitution of externality. Although the heres are also differentiated, their being different is identical with their lack of difference, and the difference is therefore abstract. Space is therefore punctiformity without points, or complete continuity. If one fixes a point, space is both interrupted and simply uninterrupted. The point has significance only in so far as it is spatial, and so external both to itself and to others. The here also has within itself an above, a below, a left and a right. If anything were no longer external to itself, but only to others it would be a point; but as no here is the last, there can be no such thing. No matter how far away I place a star, I can always go beyond it, for no one has boarded up the universe. This is the complete externality of space. This other of the point is itself just as external to itself however, and consequently both are undifferentiated and unseparated; space is still at unity with itself as its otherness beyond its limit; and it is this unity in extrinsicality which constitutes continuity. The unity of these two moments of discreteness and continuity is the objectively determined Notion of space. This Notion is however only the abstraction of space, which is often regarded as absolute space, and thought to be the truth of space. Relative space is something much higher however, for it is the determinate space of any given material body, and it is rather its being as material body which constitutes the truth of abstract space.

To ask whether space by itself is real, or whether it is only a property of things, is to ask one of the most well-worn of all metaphysical questions. If one says that it is something inherently substantial, then it must resemble a box, which, even if there is nothing in it, is still something subsisting within itself. Space is absolutely yielding and utterly devoid of opposition however; and if something is real, it is necessary that it should be incompatible with something else. One cannot point to a part of space which is space *for itself*, for space is always filled, and no part of it is separated from that which fills it. It is therefore a non-sensuous sensibility and a sensuous insensibility. The things of nature are in space, and as nature is subject to the condition of externality, space remains the foundation of nature. If one says, as Leibnitz did, that space is an order of things which does not concern the noumena, and which has its substrata in things, we assume that if one removes the things which fill space, the spatial relationships between them still persist independently. It may certainly be said that space is an order, for it is of course an external determination, but it is much more than a merely external determination, it is externality itself.

§255

Space is **implicitly** the Notion in general, and as such has the *differences* of the Notion within itself: (*a*) in its indifference it has them immediately as the three *dimensions*, which are merely *different*, and quite devoid of determination.

Remark

In so far as it is not a philosophical science, geometry may assume **the universal determinations of space** as its object, and it is not to be demanded of it that it should deduce the necessity of the three dimensions of space. The deduction of this necessity is founded upon the nature of the Notion, but because of the non-philosophical nature of geometry, it is never considered. In this primary form of extrinsicality and abstract quantity, the determinations of the Notion constitute a merely superficial and completely empty difference. Consequently one cannot say how *height*, *length*, and *breadth* differ from one another, because they are merely supposed to be distinctions. There *is* as yet no difference between them, **and no determination is added by calling a direction height, length, or breadth.** Height is more precisely determined as a direction from the middle of the earth, but **a more concrete determination of this kind** is irrelevant to the nature of space itself. **Admitting this determination, it is still a matter of indifference whether we call a certain direction** height or depth; **it is the same with** length or breadth, which is also often called depth, **for nothing is determined in this way.**

§ 256

(*b*) Spatial difference is however essentially determinate and qualitative. As such it is (1) in the first instance the point, i.e. the *negation* of the immediate and *undifferentiated* self-externality of space itself. (2) The negation is however the negation of *space*, **and is therefore itself spatial. In that** this relation **is essential to** the point, **the point is self-sublating and constitutes the** *line*, which is the primary otherness **or spatial** *being* of the point. (3) The truth of otherness is however the negation of negation, and the line therefore passes over into the *plane*. Although one aspect of the plane is that it constitutes surface in general, in that it is a determinateness opposed to line and point, it also has the aspect of being the transcended negation of space, or the reinstatement of that spatial totality which now has the negative moment within it. It is therefore an *enclosing surface*, which divides off and separates a *distinct* part of space.

Remark

It is because of their Notion that the line does not consist of points nor the plane of lines, the line being rather the *self-externality* of the point in that is *relates* itself to space and is self-sublating, and the plane likewise, being the transcended self-externality of the line. The point is here presented as that which is primary and positive, and it is from this that a beginning is made. The contrary is also true however, for space may be considered as that which is positive, the plane as the first negation of space, and the line **as the second negation,** which, because it is the second, is in truth the self-relating negation of the point. **The necessity of this transition is the same as it was in the first case. The necessity of this transition is not realized when the point and the line etc. are grasped and defined in an external manner; the former kind of transition is however grasped, as something contingent, when a manner of definition is used in which the line is said to arise from the movement of the point etc.** The other figurations of space treated in geometry are further qualitative limitations of an abstract division of space, of the plane, or of a bounded spatial unit. Moments of necessity also occur here; in the triangle for example, which is the primary rectilinear figure, to which, with the square, all other figures must be reduced if they are to be determined etc. The principle of these constructions is the identity of the understanding, which determines the figurations into *regularity* and so establishes the relationships **by which they may be understood.**

It may be noticed in passing that *Kant* was of the extraordinary opinion that the definition of a *straight line* as the shortest distance between two points is a synthetic proposition because our *conception* of *straightness* is merely qualitative and does not involve size. In this sense, every definition is a synthetic proposition; that which is defined, which in this case is the *straight line*, is primarily nothing but an intuition or representation. As we have already seen in § 229, in definitions such as this, it is the determination as the shortest distance between two points which first constitutes the *Notion*. A definition is necessary here because the *Notion* differs from the *intuition* by not being already present within it. **Kant's definition is clearly analytic, since the straight line reduces itself to simplicity of direction, which, when taken in relation to quantity, yields the determination of the smallest quantity, and consequently of the shortest distance.**

Addition. It is only the straight line which is the primary determination of spatiality, for curved lines implicitly involve two dimensions; in the circle we have the second power of the line. As the second negation, the plane has two dimensions, for the second negation is no less double than *two*. +

If certain determinations are given, it is the task of the science of geometry to discover what other determinations follow from them, the main thing being that that which is given, and that which follows, should constitute a single developed totality. The central propositions of geometry are those in which a whole is postulated, and expressed in its determinate elements. There are two such cardinal propositions involved in the complete determinability of the triangle. (*a*) If one has any three elements of a triangle, one of which has to be a side (and there are three cases of this), the triangle is completely determined. Geometry deviates here into the easier but superfluous presentation of two triangles, which under these circumstances are supposed to be congruent. In fact the proposition needs only one triangle, for the triangle in itself is such a relationship: if the first three parts of it are determined, so are the other three, for the triangle is determined by two sides and an angle, or two angles and a side etc. The + first three elements constitute the determinability or Notion of the triangle; the other three belong to its external reality, and are superfluous to the Notion. In such postulation, determination is still completely abstract, and there is only a general dependence, for the relation of specific determinateness in the size of the elements of the triangle is still lacking. This is (*b*) reached in Pythagoras's theorem, which presents the perfect determinateness of the triangle, in that in it, only the right angle is completely determined, its adjacent angle being equal to it. This theorem is therefore superior to all others as an illustration of the Idea. It presents a whole which has divided itself within itself, just as each shape in philosophy is divided within itself as Notion and reality. Here we have the same magnitude twice, first as the square of the hypotenuse, and then divided into the squares on the two cathetuses. There is a higher defini- + tion of the circle than that based on the equality of radii, in which difference is taken into account, so that the perfect determinateness of the circle is obtained. This occurs in analytical treatment, and contains nothing that is not found in Pythagoras's theorem. The cathetuses are the sine and cosine, or abscissa and ordinate, and the hypotenuse is the radius. The relationship of these three constitutes the determinateness of the circle. + This is not however a simple relationship like that in the first definition, but a relationship of different elements. Euclid also concludes his first book with Pythagoras's theorem. After this he is interested in bringing differences back to likeness, and he therefore concludes his second book by reducing the rectangle to the square. A hypotenuse contains the possibility +

of an infinite number of right-angled triangles, and a square, likewise, a number of rectangles; the circle is the place for both. It is in this way that geometry, as an abstract science of the understanding, proceeds scientifically.

B

Time

§ 257

The negativity which relates itself to space as point and develops its determinations within it as line and plane, is however also a being-*for-self* within the sphere of self-externality; **it posits its determinations within space, but at the same time, in conformity with** the sphere of self-externality, **and is therefore** apparently indifferent to the immobile collaterality of space. Thus posited for itself, this negativity is *time*.

Addition. Space is the immediate determinate being of quantity, in which everything remains subsistent, and even limit has the form of a subsistence. This is its deficiency. Space is a contradiction, for the negation within it disintegrates into indifferent subsistence. As space is merely this inner negation of itself, its truth is the self-transcendence of its moments. It is precisely the existence of this perpetual self-transcendence which constitutes time. In time therefore the point has actuality. Through the generation of difference within it, space ceases to be mere indifference, and through all its changes, is no longer paralysed, but is for itself. This pure quantity, as difference existing for itself, is that which is implicitly negative, i.e. time; it is the negation of the negation, or self-relating negation. Negation in space is negation relative to another; in space therefore the negative does not yet come into its own. In space the plane is certainly negation of the negation, but in its truth it is different from space. The truth of space is time, so that space becomes time; our transition to time is not subjective, space itself makes the transition. Space and time are generally taken to be poles apart: space is there, and then we *also* have time. Philosophy calls this 'also' in question.

§ 258

Time, as the negative unity of self-externality, is also purely abstract and of an ideal nature. **It is the being** which, in that it *is*, is *not*, and in that it is *not*, *is*. **It is intuited becoming; admittedly, its differences are therefore determined as being simply momentary; in that they immediately sublate themselves in their externality however, they are self-external.**

Remark

Time, like space, is a *pure form* of *sensibility* or *intuition*; **it is the insensible factor in sensibility.** Like space however, time does not involve the difference between objectivity and a distinct subjective consciousness. If these determinations were to be applied to space and time, the first **would** be abstract objectivity, and the second abstract subjectivity. Time is the same principle as the ego=ego of pure self-consciousness, but as time, this principle, or the simple Notion, is still completely external **and abstract** as mere intuited becoming; it is pure being-in-self, as a plain self-production.

Time is as *continuous* as space is, for it is abstract negativity *relating itself to itself*, and in this abstraction there is as yet no difference of a real nature.

It is said that everything *arises* and *passes away in* time, and that if one abstracts from *everything*, that is to say from the content of time and space, then empty time and empty space will be left, i.e. time and space are posited as abstractions of externality, **and represented as if they were for themselves.** But **everything does not appear and pass in time;** time itself is this *becoming*, arising, and passing away, it is the *abstraction* which has *being*, the *Cronos* which engenders all and destroys that to which it gives birth. That which is of a real nature is certainly distinguished from time, but is just as essentially identical with time. **It is limited, and the other involved in this negation is outside it. Consequently, the determinateness is implicitly external to itself, and is therefore the contradiction of its being. Time itself consists of the abstraction and contradiction of this externality and of the restlessness of this contradiction.** That which is finite is transitory and *temporal* **because** unlike the Notion, it is not in itself **total** negativity. It certainly contains negativity **as its** universal essence, but as it is not adequate to this essence **and is**

one-sided, it relates itself to negativity as to its *power*. The Notion however, in its **freely existing** identity with itself, as ego=ego, is in and for itself absolute negativity and freedom, and is consequently, not only free from the power of
5 time, but is neither within time, nor something temporal. It can be said on the contrary that it is the *Notion* which constitutes the power of time, for time is nothing but this negation as externality. **Only** that which is natural, in that it is finite, is subject to time; that which is true however,
10 the Idea, spirit, is *eternal*. The Notion of eternity should not however be grasped **negatively as the abstraction of time, and as if it existed outside time; nor should it be grasped** in the sense of its coming *after* time, for by placing eternity in the future, one turns it into a moment of time.

15 *Addition*. Time does not resemble a container in which everything is as it were borne away and swallowed up in the flow of a stream. Time is merely this abstraction of destroying. Things are in time because they are finite; they do not pass away because they are in time, but are themselves that which is temporal. Temporality is their objective determination. It is
20 therefore the process of actual things which constitutes time, and if it can be said that time is omnipotent, it must be added that it is completely impotent. The present makes a tremendous demand, yet as the individual present it is nothing, for even as I pronounce it, its all-excluding pretentiousness dwindles, dissolves, and falls into dust. It is the universality of
25 these present moments which *lasts*, and the sublatedness of this process of things which does not. Even if things endure, time does not rest, but continues to pass, and it is because of this that it appears to be distinct and independent of things. If we say that time continues to pass even if things endure however, we are merely saying that although some things endure,
30 change appears in other things, as for example the course of the sun; so that things still remain in time. The attribution of gradual change is employed as a last resort in order to endow things with stillness and permanence. If all stood still, even our thinking, we would be permanent, and there would be no time, but all finite things are temporal, as sooner or
35 later they are all subject to change, and their permanence is therefore only relative.

Absolute timelessness is *eternity*, which is devoid of natural time, and is therefore to be distinguished from duration. In its Notion, time itself is eternal however, for its Notion is neither the present nor any other time, but time as such. Its Notion is, like all Notion, eternal, and thus also constitutes the absolute present. Eternity will not be, nor has it been, it *is*. Duration is therefore to be distinguished from eternity, in that it is merely a relative sublation of time; eternity is however infinite, that is to say, not relative, but intro-reflected duration. That which is not in time, is without process; the most imperfect, like the most perfect, is not in time, and therefore endures. The most imperfect endures, because it is an abstract universality, such as space, and time itself; the sun, the elements, stones, mountains, inorganic nature in general, as well as works of man such as pyramids, have a barren duration. That which endures is regarded more highly than that which soon passes, but all blossom, all that is exquisite in living being, dies early. The most perfect also endures however, not only in the lifeless inorganic universal, but also in the other inherently concrete universal of the genus, the law, the idea, and the spirit. We have to decide whether something is the whole process, or merely one moment of it. As law, the universal is also inherently a process, and lives only as process; but it is not part of the process, it is not within the process, it contains its double aspect, and is itself without process. In its phenomenal aspect, law falls within time, because the moments of the Notion show themselves as independent; but in their Notion the excluded differences reconcile and relate themselves, and are harmoniously reassimilated. The Idea or spirit is above time, because it is itself the Notion of time; in and for itself it is eternal and unbreached by time, because it does not lose itself in its own side of the process. This is not the case with the individual as such, on one side of which is the genus; the finest life is that which completely unites its individuality and the universal into one form. The individual is not then the same as the universal however, and is therefore one side of the process, or mutability, in accordance with which mortal moment it falls within time. Achilles, the flower of Greek life, and the infinitely powerful personality of Alexander the Great, are no more, and only their deeds and influences remain through the world that they have brought into being. Mediocrity endures, and finally governs the world. Thought also displays this mediocrity, with which it pesters the world about it, and which survives by extinguishing spiritual liveliness and turning it into flat formality. It endures precisely because it rests in untruth, never acquires its right, fails to honour the Notion, and never realizes the process of the truth within it.

§ 259

The *present*, *future*, and *past*, the dimensions of time, constitute the *becoming* **of externality as such,** and its dissolution into the differences of being as passing over into nothing, and of nothing as passing over into being. The immediate disappearance of these **differences** into *individuality* is the present as *now*, **which, as it excludes individuality and is at the same time simply continuous in the other moments, is itself** merely this disappearance of its being into nothing, and of nothing into its being.

Remark

The *finite* present is the *now* **fixed as being,** and as the concrete unity, distinguished **from the negative,** the abstract moments **of** the past and the future, **it is therefore the affirmative factor; yet in itself this being is merely abstract, and** disappears into nothing. Incidentally, these dimensions do not occur in nature, where time is *now* as separately *subsistent* differences, for they are only necessary in subjective representation, in *memory*, and in *fear* or *hope*. The past and the future of time are space in so far as they have *being* in *nature*, for space is negated time; just as sublated space is initially the point, which **developed for itself** is time. There is no *science of time* corresponding to *geometry*, the *science of space*. Temporal differences do not have this *indifference* of self-externality which constitutes the immediate determinability of space, and unlike this determinability, do not therefore give rise to figurations. Time first becomes capable of such figurations when the understanding paralyzes it and reduces its negativity to a *unit*. This dead unity, which is thought's highest externality, gives rise to external combinations; these are the figures of *arithmetic*, which may be applied by the understanding to equality and inequality, identity and difference.

One could go further and work out the thought of a *philosophical mathematics* apprehended through notions, instead of the assumed determinations from which the method employed by the understanding derives ordinary mathematics. It is because mathematics is the science of the finite determinations of magnitude, which are supposed to remain firmly and consistently in their finitude, and may not go beyond these determinations, that it is essentially a science of the understanding; and since it is capable of realizing this science in a perfect manner, it has the advantage over other sciences of this kind, of not being contaminated by the admixture of heterogeneous notions or empirical application. It is always possible therefore that the Notion may establish **a more exact** awareness of the guiding principles of the operations of arithmetic (cf. § 102) and the theorems of geometry. 5 10 +

It would however by a superfluous and thankless task to attempt forcibly to manipulate such a refractory and inadequate medium as spatial figures and numbers into a means for expressing *thoughts*. **Because of their simplicity,** the elementary primary figures and numbers may be employed as *symbols* **without giving rise to misunderstandings, but they remain a heterogeneous and** perfunctory way of expressing thought. The first essays in **pure** thought had recourse to this means; *Pythagoras's* system of numbers furnishes the most famous example of this. Richer concepts will find these means completely inadequate however, because their *external* combination, and the contingency of connection in general, is not suited to the Notion, and where the many relations which are possible in combinations of numbers and figures should be held together, radical ambiguity is introduced. The result, in any case, is that the fluidity of the Notion is dissipated in an external medium of this kind, so that each determination falls into indifferent extrinsicality. This ambiguity could only be removed by *explanation*. The essential expression of thought is then the explanation however, and the symbolization becomes a worthless superfluity. 15 20 + 25 30

Other mathematical determinations such as the *infinite* and *its relationships*, the *infinitely small*, *factors*, *powers* etc. have their true notions in philosophy itself; it is wrong headed to think that they should be borrowed and adapted from mathematics, where they are not employed in conformity with the Notion, and where they are often taken up at random. It is rather by means of philosophy that they 35 40 can be corrected and given significance. **In order to avoid thinking and determining by means of the Notion, indolence has recourse to formulae, and deals in their ready-made schemata, which are in no way an immediate expression of thought.**

5 The truly philosophical science of mathematics considered as the *doctrine* of quantities, **would be** the science of *measures*; but this already assumes the real nature and the particularity of things, which is first present in concrete + nature. **Because of the external nature of quantity, this would 10 certainly also be the most difficult of all sciences.**

Addition. The dimensions of time complete that which is determinate in intuition in that they posit for intuition the totality or reality of the Notion of time, which is becoming. This reality consists of the abstract moments of the unity which constitute becoming, each being posited 15 for itself as a whole, although under opposite determinations. Each of these two determinations is therefore in itself the unity of being and nothing; but they are also different. This difference can only be that of arising and passing away. In the first, the principle with which one begins + is being in the past, of Hades; the past has really existed as world-history 20 or natural events, but it is approached by being posited with the determination of not-being. In the second determination, the opposite is the case. In the future the first determination is not-being, being comes later, although not in time. The middle term is the undifferentiated unity of both, in which neither the one nor the other is the determining element. 25 The present is, only because the past is not: the being of the now has the determination of not-being, and the not-being of its being is the future; the present is this negative unity. The not-being replaced by now, is the past; the being of not-being contained in the present, is the future. If one considers time positively one can therefore say that only the 30 present is, before and after is not, but the concrete present is the result of the past, and is pregnant with the future. The true present is therefore eternity.

Incidentally it would also be permissible to define mathematics as the philosophical consideration of space and time. If one attempted to treat 35 the figurations of space and of the unit philosophically however, they would lose their characteristic significance and shape; a philosophy of them would be a matter of logic, or, to the extent that one attributed a more concrete significance to the concepts, even become another concrete philosophical science. Mathematics only takes into consideration the determination of quantity involved in these objects, and as we have seen, ignores time itself, and concentrates only upon the figurations and combinations of the unit. In the theory of motion, time will certainly also be treated by this science, but applied mathematics, precisely because it is the application of pure mathematics to a given material, and the deter- 5 minations of this material are taken from experience, is in no respect an immanent science.

C

Place and motion

(*The union of space and time*)

§ 260

Space in itself is the contradiction of indifferent juxtaposition and of continuity devoid of difference; it is the pure negativity of itself, and the **initial** *transition into time*. 10 Time is similar, for as its opposed moments, held together in unity, immediately sublate themselves, it constitutes an immediate *collapse* into undifferentiation, into the undifferentiated extrinsicality of *space*. **Consequently, the negative determination here, which is the exclusive point, is no longer** 15 **merely implicit in its conformity to the Notion, but is posited, and is in itself concrete on account of the total negativity of time. This concrete point is place** (§ 255 and § 256).

Addition. If we refer back to the exposition of the Notion of duration, we see that this immediate unity of space and time is already the ground of their being. 20 The negative of space is time, and the positive, or the being of the differences of time, is space. In this analysis however, they are posited as of unequal import, or their unity is merely presented as the movement of the transition from one into the other. Consequently the beginning, and the realization, the result, fall apart. The result is the precise expression of their ground and truth however. 25 The durable element is the self-equality into which time has returned; this is space, the determinability of which is indifferent existence in general. Here the point is that which it is in its truth as a universal; it is in fact the whole of space, as a totality of all dimensions. This here is to the same extent time, and is now + an immediately self-sublating present, or a now which has been. As it is the 30 point of duration, the here is at the same time a now. This unity of here and now is place.

§ 261

Initially, the place which is thus the posited identity of space and time is also the posited contradiction set up by the mutual exclusiveness of space and time. Place is spatial and therefore indifferent singularity, and is this only as the spatial now, or time. As this place, it is therefore in a condition of immediate indifference to itself; it is external to itself, the negation of itself, and constitutes another place. This *passing away* and **self-***regeneration* of space in time and time in space, **in which time posits itself spatially as place, while this indifferent spatiality is likewise posited immediately in a temporal manner, constitutes motion.** To an equal extent however, this becoming is itself **the internal collapse of its contradiction, it is therefore the immediately** *identical* and *existent* unity of place and motion, i.e. *matter*.

Remark

The transition from ideality to reality, from abstraction to concrete existence, in this case from space and time to the reality which makes its appearance as *matter*, is incomprehensible to the understanding, for which it therefore always remains as something externally presented. Space and time are usually imagined **as being empty and indifferent to that which fills them, and yet as always to be regarded as full. They are thought** to be *empty* until they have been *filled* with matter from *without*. On the one hand material things are therefore taken to be indifferent to space and time, and yet at the same time they are accepted as essentially spatial and temporal.

It is said of matter that: (*a*) it is *composite*, which is a property it derives from its abstract extrinsicality, space. In so far as an abstraction is made of time and all form, matter is said to be eternal and immutable, which is in fact the immediate result of this; but matter in such a state is merely an untrue abstraction. (*b*) It is *impenetrable* and offers *resistance*, it can be felt, seen etc. These predicates merely indicate that matter has two determinations, according to which it exists partly for determinate perception, or more generally *for another*, and partly and equally, *for itself*. It has these two determinations as the *identity* of space and 5 time, and of immediate *extrinsicality* and *negativity*, or **as the being-for-self of singularity.** +

The *transition of ideality into reality* also expresses itself in the familiar mechanical phenomenon of reality being replaceable by ideality and vice versa, and it is only the 10 thoughtlessness of popular conception and of the understanding which prevents the identity of both from being recognized in this interchangeability. In the case of the *lever* for example, the mass may be replaced by the *distance* and vice versa, and a certain quantum of moments of 15 an ideal nature produces the same effect as the corresponding moments of a real nature. Similarly, in the *magnitude of motion*, *velocity*, which is a quantitative relationship, simply between space and time, replaces *mass*; and conversely, the real nature of the same effect is obtained by aug- 20 menting the mass and correspondingly diminishing space and time. A tile does not strike a man dead by itself, it only has this effect by virtue of the velocity it has acquired, i.e. the man is struck dead by *space* and *time*. Here the understanding gets no further than the reflectional deter- 25 mination of *force*, which it regards as fundamental, and is not therefore tempted to look further into the relationship of its determinations. Even this thought implies vaguely that the *effect* of force is a sensuous event of a real nature however, that there is no difference between the *content* 30 and expression of force, and that precisely *this force* has the *real nature* of its *expression* in the relationship between the ideal nature of the moments of space and time.

This sort of notionless reflection also thinks of what it calls forces, as being *implanted* in matter, and therefore as 35 originally *external* to it. The very identity of time and space which hovers vaguely before this reflectional determination of *force*, and which constitutes the true essence of matter, is consequently posited as something *alien* and *contingent* to it, and as **brought into it from without.** 40

Addition. One place does not merely imply another, it sublates itself into becoming another; the difference is also a sublatedness however. Each place is for itself only this place, so that all places are the same, and place is the simply mediated here. Something occupies one place, and then changes its place, passing thereby into another place; but both before and after this, it does not leave, but occupies its place. *Zeno* enunciated this dialectic within place, when he demonstrated immobility by saying that to move was to change place, but that the arrow never leaves its place. This dialectic is precisely the infinite Notion, or the here, for time is posited as being implicit. There are three different places, the present, that which is to be occupied, and the vacated. The disappearance of the dimensions of time is paralysed, but at the same time there is only one place which is common to these places, and invariable throughout all change, and this is the duration which is in immediate accordance with its Notion, i.e. motion. This demonstration of motion is self-evident, for the intuition of it coincides with its Notion. Its essence is its being as the immediate unity of space and time; it is time realizing itself and subsisting in space, or space first truly differentiated through time. We know therefore that space and time belong to motion. Velocity, which is quantum of motion, is space in relationship to a specific time elapsed. Motion is also said to be a relation of space and time; it was necessary however to grasp the more exact definition of this relation. Space and time first attain actuality in motion.

Just as time is the simply formal soul of nature, and according to Newton, space is the sensorium of God, so motion is the Notion of the true soul of the world. We habitually regard it as a predicate or state, but it is in fact the self, the subject as subject, and the persistence, even of disappearance. It is precisely because of its immediate necessity to dissolve itself that it appears as predicate. Rectilinear motion is not motion in and for itself, but motion subordinated to another term, of which, in that it has become a predicate, or sublated, it is a moment. The re-establishment of the duration of the point in opposition to its motion, is the re-establishment of the immobility of place. This re-established place is not immediate, but the return from alteration, and is the result and ground of motion. In that it is dimension, and so opposed to the other moments, it is the centre. This return as line is the circular line; it is the now, before, and after, joining itself with itself; it is the indifference of these dimensions, in which the before is just as much an after as the after is a before. This is the first necessary paralysis of these dimensions posited in space. Circular motion is the spatial or subsistent unity of the dimensions of time. The point tends towards a place which is its future, and vacates one which is the past; but that which it has behind it, is at the same time that at which it will arrive; and it has already been at the after towards which it tends. Its goal is the point which is its past. The truth of time is that its goal is the past and not the future. The motion which relates itself to the centre is itself the *plane*, that is to say the motion which, in that it forms a synthetic whole, itself contains its moments or its dissolution in the centre, as well as the radii of the circle, which relate it to the dissolution. This plane itself moves however, and so becomes its otherness, an entirety of space, i.e. the motion returns into itself, and the immobile centre becomes a universal point, in which the whole sinks into quiescence. It is in fact the essence of motion which has here sublated the now, the past, and the future, or the different dimensions which constitute its Notion. In the circle these dimensions are precisely one, and constitute the re-established Notion of duration, or of motion extinguishing itself within itself. This is posited *mass*, durability, that which has condensed itself through itself, and displays motion as its possibility.

We have now reached the following position: Where there is motion, there is something which moves, and this durable something is matter. Space and time are filled with matter. Space is not adequate to its Notion, and it is consequently the Notion of space itself which creates its existence in matter. People have often begun with matter, and then regarded space and time as its forms. This is a valid procedure in so far as matter is the reality of space and time, but for us space and time must come first because of their abstraction, and matter must then show itself to be their truth. Just as there is no motion without matter, so there is no matter without motion. Motion is the process; it is the passage of time into space, and of space into time. Matter on the contrary is the relation of time and space as a quiescent identity. Matter is the primary reality, existent being-for-self; it is not merely abstract being, it is the positive subsistence of space as exclusive of other space. The point *should* also exclude other points, but it does not yet do so, for it is merely an abstract negation. Matter is exclusive relation to self, and consequently the first real limit in space. That which is said to fill time and space, which can be grasped and felt, which offers resistance, and which is for itself in its being-for-other, is simply reached in the general unity of time and space. +

CHAPTER TWO

Matter and motion

Finite mechanics

(*Gravity*)

§ 262

Matter maintains itself **against its self-identity** and in a state of extrinsicality, through its moment of negativity, its abstract *singularization*, and it is this that constitutes the *repulsion* of matter. As these different singularities are one
5 and the same however, the negative unity of the juxtaposed being of this being-for-self is just as essential, and constitutes their *attraction*, or the **continuity of matter. Matter is inseparable from both** these moments, **and constitutes their negative** unity, **i.e. singularity. This is however still distinct**
10 **from the immediate extrinsicality of matter, and is therefore not yet posited as being a centre, a material singularity of an ideal nature,** i.e. *gravity*.

Remark

It is to be regarded as one of the many merits of Kant, that in his '*Metaphysical foundations of Natural Science*', he
15 made an attempt at a so-called *construction* of matter, and by establishing a *notion* of matter, revived the concept of a
\+ *philosophy of nature*. In so doing however, he postulated the reflective determinations of the *forces* of *attraction* and *repulsion* as being **firmly opposed to and independent of one**
20 **another,** and although *matter* had to be derived from them, assumed it to be *complete* in itself, and **therefore that that which is to be attracted and repelled is already fully constituted matter.** I have dealt more fully with the fundamental flaw in this
\+ Kantian exposition in my 'Science of Logic'. **It should be**

noted moreover that weighted matter is the first totality and real nature in which attraction and repulsion can occur; it has the ideal nature of the moments of the Notion, of singularity or subjectivity. Consequently they are not to be regarded as independent, or as self-contained forces. It is only as moments of the Notion that they result in matter, although matter is however the presupposition of their appearance.

It is essential to distinguish *gravity* from mere *attraction*, which is simply the general sublation of juxtaposition, and yields nothing but continuity. Gravity on the other hand is the reduction of juxtaposed and yet continuous particularity into unity, into negative relation to self, *singularity*, *a single subjectivity* which is however still quite abstract. In the sphere of the primary *immediacy* of nature, the self-external being of continuity is still posited as *subsistent* however. Material introflection first occurs in physics, and although *singularity* is therefore certainly present here as a determination of the Idea, it is *external to material being*. Consequently the primary essence of matter is that it has *weight*. This is not an external property which may be separated from it. Gravity constitutes the substantiality of matter, which itself consists of a tendency towards a *centre* which falls *outside it*. It is however this externality of its centre which constitutes the other essential determination of matter. As it negates its juxtaposed and continuous subsistence, one can say that matter is *attracted* to the centre, but if the centre itself is thought of as material, the attraction is merely reciprocal, and is at the same time a being attracted, so that the centre is again different from them both. The centre should not be thought of as material however, for the precise nature of material being is that it posits its centre as *external to itself*. It is therefore not the centre, but the tendency towards the centre, which is immanent in matter. Gravity is so to speak the acknowledgement by matter of its lack of independence, its state of contradiction, of the nullity of the self-externality involved in its being-for-self.

It can also be said that gravity is the *being-in-self* of matter in so far as it is not yet in its own self a centre or subjectivity, but is still indeterminate, undeveloped, occludent, and lacking as yet in material form.

Where the centre lies is determined by means of the weighted matter of which it is the centre; in so far as it is mass, it is deter-

+ **mined, and is therefore its tendency, which is consequently a determinate positing of the centre.**

Addition. Matter is spatial separation. By offering resistance it repels itself from itself, and so constitutes repulsion, through which it posits its
5 reality and fills space. The singularities, which are repelled from another,
+ all merely constitute a unit of many units; they are identical with each other. The unit only repels itself from itself, and it is this which constitutes the sublation of the separation of being-for-self, or attraction. Together, attraction and repulsion constitute gravity, which is the Notion
10 of matter. Gravity is the predicate of matter, which constitutes the substance of this subject. Its unity is a mere should, a yearning; this is the most afflicted of efforts, and matter is damned to it eternally, for the unity does not fulfil itself, and is never reached. If matter reached what it aspires to in gravity, it would fuse together into a single point. It is because repul-
15 sion is as essential a moment as attraction, that unity is not attained here. This subdued, crepuscular unity does not become free; yet since matter has as its determination the positing of the many within a unit, it is not
+ so thick as those would-be philosophers who separate the one from the many, and are therefore refuted by matter. Although the two unities of
20 repulsion and attraction are the inseparable moments of gravity, they do not unite themselves in a single unity of an ideal nature. As we shall see later, this unity reaches the first being-for-self of its existence in light. Matter searches for a place outside the many, and since there is no difference between the factors which do this, there is no reason for regarding
25 one as nearer than the other. They are at the same distance on the periphery, and the point sought is the centre; this extends to all dimensions,
+ so that the next determination we reach is the *sphere*. Gravity is not the dead externality of matter, but a mode of its inwardness. At this juncture, this inwardness has no place here however, for matter, as the Notion of
30 that which is Notionless, is still lacking in inwardness.

The second sphere which we now have to consider is therefore finite mechanics, in which matter is not yet adequate to its Notion. This finitude of matter is the differentiated being of motion and of matter as such; matter is therefore finite in so far as the motion which is its life, is external
35 to it. Either the body is at rest, or motion is imparted to it from without. This is the primary difference within matter as such, which is subsequently sublated through its nature, or gravity. Here therefore we have the three determinations of finite mechanics: *firstly* inert matter, *secondly* impact, and *thirdly* fall; this constitutes the transition to absolute mechanics,

in which the existence of matter is also adequate to its Notion. Gravity does not occur within matter in a merely implicit manner, but in so far as the implicitness already makes its appearance; in that it does this it constitutes fall, which is therefore the first occurrence of gravity. 5

A

Inert matter

(*Inertia*)

§ 263

Initially, in its mere universality and immediacy, matter has only a *quantitative* difference, and is particularized into different quanta or *masses*, which in the superficial determination of a whole or unit, are *bodies*. **The body is also immediately distinguished from its ideality; it is however within** 10 **space and time that it is essentially spatial and temporal, and it appears as their content, indifferent to this form.**

Addition. Matter fills space merely because it is exclusive in its being-for-self, and so posits a real limit in space. Space as such lacks this exclusiveness. The determination of plurality necessarily accompanies 15 being-for-self, but is as yet completely indeterminate difference, and not yet a difference implicit within matter itself; matters are mutually exclusive.

§ 264

In accordance with the spatial determination in which time is sublated, the body is durable; in accordance with the temporal + **determination in which indifferent spatial subsistence is sublated, it is transitory; in general, it is a wholly contingent unit. It is indeed the unity which binds both moments in their opposition, i.e. motion; but in its indifferent opposition to space and time (prev. §), and so to the relation of space and time in motion (§ 261),** 25 **the body has motion external to it in the same way as its negation of motion, or rest. It is in fact inert.** +

Remark

In this sphere the body is inadequate to its Notion or finite, because as matter it is only posited as the immediate abstract unity of time and space, and not as a single developed restless unity with motion immanent within it. Ordinary physical mechanics accepts the body in this determination, so that it is one of its axioms that a body can only be set in motion or come to rest through an *external cause*, motion or rest being merely a *state* of the body. Determinations such as this are vaguely envisaged as applying to selfless terrestrial bodies, as of course they do. **This is merely finite corporeality in its immediacy and abstraction however. The body as body means this abstraction of body. The imperfection of this abstract existence is sublated in concretely existent bodies however, and the positing of this sublation begins already in the selfless body. Inertia, impact, pressure, draw, fall etc., the determinations of ordinary mechanics, belong to the sphere of finite corporeality and so to finite motion, and should not therefore be transferred to absolute mechanics, where it is rather in the freedom of their Notion that corporeality and motion have their existence.**

Addition. Mass, posited immediately, contains motion as resistance; for this immediacy is being-for-other. The real moment of difference is external to mass, which has motion either as this Notion, or as sublated within it. Mass is inert when it is fixed in this way, yet it does not express rest. Duration is rest in that as the Notion of its realization, it is opposed to motion. Mass is the unity of the moments of rest and motion; both are sublated within it, for it is indifferent to both of them; it is as capable of motion as it is of rest, and in itself is confined to neither of them. In itself it neither rests nor moves, but merely passes from one state to the other through external impulse, i.e. rest and motion are posited within it by means of another. In so far as it rests, it remains quiescent, and does not, of its own accord, pass over into motion. Similarly, when in motion, it is in fact in motion, and does not pass over of its own accord into rest. Matter is implicitly inert, i.e. it is inert in so far as its Notion is opposed to its reality. Its reality has therefore separated itself and gone into opposition to it, and it is this that first constitutes its sublated reality, or that in which it exists merely as abstraction; it is this abstraction which is always regarded as the implicit nature and essence of matter by those for whom sensuous actuality is what is real, and the form of abstraction constitutes implicitness.

While finite matter is moved from without therefore, free matter moves itself; within its sphere it is therefore infinite, for within the whole, matter belongs to the stage of finitude. The just man is free, although he is bound by the laws which limit the unjust man. In nature each sphere exists not only in its infinitude, but as a finite relationship in itself. Finite relationships such as pressure and impact have the advantage of being known to us through reflection and being drawn from experience. They are defective merely because other relationships are subsumed under a rule constituted in this way. People think that things should happen in heaven as they do at home, but these finite relationships cannot show forth the infinitude of a sphere of nature.

B
Impact

§ 265

When movement which is external to an inert body and therefore finite, sets this body in motion and so relates it to another, the two form the momentary unit of a single body, for they are both masses, and only differ quantitatively. It is thus that both bodies are united by movement through the *imparting of motion*, but as each is to an equal extent presupposed as an immediate unit, they also resist one another. In the relationship between them, their *being-for-self*, which is further particularized by the quantum of mass, constitutes their relative *gravity*. This is *weight* as the gravity of a quantitatively distinct mass; it is extensive as a number of weighted parts, and intensive as a specific pressure (see § 103 Rem.). As the real determinateness, together with velocity, or the ideal nature of the quantitative determinateness of motion, it constitutes a *single* determinability (quantitas motus), within which weight and velocity can reciprocally replace one another (cf. § 261 Rem.).

Addition. The second moment in this sphere consists in matter being set in motion, and finding contact with itself in this movement. Matter is also moved because it is indifferent to place. This is contingent, and all necessity is here posited in the mode of contingency; later we shall see that the movement of matter is also necessary in existence. In impact the two colliding bodies are to be regarded as self-motivating, for they conflict

over a single place. The body which produces the impact assumes the place of the body at rest. The latter, the body which receives the impact, retains its place by also moving itself, and attempting to reassume the place which the other has occupied. It is in the *contact* produced by the
5 collision and pressure of these masses, between which there is no empty space, that the general ideality of matter begins. It is important to see how this internality of matter arises, for it is always important to see how the Notion arrives at existence. Masses create contact by being one for the other, merely because there are two material points or atoms in a single
10 moment of identity, the being-for-self of which is *not* being-for-self. No matter how hard and inflexible one imagines matters to be, it is always possible to postulate an interstice between; as long as they touch one another, they have positedness within a unit, no matter how small one
+ imagines this point to be. This is the higher continuity existing in matter,
15 which is not external and merely spatial, but real. Similarly, the point of time is the unity of the past and the future; for here there are two in one, and in that they are in one, they are also not within it. The precise nature of motion consists in being in one place while at the same time being in another, and yet not being in another, but only in this place.

20 To the extent that they are contained in one, masses also have being-for-self; this constitutes the other moment of repulsion, or the elasticity of matter. The one is merely the surface, and the whole is continuous, because the body is completely *hard*. Since only the whole is one however the one is unposited, and the body simply gives or is absolutely *soft*. By leaving its
+ whole, however, it correspondingly increases the intensity of its oneness. The very softness, the sublation of the body's outwardly exerted force, constitutes the restoration of this force through a return-into-self. The immediate reversion
+ of these two sides is *elasticity*. What is soft also repels; it is elastic, it gives way, but only to a certain extent, and it cannot be driven out of place
30 altogether. It is here that the being-for-self of matter becomes apparent, and it is by means of this being-for-self that matter asserts itself as internality (which may also be called force), against its externality, which is here its-being-for other, i.e. the being-within-it of another. The ideality of being-for-self consists in another asserting a prevalence within the
35 mass, and vice versa. This determination of ideality, which appeared to come from without, shows itself to be the peculiar essence of matter, which at the same time itself belongs to matter's internality; this is the
+ reason why reflective thought makes use of the concept of force in physics.

The strength of an impact, as an amount of activity, is merely that by
40 which matter retains its being-for-self, or resists; for impact is also

resistance; resistance however simply implies matter. That which offers + resistance is material, and conversely, it is material to the extent to which it offers resistance. Resistance implies the motion of two bodies, so that a determinate motion and a determinate resistance are one and the same thing. Bodies act upon one another only in so far as they are independent, + and they are only independent by means of gravity. Therefore, bodies only offer resistance to one another through their gravity. This gravity is relative however, it is not the absolute gravity which expresses the Notion of matter. One of the moments of the body is its weight, by which, in its tendency towards the centre of the Earth, it puts pressure on that 10 which resists it. Pressure is therefore a motion which tends to sublate the separation of one mass from another. The other moment of the body is the transversal movement posited within it, which diverges from the tendency towards the centre. The magnitude of its motion is then determined by these two moments, i.e. by its mass, and the determinability of its trans- 15 versal motion as velocity. If we posit the magnitude of this motion as internal to matter, we have what is called force. We could however dispense with this apparatus of forces, for the propositions of mechanics which deal with them are very largely tautological. As the determinate- + ness of force is the only determinateness, it is certainly true that we have 20 the same material activity whether the number of material parts is replaced by velocity, or vice versa, for material activity only occurs as self-motivating. Yet the real nature of the factor should be only partly, and not wholly replaced by its ideal nature, and vice versa. If the mass is six pounds, and the velocity 4, the force is 24; and the force is the same if 25 eight pounds move at velocity 3 etc. The ὑπομόχλιον carrying the weight, and the length of the arm on one side of it balancing the mass of the load carried on the other, also illustrates this principle. Pressure and + impact are the two causes of external mechanical motion.

§ 266

This weight, concentrated as an intensive amount into one point 30 within a body, is the body's centre of gravity; in that it is weighted, the body has its centre where it posits it however, i.e. outside itself. Consequently, impact and resistance, as well as the motion posited through them, have a substantial foundation in a centre which, while lying outside each particular body, is 35 common to them all. This explains why each contingent motion imposed on them from without, passes into rest in this centre. As +

the centre is outside matter, this rest is at the same time merely a tendency towards the centre, and as the result of the relationship of the particular bodies, and of this tendency towards the centre in the matter which is common to them, they exert pressure on 5 one another. In relationships where bodies are separated from their centre of gravity by relatively empty space, this tendency constitutes fall, i.e. essential motion, in which contingent motion conforms to the Notion and its existence, by passing over into rest.

Remark

10 It is the basic proposition of mechanics, that in external finite motion, a body at rest would continue to rest indefinitely, and a moving body would continue to move indefinitely, if they were + not forced from one condition to the other by an external cause. This proposition merely expresses motion and rest in accordance 15 with the principle of identity (§ 115): it tells us that motion is motion, and that rest is rest and that each determination is external + to the other. It is this abstract separation of motion as it is for itself, from rest as it is for itself, which gives rise to the empty postulate of a perpetual motion, which always involves certain con- + ditions. The nullity of the principle of identity, on which this postulate is based, has been shown in its proper place. As a postulate it has no empirical basis, for even simple impact is conditioned by gravity, i.e. the determination of fall. It is true that in projection there is a contingent motion opposed to the essen- 25 tial motion of fall; the abstraction however, the body considered as body, is inseparable from its gravity, and in a projection therefore, the necessity of taking this gravity into account is self-evident. One cannot have a bodiless projection existing for itself. The example usually given to illustrate motion supposed to 30 be produced by centrifugal force, is that of a stone swung round in a sling, in which there is a constant tendency to fly outwards + (Newton, phil. nat. princ. math. Defin. V). We already know perfectly well that such a direction exists however, it is its existing for itself apart from gravity, and the way in which it is to be 35 presented as a fully independent aspect of force, which has to be established. Newton, in the same place, maintains that a leaden ball, 'in coelos abiret et motu abeundi pergeret in infinitum', if (a useful word here) one could only impart the necessary velocity

to it. This separation of external from essential motion is merely a product of abstractive reflection, and belongs neither to experience nor to the Notion. It is one thing to distinguish these motions, it is in fact necessary to do so, and to consider them mathematically as separate lines, or treat them as distinct quantitative factors etc., it is another thing to regard them as physically independent existences.

In the postulated flight of this leaden ball into infinity, the resistance of air and friction is also turned into an abstraction. When a perpetuum mobile, no matter how correctly calculated and demonstrated in theory, necessarily passes over into rest in a certain period of time, an abstraction is made of gravity, and the phenomenon is attributed solely to friction. The gradual decrease in the motion of the pendulum, and its final cessation, is also attributed to the retardation of friction, as it is also said of this motion that it would continue indefinitely if friction could be removed. This resistance which the body encounters in its contingent motion, belongs of course to the necessary manifestation of its dependence. But just as the body is hindered in its effort to reach the middle of its central body without these impediments sublating its pressure and its gravity, so the resistance produced by friction checks the projectile motion of the body, without its gravity being removed or replaced by friction. Friction is an impediment, but it is not the essential obstacle to external contingent motion. Finite motion must be inseparably bound up with gravity therefore, for in its purely accidental form, it passes over into and becomes subject to the direction of gravity, which is the substantial determination of matter.

Addition. It is here that gravity itself now occurs as the principle of motion, but of motion determined as cancelling this separation or distance from the centre. This is self-generating motion, which posits its own determinateness as a manifestation. Direction is the first determinateness, and the law of fall is the other. *Direction* is the bearing upon the unit, which is sought and presupposed in gravity; it is a tendency which is not a random indeterminate spatial vacillation, but a unit which matter posits for itself as a place in space which is not however reached by it. One cannot say that this centre is present merely as a nucleus to which matter is drawn, or around which it subsequently agglomerates; the gravity of masses generates such a centre, and material points, by seeking one another, posit it as their common centre of gravity. Gravity is the positing of such a unit. Each particular mass is the positing of the same, and by this it seeks a unit in itself, and so gathers the whole of its quantitative relationship to others into a single point. This subjective unit, which as mere tendency constitutes the objective unit, is a body's centre of gravity. Every body has a centre of gravity, by which it has its centre in another body, and it is only in so far as it possesses this centre that the mass constitutes an actual unit or body. The centre of gravity is therefore the primary reality of the unit of gravity, the tendency in which the entire weight of the body is concentrated. A mass cannot be at rest unless its centre of gravity is supported, but if it is supported, the rest of the body might just as well not be there, for its gravity is completely withdrawn into one point. As a line, this point is the *lever*, to which each part of this unit belongs, and in which the centre of gravity divides itself as middle into points of extremity, the continuity of which constitutes the line. Gravity is equally the whole of this unit; the surface constitutes the unit, but the unit is taken back into the centre as a whole. Whatever exhibits itself here as the juxtaposition of dimensions, is in its immediacy a unit. It is in this way that the centre of gravity makes itself into the whole individual body.

Each individual mass is then such a body, which strives towards its centre, i.e. the absolute centre of gravity. In so far as matter determines a centre towards which it strives, and this centre is a point of unity while matter remains a multiplicity, matter is determined as proceeding out if itself and out of its place. By proceeding out of itself, it also proceeds out of its self-externality, and as sublation of externality, this is the first true inwardness. All mass belongs to such a centre, and each particular mass is dependent and contingent as against this truth. It is because of this contingency, that an individual mass can be separated from this central body. In so far as the specific mass which intervenes offers no resistance, the body will not be prevented from moving towards the centre; it will then move on account of there being no impediment, or rather fall on account of there being no support. The rest into which external motion is brought by fall is certainly still a tendency, but unlike the first kind of rest, it is not contingent, nor is it a mere condition, or posited externally. The rest we have now is posited through the Notion, like fall, the motion which is posited through the Notion and sublates external and contingent motion. Here inertia has disappeared, for we have reached the Notion of matter. In that each mass, through its weight, has a tendency towards the centre, and therefore exerts pressure, its motion is only an attempted motion, which makes itself effectual within another mass, and so posits its ideal nature. Similarly, by offering resistance and maintaining itself, this second mass posits the ideal nature of the first. In finite mechanics both kinds of rest and motion are placed on the same level. Everything is reduced to interrelated forces differing only in direction and velocity; consequently the result becomes all-important. Thus, the motion of fall, which is posited by the force of gravity, is placed on the same level as the force of projection. 5

It is imagined that if a cannon-ball were to be shot forth with a force greater than that of gravity, it would escape at a tangent, if, it is added, there were no resistance from the air. It is also thought that the pendulum + would go on swinging indefinitely if the air offered no resistance. 'The pendulum', it is said, 'describes an arc. By falling into the perpendicular, 10 it has acquired a velocity by virtue of which it must reach a height on the other side of the arc equal to that of the point from which it started. It must therefore continue to move from side to side'. On one side the pendulum follows the direction of gravity, and this direction is then sublated; that is to say that it is removed from the direction of gravity by 15 the communication of a new determination. It is this second determination which produces the lateral motion. It is then asserted that, 'It is *primarily* because of resistance, that the arc of oscillation becomes progressively smaller and the pendulum finally comes to rest, for if there were no resistance, the oscillatory motion *itself* would continue indefinitely'. + Gravitational and transversal motion are not however two opposed kinds of movement. The first is the substantial movement, within which the second is contingently absorbed. Friction itself is not contingent however, for it is the result of gravity, although it can also be reduced. Francoeur realized this ('Traité élémentaire de méchanique', p. 175 n. 4–5) when he 25 said, 'Le frottement ne dépend pas de l'étendue des surfaces en contact, le poid du corps restant le même. Le frottement est proportionel à la *pression*'. Friction is therefore gravity in the form of an external resistance; + it is pressure as a mutual drawing towards the centre. In order to counteract the variable motion of the body, it has to be attached to something else. 30 This material connection is necessary, but it disturbs the motion and so gives rise to friction. Friction is therefore a necessary factor in the construction of a pendulum, and can be neither eliminated nor thought away. If one imagines what it would be like without it, one is dealing with an empty concept. It is not only friction which brings the movement of 35 the pendulum to rest however, for even if friction ceased, the pendulum would still come to rest. Gravity is the power which brings the pendulum to rest in conformity with the Notion of matter, for as the universal principle of matter, it maintains its preponderance over what is alien, and oscillation ceases in the line of fall. This necessity of the Notion appears in +

this sphere of externality as an external impediment or as friction. A man can be struck dead, but this external circumstance is contingent; the truth of the matter is that the man himself dies.

The combinations of fall with contingent motion, in projection for example, do not concern us here, where we have to consider the sublation of purely contingent motion. In projection the magnitude of the motion depends upon the force of the projection and the weight of the mass. It is this very weight however, which is at the same time gravity; in that it gains preponderance as the universal, it overcomes the determinateness posited within it. The body is projected only by means of gravity; it passes out of its determinate direction however, although only to return into the universal and become simple fall. This return gives a further determinability to gravity, in which motion comes still closer to its unity with it. In projectile motion weight is only one moment of the motive force, it is the transition by which the force lying outside gravity is posited within it. This transition increases the extent to which gravity constitutes all motive force. The principle of motion is certainly still external to it, but in a completely formal way as mere impulse, which in fall is simple removal. It is in this way that projection constitutes fall, and both of these occur simultaneously in the motion of the pendulum. Gravity is removal-from-self, a presentation of itself as self-sundering, but everything is still external. The fixed point, the removal from the line of fall, the holding at a distance of the motivated point, and the moments of the actual motion, belong to something else. The return from projection into the line of fall is itself projection, and the oscillation of the pendulum is the falling self-producing sublation of projection.

C

Fall

§ 267

Fall is *relatively free* motion: **free, in that it is posited through the Notion of the body and is the** manifestation of the body's own **gravity;** within the body **it is** therefore *immanent.* **At the same time, it is however only the primary negation of externality, and is therefore conditioned. Separation from the connection**

with the centre is therefore still a *contingent* determination, posited *externally*.

Remark

The laws of the motion are concerned with *quantity*, and in particular with distances traversed in periods of time, and the highest credit accrues to the analysis of the understanding by reason of the immortal discoveries it has made in this field. The further non-empirical *proof* of these laws has been provided by mathematical mechanics however, for even science which bases itself upon empiricism discovers the inadequacy of the purely empirical mode of demonstration. In the a priori proof in question, it is assumed that velocity is *uniformly* accelerated. However, the proof consists in the transformation of the *moments* of the *mathematical* formula into *physical* forces, i.e. into an *accelerative* force which produces a uniform impulse in each moment of time, and a force of *inertia*, which is regarded as maintaining the increased velocity acquired in each moment of time. These determinations are completely lacking in empirical confirmation, and are in no way in conformity with the Notion. Consequently, the quantitative determination, which here contains a *potency* relationship, is formed into a *sum* of two mutually independent elements, so that the qualitative determination, which is connected with the Notion, is eliminated. One of the *corollaries* drawn from the law supposed to have been proved in this way is, 'That in uniformly accelerated motion, the velocities are proportional to the times.' In fact this proposition is nothing more than the completely straightforward definition of uniformly accelerated motion. In simply uniform motion the spaces traversed are proportional to the times elapsed; in *accelerated* motion, *velocity* increases in each successive unit of time; consequently, in *uniformly* accelerated motion, the velocities are proportional to the times elapsed; hence $\frac{V}{t}$, i.e. $\frac{s}{t^2}$. This is the simple, genuine proof. V is the *general* velocity, which is as yet *indeterminate*, and so *at the same time abstract*, i.e. simply uniform. The difficulty of the proof consists in V being considered at first as an indeterminate velocity, and yet presenting itself in the mathematical expression as $\frac{s}{t}$, i.e. as purely uniform. The roundabout procedure of the proof

borrowed from the mathematical exposition, makes it possible to accept velocity as simply uniform $\frac{s}{t}$, and to pass over from there to $\frac{s}{t^2}$. In the proposition that the velocity is proportional to times, it is primarily velocity in general that is referred to, so that it is superfluous to represent it mathematically as $\frac{s}{t}$, to posit it as simply uniform, to introduce the force of inertia, and then to attribute to it this moment of purely uniform velocity. If velocity is to be proportional to times, it must be as uniformly accelerated velocity, $\frac{s}{t^2}$. Consequently, the determination $\frac{s}{t}$ has no place here, and is excluded.

As against the abstract uniform velocity of lifeless and externally determined mechanism, the law of *fall* is a *free* law of nature, i.e. it has a side to it which determines itself from the *Notion* of the body. Since it follows from this that the law must be deducible from this Notion, it has to be shown how Galileo's law, 'That the spaces traversed are as the *squares* of the times elapsed', accords with the determination of the Notion.

The connection here lies simply in this, that since the Notion is here the determinant of motion, time and space, as Notional determinations, become free with regard to one another, i.e. their *quantitative determinations* conform to their Notional determinations. Now since *time* is the moment of *negation*, of being-for-self, and the principle of the unit, its magnitude (any empirical number) in relationship to space is to be considered as *the unit* or denominator. *Space* on the contrary is *juxtaposition*, the extent of which is determined *only* by the extent of time, for in the velocity of this *free* motion, space and time are not mutually *external* and contingent, but constitute a *single* determination. The form of the extrinsicality of space, which is opposed to unity as the form of time, and which is unmixed with any other determinateness, is the *square*; it is quantity *coming out of itself*, positing itself in a second dimension, and so augmenting itself, although *only* in accordance with its *own* determinability. This self-extension sets its own self as limit, so that by becoming an other, it merely relates itself to itself.

Here the proof of the law of fall is drawn from the *Notion* of

the matter. The potency relationship is essentially qualitative, and is the only relationship which belongs to the Notion. It should be added in connection with what follows, that since fall, in its freedom, still contains conditionality, time remains an immediate number, a merely abstract unit, and the quantitative determination of space only attains to the second dimension.

Addition. The tendency towards the centre is the only absolute factor in fall; we shall see later how the other moment, which is diremption, difference, the removal of the body into a state of supportlessness, also derives from the Notion. In fall mass does not separate itself of its own accord, but when it is separated, it returns into the unity. The motion which produces itself in fall constitutes the transition therefore, it is a middle term between inert matter, and matter in which its Notion finds absolute realization, i.e. absolutely free motion. As merely quantitative indifferent difference, mass is a factor in external motion, but here, where motion is posited through the Notion of matter, purely quantitative difference between masses has, as such, no significance, for masses fall not as masses but as matters in general. In fall it is in fact merely the weightedness of bodies which comes under consideration, and a large body is as heavy as a smaller one, i.e. one of less weight. We know well enough, that a feather does not fall like a plummet, but this is the result of the medium which has to give way, i.e. masses behave in accordance with the qualitative difference of the resistance they encounter. A stone falls faster in air than it does in water for example, but in airless space bodies fall in the same way. Galileo put forward this proposition, and expounded it to certain monks. Only one of the fathers got a slant on it when he said that a pair of scissors and a knife would reach the earth at the same time; but the matter cannot be decided so easily. Knowledge of this kind is worth more than thousands upon thousands of so-called brilliant thoughts.

The empirical extent of the fall of a body is a little over 15 feet per second, although there is a slight variation at different latitudes. If a body falls for two seconds, it covers not double, but four times the distance, i.e. 60 feet; in three seconds 9×15 feet, and so on. If one body falls for three seconds and another for 9, the spaces traversed are related not in the ratio of 3:9, but of 9:81. Purely uniform motion is ordinary mechanical movement; motion which is not uniformly accelerated is capricious; uniformly accelerated motion is that in which the law of living natural movement begins to appear. Velocity increases with time therefore, i.e.

$t = \frac{s}{t}$, i.e. $s = t^2$, for $s = t^2$ is the same as $\frac{s}{t^2}$. In mechanics this is proved mathematically by representing the so-called force of inertia by a square, and the so-called accelerative force by the addition of a triangle. This is an interesting procedure, and may well be necessary for mathematical exposition; but this is its only use, and it is a forced representation. Proofs of this kind always assume what has to be proved, so they certainly describe what happens. Mathematical imagination arises out of the need for a transformation of the potency relationship into a more manageable form, e.g. by reducing it to addition, or subtraction and multiplication. It is because of this that the motion which occurs in fall is analysed into two parts. The division has no reality however, and is an empty fiction which merely serves the convenience of mathematical exposition.

§ 268

Fall is merely the abstract positing of a single *centre*, in the unity of which the difference between particular masses and bodies posits itself as sublated; consequently, mass or weight plays no part in the magnitude of this motion. As this *negative* relation to self, the simple being-for-self of the centre is essentially a *repulsion* of itself however. It is *formal* repulsion into many immobile centres (*stars*), and *living* repulsion in that it determines these centres according to *the moments of the Notion* and so establishes an essential relation within their Notional differentiation. This relation is the *contradiction* of their independent being-for-self, and their connectedness with the Notion; the appearance of this contradiction between the reality and ideality of these centres is motion, and indeed *absolutely free motion*.

Addition. The deficiency in the law of fall is the result of our regarding space as posited here in a simply abstract manner in its first power as line; this happens because the motion of fall is conditioned as well as being free (see prec. §). Because its condition of being removed from the centre is still contingent and not determined by gravity itself, fall is merely the primary manifestation of gravity. This contingency has still to fall away. The Notion must become wholly immanent within matter. This takes places in the third main section, in absolute mechanics, where matter is completely free, and where its determinate being is completely adequate to its Notion. Inert matter is wholly inadequate to its Notion. Weighted matter, in so far as it falls, is only partly adequate to its Notion through the sublation of plurality as the tendency of matter towards one central place. The other moment, which is the differentiation of the place within itself, is not yet posited by the Notion however; that is to say that the self-repulsion of attracted matter as weightedness is lacking as yet, and that diremption into many bodies is not yet the act of gravity itself. Matter of this kind, which is extended as a plurality and at the same time continuous within itself, and which contains the centre, must be repelled. This is real repulsion, in which the centre is formed out of self-repulsion and diversification, and a plurality of masses is consequently posited, each having its centre. The logical unit is this infinite relation with itself, which is identity with itself, but as self-relating negativity, and consequently as repulsion from itself. This is the other moment contained within the Notion. The self-positing of matter within the determinations of its moments is necessary to material reality. Fall posits matter onesidedly as attraction; it must now also appear as repulsion. Formal repulsion also has a place here, for it is a property of nature to allow an abstract and particular moment to subsist in itself. The stars are the bodies in which formal repulsion finds existence, for as bodies they are as yet simply multiple and exhibit no difference; here, they are not yet to be regarded as luminous, for this is a physical determination.

We could regard the relations between stars as being rational; but they belong to dead repulsion. Their *figurations* could be the expression of essential relations, but they do not belong to living matter, where the centre differentiates itself within itself. The host of stars is a formal world, because only this onesided determination is able to hold sway there. As a system it should not be put on a level with the solar system, which for us is the primary knowable system of real rationality within the heavens. The stars may be admired for their repose, but in worth they are not to be regarded as the equals of the concrete individual body. The content of space explodes into an infinite number of matters; this can delight the eye, but it is only the first breaking forth of matter, and this eruption of light is as unworthy of wonder as an eruption on the skin or a swarm of flies. The tranquillity of these stars means more to the heart, for the contemplation of their peace and simplicity calms the passions. Their world is not so interesting from the philosophical point of view as it is to the sentiments however. As a plurality within immeasurable spaces it is of no significance to reason; it is externality, emptiness, negative infinity. Reason knows itself to be above this, for the wonder is merely negative,

\+ an uplifting of the mind which remains strictly limited. The rationality of the stars is to be grasped in the figurations in which they are reciprocally disposed. The eruption of space into abstract matter proceeds according to an inner law, so that the stars present crystalline effects which could 5 have an inner connection, although interest in these matters can be no more than an empty curiosity. Little can be said about the necessity of these figurations. Herschel has noted forms in nebulae indicative of + regularity. The spaces are emptier as the distances from the Milky Way increase, and from this it has been concluded (Herschel and Kant), that 10 the stars form the figure of a lens; but this is something wholly indeter- + minate and general. It must not be thought that the worth of science depends upon its ability to grasp and explain all multifarious shapes. One must be content with the fact of that which has already come within one's grasp. There is still much that cannot be grasped, and this has to be ad- 15 mitted in the philosophy of nature. At present, rational interest in the + stars must confine itself solely to stellar geometry. The stars constitute the field of this abstract and infinite diremption, in which contingency has an essential influence upon the disposition of the parts.

CHAPTER THREE

Absolute mechanics
(*Astronomy*)

§ 269

Gravitation is the true and determinate Notion of material corporeality **realized as the Idea. Universal corporeality divides itself** essentially into *particular* bodies, **and links itself together in the moment of** *individuality* **or subjectivity, as determinate being appearing** in *motion*; this, in its immediacy, is thus a **system** of *many bodies*.

Remark

Universal gravitation must be recognized as a profound thought in its own right. **It has already attracted** attention and inspired confidence, particularly through the quantitative determination bound up within it, and its verification **has been pursued** from the *experience* of the solar system down to that of the phenomenon of the miniature capillary tube. **When it is** seized upon **in this way** in the sphere of reflection **however, it has a merely general abstract significance, which in its more concrete form is merely gravity in the quantitative determination of fall, and it therefore lacks the significance of the Idea developed into its reality, which is given to it in this paragraph.** Gravitation is the **immediate** contradiction of the law of inertia, and it is because of this that matter strives *out of itself* towards another.

As has already been shown, the *Notion* of *gravity* contains not only the moments of being-for-self, but also that of the continuity which sublates being-for-self. These moments of the Notion suffer the fate of being grasped as distinct forces corresponding to the forces of attraction and repulsion. They are defined more closely as the *centripetal* and *centrifugal* forces which, being mutually independent and brought to bear upon one another contingently in the body as a third element, are supposed to *work upon bodies* as + gravity does. Whatever profundity there might be in the 5 thought of **universal** gravity is annulled by this, and as long as this vaunted purveying of *forces* prevails, the Notion and reason can never penetrate into the science of absolute motion. In the syllogism which contains the *Idea* of gravity, this Idea is the Notion disclosing itself **in external reality in** 10 **the particularity of bodies, and at the same time, in the ideality and intro-reflection of these bodies, displaying its integration into itself in motion.** This contains the rational identity and inseparability of the moments **which are otherwise taken to be independent. In general, motion as such** only has signifi- 15 cance **and existence** where there is a system of *several* bodies, which are variously *determined*, and so stand in a certain relationship to one another. **The closer determination of this syllogism of totality, which is in itself a system of three syllo-** + **gisms, is given in the Notion of objectivity** (**see** § 198).

20 *Addition.* Primarily, the solar system is a number of independent bodies, which maintain themselves in this relation, and posit an external unity within another. Difference is posited therefore, and plurality is no longer indeterminate as with the stars, so that determinateness consists of absolutely universal and particular centrality. The forms of motion in which 25 the Notion of matter is achieved follow from these two determinations. The body which constitutes the relative centre is in itself the universal determinability of place, and it is into this that motion falls; but at the same time, place itself is also not determined in so far as it has its centre in another, and this indeterminateness has to find its determinate being, 30 for place determined in and for itself is a mere unit. The particular central bodies are consequently indifferent to particularity of place; this appears in the search for their centre, in which they leave their place and transport themselves to another. The third determination is that they could all be simultaneously equidistant from their centre, and that if they were, they 35 would then no longer be separated from one another. If they then moved in the same orbit, there would be no difference between them; they would be one and the same, each the mere repetition of the other, and their variety would then be purely nominal. The fourth determination is that by changing their place at different distances from one another, they

return to themselves by means of a curve, for it is only in this way that they assert their independence of the central body. Similarly, by moving around the centre in the same curve, they express their unity with it. It is because of their independence of the central body that they keep their place, and do not fall further into it.

There are therefore three movements present here; (1) mechanical motion communicated from without, which is uniform; (2) the motion of fall, which is partly conditioned and partly free, and in which the separation of a body from its gravity is still posited as contingent, although the motion already belongs to gravity itself; (3) unconditioned free motion, the main moments of which we have presented as the great mechanism of the heavens. This motion is a curve, in which the particular bodies posit the central body, which simultaneously posits them. The centre has no significance without the periphery, nor has the periphery a significance without the centre. This disposes of the physical hypotheses which proceed indiscriminately from the centre or from the particular bodies, positing first one and then the other as original. Each aspect is necessary, but is onesided when taken alone. The diremption into different terms and the positing of subjectivity is a single act, a free motion, which unlike pressure and impact, is not external. It is said that the distinct reality of the force of attraction may be seen and demonstrated in gravity. In that it brings about fall, gravity undoubtedly constitutes the Notion of matter, but it does so abstractly, and is not yet self-diremptory. Fall is an incomplete manifestation of gravity, and is therefore not real. The centrifugal force through which a body has the tendency to fly off at a tangent, is supposed, foolishly enough, to impart an impact to the celestial bodies by a swinging side-blow, to which they have evidently always been susceptible. The contingency of externally administered motion of this kind belongs to inert matter; it appears for example when a stone is attached to a string, and swung round so that it tends to fly off. We should not speak of forces therefore, but if we do so, we should remember that there is one force, and that its moments do not pull in different directions as two forces. The movement of the heavenly bodies is not a pulling hither and thither, but free motion; as the ancients said, they go their ways like the blessed gods. The corporeality of the heavens is not of a kind to have the principle of rest or of motion external to it. 'As the stone is inert, and the whole earth is composed of stones, the other heavenly bodies are precisely the same'. This syllogism puts the properties of the whole on the same level as those of the part, but impact, pressure, resistance, friction, attraction, and the like, are only valid in their application to an existence of matter distinct from that of heavenly cor-

\+ poreality. Matter is certainly common to them both, just as a good thought and a bad thought are both thoughts; but the bad is not good because the good is also a thought.

§ 270

In bodies in which **the full** freedom **of the Notion** of gravity 5 is realized, the determinations of their distinctive nature are contained as the moments of their Notion. Thus, one of the moments is the *universal* centre **of abstract relation to self.** Opposed to this extreme **is immediate** *singularity*, which is self-external and centreless, **and which also appears as an** 10 **independent corporeality.** The *particular* bodies are however + those which simultaneously stand **as much** in the determination of self-externality, as they do in that of being-in-self; they are in themselves centres and find their essential unity through relating themselves to the universal centre.

Remark

15 **As that which is immediately concrete, the planetary bodies are the most perfect form of their existence. The sun is usually regarded as the most important, for the understanding tends to prefer what is abstract to what is concrete; it is for the same reason that the fixed stars are more highly regarded than the bodies of the** 20 **solar system. Lunar and cometary bodies are the opposites into which centreless corporeality divides itself in so far as it belongs to externality.**

It is well known that the immortal honour of having discovered the laws of absolutely free motion belongs to + *Kepler*. *Kepler proved* them in that he discovered the *univer-* + *sal* expression of the empirical data (§ 227). It has subsequently become customary to speak as if *Newton* were the + first to have discovered the proof of these laws. The credit for a discovery has seldom been denied a man with more 30 unjustness. **In this connection I have the following observations to make:**

(1) **Mathematicians will admit** that Newton's formulae may be deduced from Kepler's laws. **The simply immediate derivation**

is straightforward enough. In Kepler's third law $\frac{A^3}{T^2}$ is the constant. If this is expressed as $\frac{A.A^2}{T^2}$, and Newton's definition of $\frac{A}{T^2}$ as universal gravity is accepted, one has an expression of this so-called gravity as working in inverse proportion to the squares of the distances. +

(2) Newton's proof of the proposition that 'a body subject to the law of gravitation moves in an *ellipse* about a centre' simply gives rise to a *conic section*, whereas the main proposition to be proved consists precisely in the fact that the course of such a body is *neither* a *circle nor a conic section*, 10 but *simply* the *ellipse*. **This Newtonian proof. (Princ. Math. bk. I sect. II prop. 1) needs further careful qualification; and although it is the basis of the Newtonian theory, analysis no longer uses it. In the analytical formula,** the conditions which make the path of the body a *specific* conic section **are constants; and their deter-** 15 **mination** is made to depend upon an *empirical* circumstance, i.e. a particular position of the body at a certain point of time, and the *fortuitous* strength of the original *impulse* it is supposed to have received. **In this way the circumstance which determines the curved line into an ellipse falls outside the formula** 20 **which is supposed to be proved, and the attempt to prove it is never made.** +

(3) The Newtonian law of the so-called force of gravity is also merely demonstrated from experience by means of induction. +

The only difference to be seen here is, that what Kepler expressed in a simple and sublime manner as *constituting* the *laws of celestial motion*, is changed by Newton into the *reflectional form* of the *force of gravity*, **and into the form of this force as it yields the law of its magnitude in the motion of fall. For the** 30 **analytical method, the Newtonian form is not only convenient, but necessary; this is merely the difference of a mathematical formula however, and for some time now analysis has known how to deduce the Newtonian formulation and its dependent propositions from the form of Kepler's laws. On this point I concur with** 35 **the accomplished exposition in Francoeur's, 'Traité élém. de Mécanique' Bk. II ch. II n. IV.** Taken as a whole, the **old-fashioned** + attempt at what is called a proof, presents a confused web, and entails the *lines* of a simply geometrical construction, given the physical significance of *independent forces*, and empty reflectional determinations involving the *accelerating force* and the *force of inertia* already mentioned, and particularly the relationship of what is called gravity itself to centripetal and centrifugal forces etc.

The remarks made here need a far more extensive treatment than can be given them in a compendium such as this. Propositions not in accordance with accepted opinions look like mere assertions, and when they contradict sober authorities, seem to be presumptuous, which is even worse. It is however simple facts rather than propositions which have been adduced here. The import of this reflection is merely this, that the distinctions and determinations employed by mathematical analysis, and the course to which its methods commit it, should be sharply distinguished from whatever is supposed to have a physical reality. It is not the assumptions, procedure and results which analysis requires and affords which are questioned here, but the physical worth and the physical significance of its determinations and procedure. It is here that attention should be concentrated, in order to explain why physical mechanics has been flooded by a monstrous metaphysic, which, contrary to both experience and the Notion, has its sole source in these mathematical determinations.

It is recognized that the significant moment added by Newton to the content of Kepler's laws—apart from the basis of the analytical treatment, the development of which has moreover rendered superfluous and even led to the rejection of much that belonged to Newton's essential principles and contributed to his fame—is the principle of perturbation. In so far as it rests upon the proposition that what is called attraction consists of an action between all the individual material parts of a body, the importance of this principle has to be adduced here, and is to be found in the fact that matter in general posits its centre. It follows that the mass of a particular body is to be regarded as a moment in the determination of the place which occupies the centre, and that all the bodies of a system posit their sun. The individual bodies themselves also give rise to each relative position which they assume with regard to one another in the general movement however: this is the momentary relation of gravity between them, through which they not only possess the abstract relationship of distance, but posit a particular centre amongst themselves. This centre is partly resolved again in the universal system however, and if it persists, as it does in the mutual perturbations of Jupiter and Saturn, it remains at least partly subordinate to it. +

The connection between the main determinations of free motion and the Notion has only been outlined, and as it is not possible here to develop it any further, it must be left to its fate. The principle of the matter is that the rational demonstration of the quantitative determinations of free motion can rest solely upon the Notional determinations of space and time, for these moments, in their intrinsic relationship, constitute motion. When will science reach an awareness of the metaphysical categories which it employs, and instead of taking these as basic, found itself upon the Notion of the fact in hand!

The Notion in general affects the primary form of returning into itself through a curve; this is due to the general particularity and individuality of bodies (§ 269), which have a semi-independent existence, with their centre partly in themselves, and partly in another. It is these Notional determinations which give rise to the postulation of centripetal and centrifugal forces, and which are distorted by being regarding as distinct and independent, as existing outside one another and influencing independently, and as only meeting contingently and externally in their effects. As has already been observed, these are the lines which should be reserved to mathematical determination, but which have been transformed into physical actualities.

Further, this motion is uniformly accelerated, and as it returns into itself, it is in turn uniformly retarded. In free motion, space and time occur in accordance with what they are by differentiating themselves and entering into the quantitative determination of motion (§ 267 Remark), so that they are not related as they are in abstract simply-uniform velocity. It is in the so-called explanation of uniformly accelerated and retarded motion by means of an alternating decrease and increase in the magnitude of the centripetal and centrifugal forces, that the confusion caused by the postulation of such independent forces is greatest. According to this explanation, the centrifugal force is less than the centripetal force in the movement of a planet from aphelion to perihelion; at perihelion itself however, the centrifugal force suddenly becomes greater than the centripetal force, and in the movement from perihelion to aphelion, the forces are supposed to work in the inverse relation. It is clear that it is not in accordance with the nature of forces that the preponderance acquired by one over the other should *suddenly switch* like this into subordinacy. On the contrary, it ought to be concluded that a preponderance acquired by one force over another should not only maintain itself, but lead to the complete annihilation of the other, so that motion must either pass over into rest through the preponderance of the centripetal force, and the planet crash into the central body, or pass into a straight line through the preponderance of the centrifugal force. The conclusion drawn from this is simply that it is because the body draws away from the sun after passing perihelion that the centrifugal force increases again, and that as it is furthest from the sun at aphelion, it is just there that this force is greatest. In this metaphysical chimera, two opposed and independent forces are assumed, and no further investigation of these fictions of the understanding is thought to be necessary. No enquiry is made into how an independent force of this kind is able, *of its own accord*, to make itself subordinate to the other, and then to make itself predominate, to get the other force to allow this, and to follow this up by cancelling this predominance again, or allowing it to be cancelled. If this inwardly groundless augmentation and diminution is examined more closely, points are found midway between the apsides, in which the forces are in *equilibrium*. The supposed movement of these two forces out of this equilibrium is just as unmotivated as this sudden reversal of their preponderance. It is easy enough to see how this method of explanation, in remedying a fault by means of a further determination, gives rise to further and more bewildering confusions.

A similar confusion arises from the explanation of the fact that the oscillation of the pendulum appears to be slower at the equator. This phenomenon is also attributed to a supposedly greater centrifugal force, but it could be ascribed with equal facility to an increase in the force of gravity holding the pendulum more firmly in the perpendicular, or line of rest.

In so far as it enters into the *shape of the orbit*, the *circle* is only to be grasped as the orbit of a *simply uniform* motion. It is certainly *conceivable* as it is said, that a uniformly *increasing* and *decreasing* motion should take place in a circle. This conceivability, or possibility, is only an abstract representability however, and as it leaves out the determinate situation to which it applies, it is not only superficial, but wrong. The circle is the line returning into itself; all its radii are equal, and it is therefore fully determined through its radius; this is merely a unit, and the unit constitutes 5 the whole determinateness. In free motion however, where various spatial and temporal determinations occur in qualitative relationship with one another, the relationship necessarily occurs as a spatial differentiation, which therefore requires two determinations. Consequently the form of the path returning into 10 itself is essentially an ellipse, which is the first of Kepler's laws. +

The abstract determinability which constitutes the circle, also appears in the arc or angle being independent of the two radii by which it is enclosed, and to which it is a purely empirical measure. In motion determined by the Notion however, the 15 distance from the centre, and the arc described in a certain time, must be contained in a single determinability, and constitute a single whole, for the moments of the Notion are not related contingently. It is this that gives rise to the sector, which is a two-dimensional spatial determination. The arc is therefore the 20 essential function of the radius vector, and by its variation in equal periods of time, it carries the inequality of the radii with it. That the spatial determination should appear here, by means of time, as the two-dimensional determination of a plane, is connected with what was said above (§ 267) about the exposition of the same 25 determinateness in fall: now in the root as time, and again in the square as space. Here however the quadraticity of space is confined to the sector by the return of the line of motion into itself. It will be apparent that the second of Kepler's laws, which is concerned with the sweeping out of equal sectors in equal 30 periods of time, rests upon these general principles. +

This law only touches the relation between the arc and the radius vector, and within it time is an abstract unity; as time is the unity which determines the various sectors, they are all equal. The further relationship is however that between time and the extent 35 of the orbit, or, for it comes to the same thing, the distance from the centre. Here time is not an abstract unity but the general quantum of time taken to complete the orbit. We have seen that in fall, which is an imperfectly free motion determined partly in accordance with the Notion, and partly from without, time and 40

space are related to one another as root and square. In absolute motion however, which is the realm of *free* measures, each determinateness attains its totality. As root, time is a purely empirical quantity, and in that it is qualitative, it is merely abstract unity. As a *moment* of the developed totality however, it is at the same time a determined unity, a totality for itself, which produces itself, and so relates *itself to itself*. It is however internally dimensionless, and only reaches a formal identity with itself by producing itself as the *square*. Space on the other hand, as positive extrinsicality, attains the dimension of the Notion in *the cube*. It is in this way that their realization simultaneously contains their original difference. This is the third of Kepler's laws, which is concerned with the relation between the *cubes of the distances, and the squares* of the times. The greatness of this law consists in its presentation of the *rationality of the matter* with such simplicity and immediacy. In the Newtonian formula however, it is transformed into a law applied to the *force* of gravity, and so shows how *reflection* which fails to get to the bottom of things can distort and pervert the truth.

Addition. It is here in the mechanical sphere that genuine laws make their appearance, for a law is the linking of two simple determinations so that only their simple relation to one another constitutes the whole relationship, although there must be the appearance of mutual freedom between them. In magnetism however, the inseparability of the two determinations is already posited, so we do not call it a law. In higher shapes, the determinations are linked in the individualization of the third term, so that we no longer have the direct determinations of two interrelated terms. It is only in spirit, where there is a mutual confrontation of independent entities, that laws occur again. Now the laws of this motion concern the two aspects of the form of its path, and its velocity. These have to be developed out of the Notion, but this would demand an extensive investigation, and because of the difficulty of the task, it has not yet been fully accomplished.

Kepler discovered his laws empirically, by working inductively with the observations of *Tycho Brahe*; to discover the universal law governing these fragmentary phenomena is a work of genius in this field.

(1) Copernicus still regarded the orbit as circular and the motion as eccentric. Equal arcs are not described in equal times however, and as it

is contrary to the nature of the circle, motion of this kind cannot take place within it. The circle is the curve of the understanding, and posits equality. Circular motion can only be uniform, for equal arcs can only correspond to equal radii. There is no general agreement upon this point, but if it is considered more closely, the opposite is found to be an empty assertion. The circle has only one constant, while other curves of the second order have two constants, the major and the minor axis. If different arcs are described in the same time, then they must be different not only empirically but in their function, i.e. it is in their function itself that the difference must lie. In the circle, these arcs would in fact only be distinguished from another empirically. The radius is essential to the function of an arc in that it is the relation of that which is peripheral to the centre. If the arcs are different, the radii must also differ, and the Notion of the circle be immediately transcended. Consequently, the assumption of acceleration necessarily implies a variation in the radii, for arc and radius are inseparably connected. The path must therefore be elliptical, for its complete motion is a revolution. We know from observation that the ellipse does not correspond completely to the course of the planets, and other perturbations are therefore to be assumed. It is for subsequent astronomy to decide whether or not the path of the orbit has profounder functions than the ellipse, it may perhaps be the oval line etc.

(2) Here the determinability of the arc lies in the radii by which it is intersected; these three lines together form a triangle, which is a single determinate whole, of which they are the moments. Similarly, the radius is a function of the arc, and of the other radius. It should not be forgotten that the determinateness of the whole as an empirical quantity, and a distinct determinability which may be brought into external comparisons, lies in this triangle, and not in the arc as such. The empirical determinability of the complete curve, of which the arc is a certain part, lies in the relation of its axes; the other determinateness lies in the law governing the variation of the vectors; and so far as the arc is a part of the whole, its determinability, like that of the triangle, lies in that which constitutes the general determinability of the whole path. A line can only be subsumed under a necessary determinateness if it is a moment of a whole. The extent of the line is a merely empirical element, the whole first appears in the triangle. This is the origin of the mathematical conception of the parallelogram of forces in finite mechanics, in which the space traversed is presented as the diagonal, which is therefore posited as part of a whole or function, and so susceptible to mathematical treatment. Centripetal force is the radius, centrifugal force the tangent, and the arc is the diagonal of

the tangent and the radius. These are only mathematical lines however; separate the whole from physical reality, and it becomes an empty representation. In the abstract motion of fall, the squares, that is to say the plane involved in the time factor, are only numerical determinations. The 5 square is not to be taken in a spatial sense, because in fall only a straight line is traversed. It is this which constitutes the formal element in fall, and when the space traversed in fall is also represented as a plane expressing a quadratic spatial relationship, this is therefore a merely formal construction. However, as the time which sublates itself here corresponds to a 10 plane, it is here that the self-production of time attains reality. The sector is a plane produced by the arc and the radius vector. The two determinations of the sector are the space transversed, and the distance from the centre. The radii drawn from the focus in which the central body is situated are not all the same. If two sectors are equal, the one with the 15 longer radii will have the smaller arc. Both sectors should be traversed in the same time, consequently, in the sector with the longer radii, both the distance travelled and the velocity will be less. The arc or the distance travelled is here no longer an immediate term, but by its relation to the radius, which is not yet present in fall, it is reduced to a moment, and 20 therefore to the factor of a product. Yet the spatiality determined through time here forms two determinations of the path itself, i.e. the space traversed, and the distance from the centre. The time taken determines the whole, of which the arc is only a moment. It is because of this that equal sectors correspond to equal times; the sector is determined by time, 25 so that the space traversed is reduced to a moment. The situation here corresponds to that in leverage, in which the load and the distance from the fulcrum are the two moments of equilibrium.

(3) Kepler searched for the law that the cubes of the mean distances of the various planets are as the square of the times of their revolutions, for 30 27 years. He had been on the brink of discovering it earlier, but an error in calculation had prevented him from doing so. It was his unshakeable + belief in the inherent rationality of the facts that led him to his discovery. Previous consideration has made it seem likely that time has a dimension + less than space. Since space and time are bound together here, each is 35 posited in its singularity, and their quantitative determinability is determined by their quality.

These laws are some of the finest, purest, and least contaminated with heterogeneous matter that we have in the natural sciences. It is therefore of the greatest interest to reach an understanding of them. These Keplerian 40 laws are presented in their purest and clearest form. According to the

Newtonian form of the law, gravity governs motion, and its force works in inverse proportion to the square of the distances. The honour of having discovered the law of universal gravitation has been attributed to Newton, who, by catching the popular imagination, has won the greatest applause, and obscured the glory of Kepler. The Germans have often looked on impassively while the English have assumed authority in this way. Voltaire furthered the acceptance of the Newtonian theory among the French, and then the Germans also followed along. The merit of Newton's form is of course that it has many advantages in mathematical treatment. It is often envy which motivates the debunking of great men, but on the other hand, it is a kind of superstition to regard their accomplishments as unsurpassable.

The mathematicians themselves have been unjust to Newton in so far as they have regarded gravity in two different ways. In the first instance it is simply the direction in which a stone falls at 15 feet a second on the surface of the earth, and as such it is a purely empirical determination. The law of fall is ascribed principally to gravity, but as the moon also has the earth as its centre, Newton applied it to lunar motion, so that the quantity of 15 feet is also taken as basic to the orbit of the moon. The distance of the moon from the earth is sixty times the earth's diameter, and this fact is therefore used to determine the moment of attraction in lunar motion. It is then found that the earth's power of attraction over the moon (the sinus versus, the sagitta) also determines the entire lunar orbit, and that the moon falls. This may very well work out in this way, but it remains a particular case, in which the empirical extent of fall on the surface of the earth is merely extended to the moon. It is not meant to apply to the planets, or would only be valid in the relationship between them and their satellites. It is therefore a limited principle. Fall is said to apply to the heavenly bodies. These bodies do not fall into the sun however, and in order to counteract fall, yet another motion is attributed to them. This is accomplished easily enough. Boys do the same thing when they whip the side of a top to keep it from toppling over. Such a puerile attitude towards the free motion of the planets is not to be tolerated however. Universal gravitation is therefore only the second meaning of gravity, and Newton saw in gravity the law of all motion; he therefore transferred gravity to the law governing the celestial bodies, and called it the law of gravity. It is this generalization of the law of gravity which constitutes the merit of Newton's work. We are aware of it when we watch the movement of a falling stone, and the fall of an apple from a tree is said to have motivated Newton into making this generalization.

According to the law of fall, the body moves towards its centre of gravity, and heavenly bodies have a tendency towards the sun; their direction is posited jointly by this and their tangential tendency, the result being this diagonal direction.

It seems therefore as though we have found a law here, and that it has as its moments: (1) the law of gravity as attractive force, and (2) the law of tangential force. If we examine the law of planetary revolution however, we shall discover only one law of gravity, for although the centripetal force is supposed to constitute only one of the moments, the centrifugal force is a superfluous element, and therefore disappears completely. Consequently, the construction of motion out of these forces shows itself to be futile. The law of one of these moments, i.e. that which is attributed to attractive force, is not the law of this force alone, but shows itself to be the law of the entire motion, the other moment becoming an empirical coefficient. Nothing more is heard of centrifugal force. Elsewhere these two forces are readily allowed to separate. Centrifugal force is said to be an impulse received by bodies in accordance with their direction and magnitude. Such an empirical quantity can no more constitute the moment of a law than can the 15 feet. If one wants to determine the laws of centrifugal force as they are in themselves, contradictions will present themselves, as is always the case with opposites of this kind. Sometimes they are credited with the same laws as centripetal force, and sometimes with others. The greatest confusion arises however if one attempts to separate the action of these two forces when they are no longer in equilibrium, but one is greater than the other, and one is supposed to be increasing while the other diminishes. The centrifugal force is said to be at its maximum in aphelion, and the centripetal force in perihelion. One could just as well assert the opposite however. If the attractive force of the planet is greatest when it is closest to the sun, it is precisely at this point that the centrifugal force ought also to be at its maximum, in order to prevail as the distance from the sun begins to increase again. If one assumes a gradual increase in the force in question instead of a sudden switchover, one has to assume an even greater increase in the other force, so that the opposition admitted for the purpose of explanation, breaks down. In some expositions the increase in one is taken to be different from the increase in the other, but the result is the same. This switching around, in which each is always supposed to be prevailing over the other, merely leads to confusion. It is the same in medicine, when irritability and sensibility are regarded as in inverse ratio to one another. This form of reflection ought to be dispensed with completely.

Experience shows that because the pendulum swings slower at the equator than at higher latitudes, it has to be shortened there in order to increase the rapidity of its oscillations. This is supposed to be evidence of a more powerful centrifugal force at the equator, for in the same time a point at the equator will describe a greater circle than the pole, 5 and it is supposed to be the resultant increase in centrifugal force which counteracts the pendulum's force of gravity, or tendency to fall. The opposite might be asserted with equal plausibility and rather more truth. Slower oscillation means that the direction of the vertical, or the line of the rest, is stronger; here therefore motion in general is weakened; the 10 motion is deviation from the direction of gravity; consequently, the truth of the matter is that gravity is augmented. This is the outcome of such oppositions. +

It was not Newton but Kepler who first thought of the planets as standing in immanent relation to the sun, and it is therefore absurd to 15 regard their being drawn as a new idea originating with Newton. What is more, 'attraction' is not the right word here, for it is the planets rather than the sun, which take initiative. Everything depends upon the proof + that they move in an ellipse. This is the crux of Kepler's law, but the proof of it was never attempted by Newton. *Laplace* ('Exposition du 20 système du monde', vol. II p. 12–13.) admits that, 'Infinitesimal analysis, which on account of its generality embraces everything that may be deduced from a given law, makes it clear that not only the ellipse, but every conic section, may be described by means of the force which maintains the planets in their orbits'. It is in this essential fact that the 25 complete inadequacy of the Newtonian proof becomes apparent. In the + geometrical proof Newton employs the infinitely small; it is not a rigorous proof, and modern analysis has therefore abandoned it. Instead of proving the laws of Kepler, Newton did the opposite. An explanation of the matter was called for, and Newton was content with a bad one. The idea 30 of the infinitely small stands out in this proof, which depends upon Newton's having posited all triangles in the infinitely small as equal. The sine and the cosine are unequal however, and if one then says that they are equal when posited as infinitely small quanta, the proposition will certainly enable one to do anything. When it is dark, all cows are black. 35 The quantum has to disappear, but if qualitative difference is also eliminated in the process, there is no end to what can be proved. It is upon such + propositions that the Newtonian proof is based, and that is why it is such an utterly bad one. Analysis goes on to deduce the other two laws from the ellipse; it has found a non-Newtonian way of doing this, but it is 40 precisely the first law, the foundation of the deduction, which remains unproved. In Newton's law, in so far as gravity diminishes with the distance, it is merely the velocity at which bodies move. The mathematical determination $\frac{S}{T^2}$ was stressed by Newton when he arranged Kepler's laws in order to express gravity, but it was already present in these laws. The deduction is made in a manner resembling the definition of the circle as $a^2 = x^2 + y^2$, i.e. as the relationship between the invariable hypotenuse (of the radius) and the two cathetuses which are variable (abscissa or cosine, ordinate or sine). The abscissa for example, may be deduced from this formula in the following way: $x^2 = a^2 - y^2$, i.e. $(a+y)(a-y)$ or the ordinate thus: $y^2 = a^2 - x^2$, i.e. $(a+x)(a-x)$. We are therefore able to discover all other determinations from the original function of the curve. Gravity might be elicited as $\frac{A}{T^2}$ merely by arranging Kepler's formula so as to deduce this determination. This may be done with each of Kepler's laws, with his law of ellipses, and with his law concerning the proportionality of times and sectors, but most simply and directly with the third. This law has the following formula: $\frac{A^3}{T^2} = \frac{a^3}{t^2}$. We want to deduce $\frac{S}{T^2}$ from it. S is the space traversed as part of the orbit; A is the distance from the sun; both are interchangeable, and may be substituted for one another, because the distance (diameter) and the orbit as a constant function of the distance stand in relationship to each other. The diameter being determined, I also know the curve of the revolution, and vice versa, for I have here a single determinability. I now take the formula $\frac{A^2 A}{T^2} = \frac{a^2 a}{t^2}$, i.e. $A^2 \frac{A}{T^2} = a^2 \frac{a}{t^2}$, and remove gravity $\left(\frac{A}{T^2}\right)$, substituting G for $\frac{A}{T^2}$, and g for $\frac{a}{t^2}$ (the different gravitations). I then have $A^2G = a^2g$. If I then state this relation as a proportion, I have $A^2 : a^2 = g : G$, which is Newton's law.

So far we have had two bodies in celestial motion. As subjectivity and determinateness of place in and for itself, the central body had its absolute centre in itself. The other moment is the objectivity confronting this determinedness in and for itself, i.e. the particular bodies which have a centre not only in themselves but also in another. Since these bodies are no longer the body which expresses the abstract moment of subjectivity, their place is certainly determined, for they are outside it; their place is not absolutely determined however, the determinateness of the place being indeterminate. The various possibilities are realized by the body as it moves in the curve. Each place on the curve is in fact indifferent to the body, which demonstrates this by simply moving in them around the central body. In this primary relationship, gravity has not yet unfolded 5 into the *totality* of the Notion; for it to do so, it is necessary that the particularization into many bodies by which the subjectivity of the centre objectifies itself, should be further determined within itself. Firstly we have the absolute central body, secondly the dependent bodies with no centre in themselves, and thirdly relative central bodies. The whole 10 gravitational system is complete only if it includes these three types of body. It is said that there must be three bodies present in order to decide which body is moving, as when we are in a boat, and the shore is moving past us. Determinateness could be said to be already present in the plurality of planets; but this is a simple plurality, not a differentiated determinate- 15 ness. If only the sun and the earth are under consideration, it is a matter of indifference to the Notion which of them moves. Tycho Brahe concluded from this that the sun moved about the earth, and the planets about the sun, and although this tends to make calculations more difficult, it is just as feasible. It was Copernicus who hit upon the truth of the matter; + astronomy was providing no real reason when it explained this by saying that it is more fitting that the earth should move about the sun because the sun is larger. If mass is also brought into consideration, the + question of the larger body having the same specific density also arises. The law of motion remains essential. The central body represents abstract 25 rotatory motion; the particular bodies simply move about a centre, without independent rotatory movement. The third mode in the system of free motion is movement about a centre combined with a rotatory motion which is independent of this centre.

(1) The *centre* is supposed to be a point, but as it is body and composed 30 of parts which tend towards a centre, it is at the same time extended. This dependent matter involved in the central body causes the latter to rotate about itself, for the dependent points, which are at the same time kept away from the centre, have no self-relating and clearly determined place; they are merely determined in a single direction as falling matter. All 35 other determinateness is lacking, and each point must therefore occupy all the places it is able to. Only the centre is determined in and for itself; the rest, forming as it does the extrinsicality of the centre, is indifferent, for it is merely the distance of each point from the centre which is determined here, not the point's place. This contingency of determination comes 40

into existence when matter changes its place. The *internal rotation of the sun* about its centre is the expression of this. This sphere is therefore mass in its immediacy as a unity of rest and motion, or it is self-relating motion. Axial rotation does not constitute a change of place, for all points keep the same 5 place in relation to one another. The whole is therefore quiescent motion. In order that it should be an actual motion, the axis should not be indifferent to the mass, and must not remain still while the mass is in motion. There is no real difference between this which moves and its rest, because there + is no difference in mass. That which rests is not a mass, but a line, and that which 10 is moved is distinguished solely by places, not by masses.

(2) The dependent bodies do not constitute the connected parts in the extension of a body endowed with a centre, for they have at the same time apparently free existence, and hold themselves at a distance from the + central body. They also rotate, but as they have no centre in themselves, + not upon their axis. They therefore rotate about a centre belonging to another individual body, by which they are repelled. They are completely indifferent to particularity of place, and they express this contingency of determinate place by rotation. As they remain in the same spatial determination with regard to the central body, they move about it in an inert 20 rigid manner; the relationship of the moon to the earth is an example of this. A certain place A in the mobile peripheral body will always remain in the straight line joining the absolute and relative centres, and every other point B constantly maintain its determinate angle. It is as a mere mass that the dependent body moves about the central body therefore, not 25 as a self-related individual body. It is the dependent heavenly bodies which constitute the aspect of particularity; this is why they fall apart and differentiate themselves, for in nature particularity exists as duality, and not as unity, as it does in spirit. If we regard this double nature of dependent bodies as a mere difference of movement, we have the two 30 aspects of the motion as follows:—

(*a*) The first posited moment is that in which quiescent motion becomes this + restless movement, which is a sphere of *aberration*, or of effort to break out of immediate existence into what is beyond its self. This moment of self-externality, as a mass and sphere, is itself the moment of substance, for each moment 35 here contains its special existence, or has within it the reality of the whole which constitutes a sphere. The second of these is the cometary sphere, and expresses this whirling which makes a permanent effort to disperse and scatter itself into the infinite or void. In this context, the shape of a body, and the whole conception of the comets and celestial bodies which deals merely with 40 their contingency, and is based upon knowledge accumulated simply by looking at them, has to be put out of mind. According to this way of thinking, the comets might just as well not be there, and the recognition of their necessity, the grasping of their Notion, may even seem laughable, used as this mental attitude is to regarding such things as quite beyond our comprehension, and consequently of the Notion too. All the imaginative theories of what is called 'explaining the origin', according to which the comets may be ejected from the sun, atmospheric vapours and so on, belong without exception to this way of thinking. Explanation of this kind may well attempt to state what the comets are, but it merely bypasses the essential point, which is their necessity; and it is precisely the necessity which constitutes the Notion. There is therefore no particular excuse for our taking up these phenomena and tinselling them with a glitter of thought. The cometary sphere threatens to break away from the universal self-relating order, and lose its unity. It is formal freedom, which has its substance outside itself, a pushing out into the future. In so far as it constitutes a necessary moment of the whole however, it does not escape from this whole, and so remains included within the first sphere. Nevertheless it is uncertain whether such a sphere dissolves itself as an individual and other individuals come into existence, or whether it is perpetually moving as a motion about the first sphere, which is external to it, and in which it has its repose. Both possibilities belong to the contingency of nature, and this division or transition by stages from the determinateness of this sphere into another, is to be reckoned with as proper to material existence. Nevertheless, the extreme limit of the aberration itself consists necessarily in an indefinite approach to the subjectivity of the central body, until the point is reached at which repulsion takes place.

(*b*) It is precisely this moment of unrest in which the moment of whirling attains its centre however; this is not a transition of simple change, for in its self-immediacy this otherness is the opposite of itself. The opposition is the duality of the immediate otherness and the cancellation of this otherness. It is not a pure flux or the opposition as such however, but this opposition as it seeks its rest or centre. It is sublated future, the past as moment, in which the opposition is sublated in its Notion, although not yet in its determinate being. This is the *lunar* sphere, which is not the aberration or issuing forth of determinate being, but relation to self, to what has become, or to the being-for-self. Thus, while the cometary sphere is only related to immediate rotation about an axis, the lunar sphere is related to the new intro-reflected centre, the planet. A satellite does not yet have its being-in-and-for-self within itself nor does it revolve about its axis; its axis is outside it, but it is not the axis of the solar sphere. Considered purely as a motion, the lunar sphere is rigidly controlled by a single centre, to which it is simply *subservient*, and the sphere of aberration is just as dependent. The first is abstract obedience, and conformity to another, the second is merely intended freedom. The cometary sphere constitutes an eccentricity controlled by an abstract whole, while the lunar sphere is quiescent inertia.

5 (3) The final sphere is the *planetary*, which is in and for itself, and constitutes relation to self and to another; it is formed as much by motion rotating about an axis, as by having its centre outside itself. Consequently, although the planet also has its centre in itself, it is a merely relative centre, and as it does not contain its absolute centre, it is not independent. The 10 planet has both determinations within it, and displays them by its change of place. It shows its independence only by its parts' changing place in relation to the position which they hold with regard to the straight line joining the absolute and relative centres; it is this which is the basis of the rotatory motion of the planets. The precession of the equinoxes is caused + by the movement of the orbital axis. The axis of the earth also has a nutation, + and its poles describe an ellipse. As it constitutes the third sphere, the planet concludes and completes the whole. This quadruplicity of celestial bodies forms the completed system of rational corporeality. It is necessary to a solar system, and is the developed disjunction of the Notion. These 20 four spheres between them show forth the moments of the Notion within the heavens. It may seem strange to attempt to fit the comets in here, but that which is present must necessarily be contained in the Notion. Differences are still thrown freely apart here. We shall pursue the solar, planetary, lunar, and cometary spheres through all the subsequent stages 25 of nature. The deepening of nature is merely the progressive transformation of these four. It is because planetary nature is the totality, the unity of opposites, while the other spheres, being its inorganic nature, merely exhibit its particular moments, that it is the most perfect to come under consideration here; and this is also true of it as a motion. It is for 30 this reason that living being occurs only on the planets. Ancient peoples + have glorified the sun and worshipped it; we do the same when we recognize the final supremacy of the abstract understanding, and so determine God for example, as the supreme essence.

This totality is the ground and universal substance on which that which fol- 35 lows is borne. This totality of motion is everything, but everything withdrawn into a higher being-in-self, or, to express it differently, realized as a + higher being-in-self. Everything has this totality within it, but is indifferent to it, leaves it behind as a particular existence, as a history, or as the origin against which the being-in-self has turned in order to be for itself. Everything lives in 40 this element therefore, and also frees itself from it, for only feeble traces of everything subsist there. Terrestrial being, and more particularly organic being and self-consciousness, has escaped from the motion of absolute matter but remained in sympathy with it, and lived on with it as within its own inner element. The changes of the seasons and times of day, and the changeover from waking to sleep, constitute the terrestrial life in organic being. In itself each of these moments constitutes a sphere of proceeding out of self, and of returning into its central point or power, so that it embraces or subdues all the multifarious elements of consciousness. Night is the negative to which everything returns, and organic being therefore derives its strength and consequently its negative being from thence, so that it may return again refreshed to the waking multifariousness of existence. Each has the universal sphere within it therefore, and is a sphere periodically returning into itself, and expressing the universal through its determinate individuality. The magnetic needle does so by its periodic deviations; according to *Fourcroy's* observations, man does so partly by his four-day periods of increasing and decreasing, in which he puts on for three days, and on the fourth returns to his original dimensions. The periodic courses of diseases might also be cited here. It is however in the circulation of the blood, the rhythm of which differs from that of the respiratory sphere, and thirdly in peristaltic movement, that the fully developed totality of the sphere occurs. The generally higher nature of physical being prevents this sphere from expressing its peculiar freedom however, and in order to study universal motion, one must concentrate upon its freedom, not upon these trivial appearances. In individuality it is not its free existence, but a mere internality or intention which is present.

The exposition of the solar system has not yet been completed by what has been said, and although the basic determinations have been adduced, there are still supplementary determinations which could be added. The relationship between the orbits of the planets, their reciprocal inclinations, and the inclinations of comets and satellites to them, are all fields of enquiry which could still be of interest to us. The orbits of the planets do not lie in a single plane, and what is more, the courses of the comets cut across the planetary orbits at very different angles. These do not deviate from the ecliptic, but they change the angle of their reciprocal relations; the motion of nodes is secular. It is more difficult to develop these occurrences, and we are not yet able to do so. We have only concerned ourselves with the planet in general, but the distances between the planets should also be considered, for although it is as yet undiscovered, there may well be a law governing the *series* in the distances between the planets. Astronomers tend on the whole to scorn the idea of there being such a law, and will have nothing to do with it, but it is necessary that this should remain an open question. Kepler considered the numbers in Plato's 'Timaeus' for example. Taking these as a basis, something like the following conjecture might now be made:—Mercury is the first of the planets and if its distance is a, then the orbit of Venus is a + b, the orbit of the Earth a + 2b, and that of Mars a + 3b. In this way it will certainly become apparent that these first four planets form a whole. One might say that the first four bodies of the solar system, constitute a single system in themselves, and that another order subsequently commences, both in the numbers, and in the physical constitution of the planets. These four move in a uniform manner, and it is worth noting that there are four with such a homogeneous nature. Of these four, only the Earth has a satellite, and it is therefore the most perfect. Between Mars and Jupiter there is a sudden wide gap, and a + 4b was not permissible until more recent times, when the discovery of the four smaller planets Vesta, Juno, Ceres, and Pallas, filled it and formed a new group. The unity of the planet is here sundered into a crowd of asteroids, all of which have approximately the same orbit. Dispersion and separation predominate in this fifth position. Then comes the third group. Jupiter with its many satellites is a a + 5b etc. This only works out approximately, and the rationality of it is not yet recognizable. This great mass of satellites is different again from the kind of arrangement found in the first four planets. Then comes Saturn with its rings and seven satellites, and Uranus, which was discovered by Herschel, with a host of satellites which few have seen as yet. Here we have a point of departure for the preciser determination of planetary relationships. It is not difficult to see that the law will be discovered in this way.

Philosophy has to proceed on the basis of the Notion, and even if it demonstrates very little, one has to be satisfied. It is an error on the part of the philosophy of nature to attempt to face up to all phenomena; this is done in the finite sciences, where everything has to be reduced to general conceptions (hypotheses). In these sciences the empirical element is the sole confirmation of the hypothesis, so that everything has to be explained. Whatever is known through the Notion is its own explanation and stands firm however, so that philosophy need not be disturbed if the explanation of each and every phenomenon has not yet been completed. Here I have merely traced the foundations of a rational interpretation, as this must be employed in the comprehension of the mathematical and mechanical laws of nature within the free realm of measures. Specialists do not reflect upon the matter, but a time will come when the rational concept of this science will be demanded!

§ 271

Gravity, which is the substance of matter, no longer has the self-externality of matter external to it when it is developed into totality of form. The form appears first in its differences in the ideal determinations of space, time, and motion, and in accordance with its being-for-self, as a determinate centre outside self-external matter. In developed totality however, this extrinsicality is posited as determined solely by the totality; this is the juxtaposition of matter, outside of which it has no existence. It is in this way that form is materialized. Looked at in the opposite way, matter has itself attained implicit determinateness of form in this negation of its self-externality in the totality, which was formerly merely the centre which it sought. Its abstract and subdued being-in-self, general weightedness, has been resolved into form; it is qualified matter, or physics.

Addition. In this way we conclude the first part; mechanics now constitutes a distinct whole. When Descartes said, 'Give me matter and motion and I will construct the world', he took the standpoint of mechanics as his first principle, and in these words he shows a greatness of spirit which we should not deny, despite the inadequacy of this standpoint. In motion, bodies are mere points, and gravity only determines the spatial relations between points. The unity of matter is simply the unity of place which matter seeks, it is not a single concrete unit. It is in the nature of this sphere that this externality of determinedness should constitute the peculiar determinateness of matter. Matter is weighted being-for-self seeking its being-in-self; in this infinity the point is merely a place, so that the being-for-self is not yet real. It is only in the whole solar system that the totality of being-for-self is posited, so that what the solar system is as a whole, matter should be in particular. The complete form of the solar system is the Notion of matter in general; its self-externality should now be present in each determinate existence of the completely developed Notion. Matter should find its unity by being for itself in the whole of its determinate being, which is the being for self of being-for-self. Put in another way, the self-motivation of the solar system is the sublation of the merely ideal nature of being-for-self, of mere spatiality of determination, of not-being-for-self. In the Notion, the negation of place does not merely give rise to its re-instatement; the negation of not-being-for-self is a negation of the negation, i.e. an affirmation, so that what comes forth is real being-for-self. This is the abstractly logical determination of the *transition*. It is precisely the total development of being-for-self which is real being-for-self; this might be expressed as the freeing of the form of 5 matter. The determinations of form which constitute the solar system are the determinations of matter itself, and these determinations constitute the being of matter, so that determination and being are essentially identical. This is of the nature of quality, for if the determination is removed here, being also disappears. This is the transition from mechanics to physics.

NOTES

179

Karl Ludwig Michelet (1801–1893) came of a French Calvinist family. He was born in Berlin and educated at the French Grammar School there. In 1819 he was matriculated at Berlin University and began to study law, but Hegel's lectures on logic and the philosophy of right broadened his interests, and in 1824 he took his doctorate in philosophy. In 1826 he qualified as a university teacher and lectured at Berlin until 1874. He was appointed professor there in 1829, and from 1825 until 1850 was also a teacher at his old school.

He tended to belong to the Hegelian left, and did a great deal of work faithfully defending what he considered to be orthodox Hegelianism. He joined the 'Society for scientific criticism' in 1827, and contributed to its 'Jahrbücher für wissenschaftliche Kritik'. He edited vol. I, 'Hegel's philosophische Abhandlungen' and vols. XIII–XV, 'Geschichte der Philosophie', as well as this volume of the complete edition of Hegel's works.

He wrote three works on the ethics of Aristotle (1827, 1835, 1836), and several works on the history of philosophy: see for example 'Geschichte der letzten Systeme der Philosophie in Deutschland von Kant bis Hegel' (2 vols. Berlin, 1837–1838). Although he is a competent scholar he does not show much originality as a thinker. This is particularly noticeable in his 'Das System der Philosophie' (4 vols. Berlin, 1876–1879) which is very largely a mere paraphrase of Hegel's system. Volume 3 of this work (Berlin, 1876, p. 486) is devoted entirely to the *philosophy of nature*, but it shows very little intelligent assessment of the scientific developments that had taken place since Hegel lectured.

See the article by Adolf Lasson in 'Allgemeine Deutsche Biographie' vol. 55 pp. 842–844 (Leipzig, 1910): E. H. Schmitt 'Michelet und das Geheimnis der Hegelschen Dialektik' (Frankfurt-on-Main, 1888): Pasquale d'Ercole 'C. L. Michelet e l'Hegelianismo' ('Riv. Ital. di Filos.' IX, 1894).

179, 1

See Schelling's 'Erster Entwurf eines Systems der Naturphilosophie. Für Vorlesungen' (1799), republished in 'Schellings Werke' vol. II pp. 1–268 (ed. M. Schröter, Munich, 1958), ‚Da über Natur philosophiren so viel heißt, als die Natur schaffen, so muß der Punkt gefunden werden, von welchem aus die Natur ins *Werden* gesetzt werden kann‚. (op. cit. p. 5).

179, 11

Hegel and Schelling founded the 'Kritisches Journal der Philosophie' in order to attack the philosophy of reflection with 'cudgels, whips and swishes' (Hegel's letter to Caroline Hufnagel, December 30, 1801). Hegel's contributions to it (1802–1803) are to be found in the first volume of his 'Sämtliche Werke' (ed. H. Glockner, Stuttgart, 1958), 'Aufsätze aus dem kritischen Journal der Philosophie und andere Schriften aus der Jenenser Zeit'.

180, 31

Goethe 'Zur Morphologie' (1817) vol. I p. vi. See 'Goethe, die Schriften zur Naturwissenschaft' edited for the 'Deutschen Akademie der Naturforscher' part I vol. ix 'Morphologische Hefte' (ed. D. Kuhn, Weimar, 1954).

180, 39

Adam Karl August Eschenmayer (1768–1852); his Christian names are variously given as Christoph Adam, Carl Adolph August, or Karl August: born at Neuenberg in Württemberg, July 4, 1768. He was appointed professor of medicine and philosophy at Tübingen in 1811, and in 1818 professor of practical philosophy at the same university.

In the late 1790's he came under the influence of Schelling, and it is probably the works he published at this time that Michelet has in mind: see 'Sätze aus der Natur-Metaphysik auf chemische und medicinische Gegenstände angewandt' (Tübingen, 1797); 'Versuch, die Gesetze magnetischer Erscheinungen aus Sätzen der Naturmetaphysik, mithin a priori zu entwickeln' (Tübingen, 1797). He subsequently concerned himself with animal magnetism, somnambulism etc.: see 'Psychologie, in drei Theilen, als empirisch, reine und angewandte' (Stuttgart and Tübingen, 1817), and his articles in the 'Archiv für den thierischen Magnetismus' (1817–1822).

He published several philosophical works: see 'System der Moralphilosophie' (Stuttgart, 1818): 'Normalrecht' (Stuttgart, 1819, 1820): 'Religionsphilosophie' (3 pts. Tübingen, 1818–1824) and 'Grundriss der Naturphilosophie' (Tübingen, 1832). His last works were concerned with religion: see his attack on Hegel, 'Die Hegel'sche Religionsphilosophie verglichen mit dem christlichen Princip' (Tübingen, 1834).

'Neuer Nekrolog der Deutschen' Jahrg. XXX, 1852, II p. 785: Roller in 'Allgemeine Zeitschrift für Psychiatrie' vol. X, 1853, p. 142: 'Allgemeine Deutsche Biographie' vol. VI pp. 349–350: Haberling-Hübotter-Vierordt 'Biographisches Lexikon der hervorragenden Ärtzte' vol. II pp. 432–433 (Berlin und Vienna, 1930): A. C. P. Callisen 'Medicinisches Schriftsteller Lexicon' vol. VI pp. 111–114: vol. XXVII pp. 474–475 (Copenhagen, 1831, 1839).

181, 4

Heinrich Friedrich Link (1767–1851) see the note III. 263. Michelet is quoting from his 'Grundlehren der Anatomie und Physiologie der Pflanzen' (Göttingen, 1807) pp. 245–246 (Additions I p. 59); pp. 5–6.

181, 9

Dietrich Georg Kieser (1779–1862), famous mainly as a doctor. For his views on plants see 'Aphorismen aus der Physiologie der Pflanzen' (Göttingen, 1808), 'Mémoire sur l'organisation des plantes' (Haarlem, 1812).

On Kieser himself see Haberling-Hübotter-Vierardt 'Biographisches Lexikon' vol. III pp. 519–521 (Berlin and Vienna, 1931), and 'Allgemeine Deutsche Biographie' vol. XV pp. 726–730 (Leipzig, 1882).

181, 22

See for example the articles by Claude Perrault (c. 1613–1688), Louis Carré (1663–1711) and Philippe de la Hire (1640–1718) in 'Mémoires de l'Academie Royale des Sciences' vol. I p. 145; 1704 Hist. p. 88; 1716 p. 262.

181, 25

See Michelet's article 'Zugeständnisse der neuesten Physik in Bezug auf Göthe's Farbenlehre' ('Hallische Jahrbücher für deutsche Wissenschaft und Kunst' (ed. A. Ruge and T. Echtermeyer, nos. 305–307, Dec. 1838).

183, 26

Goethe 'Zur Morphologie' (1817) vol. I p. 122: see the note I.285. Alexander von Humboldt (1769–1859), the explorer, geographer and natural scientist.

184, 25

Lorenz Oken (1779–1851): see the note III.278. Michelet evidently has in mind his 'Lehrbuch der Naturphilosophie' (3 vols. Jena, 1809–1811). A. Tulk published an English translation of this work for the Ray Society, see 'Elements of Physiophilosophy' (London, 1848).

184, 39

Schelling criticized the transition from logic to nature in the Hegelian system in the lectures he delivered at Munich in 1827. See 'Zur Geschichte der neueren Philosophie' ('Werke' ed. M. Schröter, vol. V pp. 196–234, Munich, 1959). W. T. Stace, in 'The Philosophy of Hegel' (London, 1923, Dover ed. 1955) discusses the subject at some length in his treatment of the philosophy of nature.

Michelet is referring here to the preface Schelling wrote to 'Victor Cousin über französische und deutsche Philosophie' (Stuttgart and Tübingen, 1834). This was a translation of Cousin's 'Fragments philosophiques' (Paris, 1833) by Hubert Beckers (1806–1889): see Schelling's 'Werke' vol. V p. 456.

186, 9

Michelet did not know of Hegel's lectures on the philosophy of nature delivered at Jena in 1803–1804: see Johannes Hoffmeister 'Jenenser Realphilosophie I. Die Vorlesungen von 1803–04' (Leipzig, 1932). An even earlier treatment of the subject (1801–1802) is to be found in Georg Lasson's 'Jenenser Logik, Metaphysik und Naturphilosophie' (Leipzig, 1923).

Hegel's Heidelberg Encyclopaedia has recently been republished by Hermann Glockner: see 'Enzyklopädie der philosophischen Wissenschaften im Grundrisse' (Stuttgart, 1956).

186, 24

Karl Gustav von Griesheim (1798–1854) was the son of an infantry captain. He was born in Berlin, and attended the Frederick William Grammar School there. He volunteered for the army during the War of Liberation, but did not see active service on account of a physical disability. He was commissioned on July 3, 1815 however, and marched into Paris with the victorious allies. During this period he kept a very detailed diary.

In 1819 he became adjutant of his regiment and regimental judge for three battalions. This gave him practice in the law, and in his spare time he attended the lectures given by Hegel, Erman, Ritter and Humboldt at the University in Berlin. His notes were also used by Eduard Gans (1798–1839) for the standard edition of Hegel's 'Lectures on the Philosophy of History' (Berlin, 1837). He contributed to the 'Jahrbücher für wissenschaftliche Kritik', the official publication of the Hegelian school.

He was appointed captain of the seventh company of the second Guards regiment in 1831, and later distinguished himself in army reorganization work, as a writer on military matters, and as a staunch opponent of the leftists during the turmoil of 1848. He died of Bright's disease on January 1, 1854. See his 'Der Compagnie-Dienst' (Berlin, 1837): 'Die deutsche Centralgewalt und die preussische Armee' (Berlin, July 23, 1848).

186, 25

Heinrich Gustav Hotho (1802–1873) was born in Berlin and educated at the Joachimsthal Grammar School there. At the Humboldt University he began to study law, but Hegel's lectures interested him in philosophy. He studied this subject in Breslau, and then travelled, visiting London, Paris, Belgium, Holland and Italy, and studying the history of art. On his return to Berlin, he qualified as a teacher of aesthetics and the history of art at the university (1826–1827). In 1829 he was appointed professor, and in 1830 given a post in the art gallery.

He edited Hegel's 'Vorlesungen über Aesthetik' (3 vols. Berlin, 1835) and published several works on the history of painting: 'Geschichte der deutschen und niederländischen Malerei' (2 vols. Berlin, 1842): 'Die Malerschule Huberts von Eyck' (2 vols. Berlin, 1855): 'Geschichte der christlichen Malerei' (Stuttgart, 1867–1872).

186, 26

Friedrich Wilhelm Ludwig Geyer was the son of a Berlin painter, and must have been born in the city about 1809–1810. He attended the Frederick William Grammar School, and on October 9, 1828 was matriculated at the Humboldt University in order to read theology. His father must have died by this time, for in the records of the University, a Berlin tobacco merchant is quoted as being his guardian. During his stay at the University he changed lodgings twice, but from the Michaelmas Term of 1830 until Easter 1831 he lived at no. 43 Kochstrasse with his schoolfriend and namesake Friedrich August Meyer, who was also reading theology: see 'Amtliches Verzeichniss des Personals und der Studirenden auf der Königl. Friedrich-Wilhelms Universität zu Berlin, Auf das Winterhalbjahr von Michaelis 1830 bis Ostern 1831' (Berlin, 1831). He finally left the University, without having taken his degree, on March 1, 1832, evidently on account of his not having been able to pay his fees. There is no evidence of his having studied elsewhere, and his position as 'vice-principal' probably indicates that he stayed in *Berlin* as a *schoolmaster*. This would account for Michelet's having known him.

Geyer attended many of Hegel's courses. His leaving certificate is preserved in the archives of the Humboldt University: see 'Universitäts-Archiv der Humboldt-Universität Berlin, Abgangs Zeugnisse 1832 Litt. A no. 6 vol. XCI Blatt 6–10'. From this it appears that he was no. 10 on Hegel's list of those attending the lectures on logic and the philosophy of nature delivered during the summer of 1830. On his birthday (Aug. 27th) Hegel commented on Geyer's attendance, ‚Den fleißigen Besuch bezeuge – Hegel'. This document also indicates that Geyer attended Hegel's lectures on aesthetics (Winter 1828–9), the existence of God (Summer, 1829), the history of philosophy (Winter, 1829–30), the philosophy of history (Winter, 1830–31), and the philosophy of religion (Summer, 1831), and that he had also signed (no. 15) for the lectures on the philosophy of right which were to have been given during the winter of 1831–1832, but which were cancelled on account of Hegel's death.

186, 29

E. S. Haldane and F. H. Simson published a translation of this work, 'Hegel's lectures on the History of Philosophy' (3 vols. London, 1892: reprint London, 1955, 1963), but they merely summarized Michelet's foreword. Cf. 'Vorlesungen über die Geschichte der Philosophie' (3 vols. ed. Glockner, Stuttgart, 1959) vol. I pp. 1–14. The first edition of Michelet's work appeared in 1833.

187, 36

See the excellent edition of this note-book by Johannes Hoffmeister 'Jenenser

Realphilosophie II. Die Vorlesungen von 1805–06' (Leipzig, 1931). T. L. Haering, in his 'Hegel, sein Wollen und sein Werk' (2 vols. Leipzig, 1938) discusses the *development* of Hegel's treatment of the natural sciences.

188, 23

See Sir Edmund Whittaker 'History of the Theories of Aether and Electricity' (3 vols. Nelson, 1962). The best exposition in English of Fichte's idealism is still to be found in Robert Adamson's 'Fichte' (Blackwood's Philosophical Classics, 1881). Michelet probably has in mind Schelling's 'Darlegung des wahren Verhältnisses der Naturphilosophie zu der verbesserten Fichteschen Lehre. Eine Erläuterungsschrift der ersten.' (1806): see 'Schellings Werke' vol. III pp. 595–720 (ed. M. Schröter, Munich, 1958).

188, 30

In the manuscript there is a pencilled note in the margin at this point ('Jenenser Realphilosophie' II ed. Hoffmeister, 1931 p. 3), evidently by Michelet, ,Nicht zugunsten des Physikers — absoluter Kampf, epochemachende Umwälzung — Versuch, den Verstand des Physikers zur Vernunft zu bringen—Vernunft, Geist, absolutes Prinzip'.

189, 7

This translation has been made from Hoffmeister's version of this sentence, not Michelet's, ,Insofern gesagt wird, er sei Äther oder absolute Materie, ist er *in sich* oder reines Selbstbewußtsein, dies als *seiend* überhaupt, nicht als daseiend oder reell bestimmt;'

189, 13

For the original version of this passage see Johannes Hoffmeister 'Jenenser Realphilosophie II' (Leipzig, 1931) pp. 3–4. Michelet does not indicate the emphasized words.

189, 24

In 1841 Schelling was appointed Prussian privy councillor and member of the Berlin Academy. This gave him the right to deliver lectures in the university, and he was requested to exercise it. Hegel's *philosophy of religion* had become involved in the split between the Hegelian left and the Hegelian right through the writings of Bruno Bauer (1809–1882), David Friedrich Strauss (1808–1874), Ludwig Feuerbach (1804–1872), Heinrich Eberhard Gottlob Paulus (1761–1851), and Philipp Konrad Marheineke (1780–1846), and Schelling therefore chose to lecture on the philosophy of mythology and revelation. Kierkegaard heard these lectures, and his journal and letters from this period give a brilliant picture of Schelling's manner of delivery, the crowded auditorium, and the excited and attentive audiences. He mentions the publication of this preface in a letter to Spang, '"What's the news?" you'll probably ask. Literary news we have little of, apart from Schelling's behaviour, which continues to have the interest of novelty. The second volume of Hegel's *Encyclopaedia* has appeared, and Michelet has written an introduction to it in which he somewhat savagely attacks Schelling. Schelling is looking as testy as a vinegar-maker'. Cf. P. Rohde 'Søren Kierkegaard' (tr. A. M. Williams, London, 1963) pp. 72–78.

Schelling's lectures are to be found in his 'Werke' (ed. M. Schröter, Munich, 1959–1960) vols. V, VI, and suppl. col. VI. In this paragraph, Michelet is quoting from the first lecture of this series, which was delivered on November 15, 1841, only four weeks before he finished this preface: see 'Schelling's Werke' vol. VI pp. 749–759: see also the first lectures on the philosophy of revelation (suppl. vol. VI).

191, 4

'Philosophia est divinarum humanarumque rerum in quantum homini possibile est, probabilis scientia': see F. M. A. Cassiodorus (485–580) 'Institutiones' (ed. Mynors, Oxford, 1937) II iii 5, p. 110. 'Philosophia est disciplina omnium rerum humanarum atque divinarum rationes plene investigans': see Hugh of St. Victor (1096–1141) 'The Didascalicon' (ed. Taylor, New York and London, 1961) I iv p. 51.

Cf. Cicero 'De oratore' I xlix, 212; 'De officiis' II ii 5; Augustine 'Contra academicos' I vi; F. A. Alcuin (735–804) 'De dialectica' i; Raban Maur (776–856) 'De universo' XV i; St. Isidore (570–636) 'Etymologiae' II xxiv I, 9.

On the 9th and 10th of March 1787, Hegel copied out the following passage from the 'Kurzer Begriff aller Wissenschaften' (2nd ed. Leipzig, 1759) by J. G. Sulzer (1720–1779), ,Unter der Philosophie verstehen wir hier diejenigen Wissenschaften, welche eine nähere Beziehung auf die sittliche Kenntnis der Welt und des Menschen haben'. See Johannes Hoffmeister 'Dokumente zu Hegels Entwicklung' (Stuttgart, 1936) p. 109.

191, 20

'Phänomenologie des Geistes' (Bamberg and Würzburg, 1807): see J. B. Baillie 'G. W. F. Hegel. The Phenomenology of Mind' (2nd ed. revised, London, 1949); Jean Hyppolite 'Genèse et Structure de le Phénomenologie de l'Esprit de Hegel' (Paris, 1946); Alexandre Kojève 'Introduction à la Lecture de Hegel' (Paris, 1947).

192, 2

F. W. J. Schelling (1775–1854): see his 'Werke' (12 vols. ed. M. Schröter Munich, 1960), vols. I, II, III, and the supplementary vols. I and II contain his writings on the philosophy of nature. Raph. Koeber 'Die Grundprinzipien der Schellingschen Naturphilosophie' in 'Sammlung gemeinverständlicher Vorträge' (ed. Virchow and Holtzendorff, Berlin, 1881) no. 381; Max Hoppel 'Schellings Einfluss auf die Naturphilosophie Görres' (Fulda, 1931); Kurt Schilling 'Natur und Wahrheit' (Munich, 1934). Cf. G. A. C. Frantz 'Schellings Positive Philosophie' (3 vols. Köthen, 1879–1880); John Watson 'Schelling's Transcendental Idealism' (Chicago, 1882).

193, 12

See Aristotle 'The Physics' (tr. Wicksteed and Cornford, 2 vols. Loeb, 1929, 1934); W. D. Ross 'Aristotle's Physics' (Oxford, 1936).

193, 16

Christian Wolff (1679–1754), the interpreter and systematizer of the teaching of Leibniz. His philosophy held almost undisputed sway in Germany until it was displaced by Kantianism. Hegel gives a perceptive and sensitive survey of it in his 'History of Philosophy' (tr. Haldane and Simson 3 vols. London, 1963) vol. III pp. 348–356.

At this juncture he probably has in mind that Wolff's 'Vernünftige Gedanken von den Wirkungen der Natur' (Halle, 1723), which deals with cosmology or the philosophy of nature, is concerned with abstract or quite general philosophical categories, whereas it is in his 'Vernünftige Gedanken von den Teilen der Menschen, Tiere und Pflanzen' (Frankfurt, 1725), that he deals with much of the material assessed by Hegel in these lectures.

See F. W. Kluge 'Christian von Wolff der Philosoph' (Breslau, 1831); W. Arnsperger 'Christian Wolff's Verhältniss zu Leibniz' (Heidelberg, 1897); E. Kohlmeyer 'Kosmos und Kosmonomie bei Christian Wolff' (Göttingen, 1914).

194, 7

'Metaphysics' bk. I pt. 2 982^{b} 'For it is owing to their wonder that men both now begin and at first began to philosophize; they wondered originally at the obvious difficulties, then advanced little by little and stated difficulties about the greater matters, e.g. about the phenomena of the moon and those of the sun and of the stars, and about the genesis of the universe'.

Hegel is fond of this observation and also mentions it in the addition to § 449 of the 'Encyclopaedia' and his 'Philosophy of History' (tr. Sibree, Dover, ed. 1956) p. 234. Cf. Goethes 'Faust' I 766. ‚Das Wunder ist des Glaubens liebstes Kind'.

194, 12

‚Und in allem diesen Reichthum der Erkenntniß kann uns die Frage von Neuem kommen, oder erst entstehen: Was ist die Natur?'

194, 17

In Greek mythology, Proteus was a prophetic old man of the sea who knew all things past, present and future, but was loth to tell what he knew. Those who wanted to consult him had first to surprise and bind him during his noonday slumber in a cave by the sea. Even when he was caught he would try to escape by assuming all sorts of shapes, but if his captor held him fast the god at last returned to his proper shape, gave the wished-for answer, and then plunged into the sea. From his power of assuming whatever shape he pleased he came to be regarded, especially by the Orphic mystics, as a symbol of the original matter from which the world was created: see C. A. Lobeck 'Aglaophamus, sive de theologiae mysticae Graecor' (Regiomonti, 1829).

> 'Proteus, a name tremendous o'er the main,
> The delegate of Neptune's watery reign.
> Watch with insidious care his known abode;
> There fast in chains constrain the various God:
> Who bound, obedient to superior force,
> Unerring will prescribe your destin'd course.
> If, studious of your realms, you then demand
> Their state, since last you left your natal land;
> Instant the God obsequious will disclose
> Bright tracks of glory, or a cloud of woes'
>
> —'Odyssey' bk. IV 351 (Pope)

See also Virgil's 'Georgics' iv 386: Herodotus 'The Histories' bk. ii 112, 118.

195, 15

See 'The Logic of Hegel' (tr. Wallace, Oxford, 1963) pp. 346–351.

195, 32

'Wonders are many, and none is more wonderful than man; . . .
Nothing destined to befall him finds him without resources.'

—'Antigone' lines 332–3 and 360.

Cf. 'Hamlet' II ii 316, 'What a piece of work is man, how noble in reason, how infinite in faculties'. Cf. Heinz Oeben 'Hegels Antigone-Interpretation' (Dissertation, Univ. of Bonn, July 1, 1953).

196, 19

The idea may have owed its wide currency in the West to the most used textbook of the mediaeval scholastics: see Peter Lombard (c. 1095–1160) 'Libri Sententiarum' (2 vols. Florence, 1916) II i 8, 'As man is made for the sake of God, namely, that he may serve Him, so is the world made for the sake of man, that it may serve him'. Bacon makes mention of it in 'De sapientia veterum'; see 'The Works of Francis Bacon' (7 vols. London, 1889–1892) vi p. 747, 'Man, if we look to final causes, may be regarded as the centre of the world; insomuch that if man were taken from the world, the rest would seem to be all astray, without aim or purpose, to be like a besom without a binding, as the saying is, and to be leading to nothing. For the whole world works together in the service of man; and there is nothing from which he does not derive use and fruit. Plants and animals of all kinds are made to furnish him either with dwelling and shelter or clothing or food or medicine or to lighten his labour or to give him pleasure and comfort; insomuch that all things seem to be going about man's business and not their own'.

One of the most popular protestant theological works of the eighteenth century made use of the idea: see Jacques Abbadie (1654–1727) 'Traité de la Vérité de la religion chrétienne' (2 vols. Rotterdam, 1684; 8th ed. The Hague, 1771; English tr. H. Lussan, London, 1694) I p. 95, 'If we consider closely what constitutes the excellence of the fairest parts of the Universe, we shall find that they have value only in their relation to us, only in so far as our soul attaches value to them; that the esteem of men is what constitutes the chief dignity of rocks and metals, that man's use and pleasure gives their value to plants, trees and fruits'.

Cf. C. G. Gillipsie 'Genesis and Geology' (Cambridge, Mass., 1951) ch. vii.

196, 25

In their 'Xenien', which is a series of 926 epigrams modelled on the thirteenth book of Martial, and published mainly in their periodical 'Die Horen' (1796–1797), Goethe and Schiller lampooned many of their contemporaries in a style reminiscent of Pope's 'Dunciad'. Writing of this kind helped to check the excesses of the romantic movement, but involved them in a number of literary battles: see Eduard Boas 'Schiller und Goethe im Xenienkampf' (2 pts. Stuttgart and Tübingen, 1851).

Hegel is referring here to no. 286 of the series:

> ,Der Teleolog.
> Welche Verehrung verdient der Weltenschöpfer! der, gnädig,
> Als er den Korkbaum schuf, gleich auch die Stöpfel erfand!'

Goethe refers to it in a conversation with Eckermann on April 11, 1827: see Erich Schmidt and Bernhard Suphan 'Xenien 1796' (Weimar, 1893) pp. 32, 143; Boas op. cit. pp. 55–56.

This particular epigram is evidently directed at Friedrich Leopold zu Stolberg (1750–1819), who, in his 'Reise in Deutschland, der Schweiz, Italien und Sicilien in den Jahren 1791 und 1792' (4 vols. Königsberg and Leipzig, 1794, English tr. T. Holcroft, 2 vols. London, 1796–1797): see 'Gesammelte Werke'

(20 vols. Hamburg, 1820–1825) vol. viii p. 198, observes of the cork trees growing between Bari and Gioja that, ,Aus der Rinde des Baumes werden Propfen zu Flaschen gemacht . . . Dieser Baum kann seine so nützliche, zu unserm Gebrauch von Gott bestimmte Rinde entbehren, da jeder andre Baum stirbt, wenn man ihm die Rinde nimmt'. See Wilhelm Keiper 'Stolbergs Jugendpoesie' (Dissertation, Berlin, 1893).

196, 32

Hegel deals with this at some length in his 'History of Philosophy' (tr. Haldane and Simson, 3 vols. London, 1963) vol. II pp. 157–163, and makes special reference to Aristotle's 'Physics' II 8, 9: see the tr. by Wicksteed and Cornford (2 vols. Loeb, 1929, 1934), and W. D. Ross 'Aristotle's Physics' (Oxford, 1936).

197, 10

i.e. to the whole 'Encyclopaedia': see 'The Logic of Hegel' (tr. W. Wallace, Oxford, 1963) pp. 3–29.

199, 25

See Goethe's and Schiller's lampooning of Friedrich Schlegel (1772–1829) in 'Xenien' no. 844 (331):

,Die Sonntagskinder.
Jahre lang bildet der Meister und kann sich nimmer genug thun,
Dem genialen Geschlecht wird es im Traume beschert'.

A 'Sunday child' is supposed to be particularly lucky and successful in all it does: see Alvin Schultz 'Alltagsleben einer deutschen Frau zu Anfang des 18. Jahrhunderts' (Leipzig, 1890) p. 195; J. C. Maennling 'Denckwürdige Curiositaeten' (Frankfurt and Leipzig, 1713); Alois Lütolf 'Sagen, Bräuche, Legenden aus den fünf Orten Lucern, Uri, Schwiz, Unterwalden und Zug' (Lucerne, 1862).

199, 35

This is almost certainly a reference to one of Schelling's first published works, 'Ueber Mythen, historische Sagen und Philosopheme der ältesten Welt' (1793): 'Werke' ed. M. Schröter, vol. I pp. 1–43 (Munich, 1958). Cf. his 'Philosophie der Mythologie' (1842): op. cit. 5th supplementary volume. See the curious exposition of similar views in a sort of intoxicated carlylese in 'Nordens Mythologi' (Copenhagen, 1832) by N. F. S. Grundtvig (1783–1872): cf. C. I. Scharling 'Grundtvig og Romantiken' (Copenhagen, 1947).

200, 24

See Kant's doctrine of the 'thing in itself', formulated most clearly in his 'Critique of Pure Reason'. Cf. Hegel's treatment of Kant in the 'Lectures on the History of Philosophy' (tr. Haldane and Simson, 3 vols. London, 1963) vol. III pp. 423–478. Cf. E. Adickes 'Kant und das Ding an sich' (Berlin, 1924): H. J. Paton 'Kant's Metaphysic of Experience' (2 vols. London, 1936): T. D. Weldon 'Kant's Critique of Pure Reason' (2nd ed. Oxford, 1958): G. Bird 'Kant's Theory of Knowledge' (London, 1962): R. Eisler 'Wörterbuch der Philosophischen Begriffe' (3 vols. Berlin, 1927–1930) vol. I pp. 280–285.

200, 37

See J. A. Stewart 'Plato's Doctrine of Ideas' (Oxford, 1909): Paul Natorp 'Platos Ideenlehre' (Leipzig, 1921): Sir David Ross 'Plato's Theory of Ideas' (Oxford, 1951). Hegel deals at length with Plato's philosophy in his 'Lectures on the History of Philosophy' (tr. Haldane and Simson, 3 vols. London, 1963) vol. II pp. 1–117.

200, 40

See E. A. Wallis Budge 'The Gods of the Egyptians' (2 vols. London, 1904) vol. II pp. 202–240: W. H. Roscher 'Ausführliches Lexikon der Griechischen und Römischen Mythologie' (6 vols. Leipzig, 1890–1897) vol. II cols. 360–549.

In art, Isis is often represented as a matron, standing, draped in a long robe reaching to the ankles, mantle thrown over the shoulders and crossing the breast, where it is made into a large and very apparent knot, and often a veil, symbolic of secrecy. In her right hand is the sistrum, in her left a small ewer. Her hair is abundant, and on her forehead rises the lotus, emblem of the resurrection.

See George Sarton 'Why Isis' ('Isis' 1953 pp. 232–242).

201, 3

Johann Georg Hamann (1730–1788), the religious thinker and friend of Kant. His aphoristic and somewhat obscure style earned him the title of 'The Magus in the North'. In the intellectual history of his time he is mainly important on account of his rejection of the popular rationalistic philosophy of Moses Mendelssohn (1729–1786), his upholding of Christianity as the historical revelation of the Triune God, of Atonement and of Redemption, and his insistence on the importance of *inner experience*, expecially in matters of religion. His works were edited by F. Roth and G. A. Wiener (8 pts. in 9 vols. Berlin and Augsburg, 1821–1843), and while the first volumes of this edition were appearing, Hegel published a lengthy review of them: see 'Jahrbücher für wissenschaftliche Kritik' (1828 no. 77–80, 109–114), and 'Vermischte Schriften aus der Berliner Zeit' (ed. Glockner, Stuttgart, 1958) pp. 203–273: in which he indicates Hamann's importance in the reaction against the 'enlightenment' of the mid-eighteenth century. He also discusses the attitude towards word-analysis (pp. 248–253), but makes no mention of the observation cited here.

Joseph Nadler, in his 'Johann Georg Hamann. Sämtliche Werke' (6 vols. Vienna, 1949–1957) vol. vi p. 263 lists all the references to 'nature' to be found in these volumes, and observes that this is a key word in the formulation of Hamann's world-view. There is however no trace in this list of the passage, referred to by Hegel. Cf. R. Unger 'Hamanns Sprachtheorie' (Munich, 1904), Herbert Heinekamp 'Das Weltbild Johann Georg Hamanns' (Dissertation, Bonn, 1936), E. Jansen Schoonhoven 'Natuur en Genade bij Hamann' (Dissertation, Leyden, 1945), E. Metzke 'J. G. Hamanns Stellung in der Philosophie des 18 Jahrhunderts' (Halle, 1934), R. G. Smith 'J. G. Hamann, with Selections from his Writings' (London, 1960).

The point of Hamann's remark is that the understanding has to *interpret* nature if it is to make it intelligible, just as the pronunciation of Hebrew words has to be indicated by inserting punctuation. He is not saying that the word 'nature' (Germ. Natur, Latin natura, from 'nasci' to be born or to emerge) is of Hebrew *origin*.

201, 27

Schelling first gave it this name in 1801. The philosophy attempted to demonstrate that subject and object, thought and being, mind and matter, are merely various aspects or phenomenal forms of a single actuality, that they are in fact 'identical', or rather that they all cohere in the ultimate, indeterminate and absolute foundation of things. See his 'Werke' ed. M. Schröter, vol. iii (1801–1806), supplementary volume ii (1804), (Munich, 1958): cf. R. Eisler 'Wörterbuch der Philosophischen Begriffe' (3 vols. Berlin, 1927–1930) vol. i pp. 708–713.

201, 31

See § 330.

202, 32

Goethe 'Faust' pt. i lines 1938–1941. Hegel misquotes the original somewhat and gives it as follows:

'Ενχείρησιν naturae nennt's die Chemie,
Spottet ihrer selber und weiß wie,
Hat freilich die Theile in ihrer Hand,
Fehlt leider nur das geistige Band.'

Cf. E. O. von Lippmann 'Encheiresis naturae' in 'Chemiker Zeitung' Jahrgang 31 p. 172 (Cöthen, 1907), 'Goethe Jahrbuch' 1908 p. 163 ff., 'Abhandlungen und Vorträge zur Geschichte der Naturwissenschaft' vol. II pp. 439–449 (Leipzig, 1913).

'Encheiresis naturae' means literally grasping nature with one's hands. The chemist J. K. Spielmann (1722–1783), whom Goethe had as a teacher in Strassburg, used the expression to describe the method of research which attempts to trace the creativeness of nature by breaking living being down into its parts. Cf. H. Kopp 'Aurea catena Homeri' (Braunschweig, 1880) pp. 5–7.

203, 8

Der philosophischen Allgemeinheit sind die Bestimmungen nicht gleichgültig'. Literally, 'To philosophic universality, the determinations are not indifferent'.

203, 35

Hegel is evidently quoting this poem from memory, for he makes twelve minor changes in it. It was published by *Goethe* in his 'Zur Morphologie' (1820): see 'Morphologische Hefte' (ed. D. Kuhn, Weimar, 1954) vol. I sect. iii p. 223, and introduced in the following way:

'Friendly Acclamation.

I am unable to conclude here without expressing a joy I have experienced repeatedly during the last few days. I feel the happiness of being in harmony with earnest and active investigators wherever they may be, for they are ready to emphasize that while an unsearchability has to be presumed and admitted, no limits ought to be placed upon the investigator.

Am I not bound to assume and allow my own being without ever actually knowing how I am constituted? Do I not continue to study myself without ever fully comprehending either myself or others? And yet despite this there is the continuous joy of perpetual progress.

So too with the world! May there be neither beginning nor end to what lies before us, may the vistas be without limit and that which is close to us impenetrable. Let this be so, for the extent and the depth to which the human spirit is able to penetrate into its own and the world's secrets can never be determined or circumscribed.

The expression of this joy in the following rhymes is to be taken and interpreted in the light of these remarks.'

Goethe is quoting the famous lines (289–290) in 'Die Falschheit menschlicher Tugenden' (1730) by Albrecht von Haller (1708–1777):

,Ins Innre der Natur dringt kein erschaffner Geist,
Zu glücklich, wann sie noch die äußre Schale weist!'

Kant's philosophy had thrown new light on Haller's assertion, and similar sentiments were expressed by Lessing and Wieland. It is not likely however that Goethe had any particular person in mind when he wrote, although it is just possible that 'Ueber meine gelehrte Bildung' (Berlin, 1799) by the author and bookseller C. F. Nicolai (1733–1811) caused him to *develop* the views he expresses. Cf. 'Faust' pt. i. 672–675.

204, 34

Genesis II 23.

205, 4

Plato 'Timaeus' 34c–35b, 'God, however, constructed Soul to be older than Body and prior in birth and excellence, since she was to be mistress and ruler and it the ruled; and He made her of the materials and in the fashion which I shall now describe.

Midway between the Being which is indivisible and remains always the same and the Being which is transient and divisible in bodies, He blended a third form of Being compounded out of the twain that is to say, out of the Same and the Other; and in like manner He compounded it midway between that one of them which is indivisible and that one which is divisible in bodies. And He took the three of them, and blent them all together into one form'.

Cf. A. E. Taylor 'A Commentary on Plato's Timaeus' (Oxford, 1928): G. M. A. Grube 'Plato's Thought' (London, 1935) ch. V: Hegel's 'Lectures on the History of Philosophy' (tr. Haldane and Simson, 3 vols. London, 1963) vol. II pp. 1–117.

205, 6

See Klopstock's famous question:

'Warum, da allein du dir genug warst, Erster, schaffst du? . . .
Wurdest dadurch du Seliger, daß du Seligkeit gabst?'

Schiller, in his poem 'Die Freundschaft', answers it in a way which Hegel evidently found very largely acceptable, since he refers to it in order to round off the peroration at the end of the 'Phenomenology of Spirit':

'Freundlos war der große Weltenmeister,
Fühlte Mangel — darum schuf er Geister,
Sel'ge Spiegel seiner Seligkeit!
Fand das höchste Wesen schon kein Gleiches,
Aus dem Kelch des ganzen Seelenreiches
Schäumt ihm — die Unendlichkeit.'

205, 27

Philo of Alexandria (c. 20 B.C.–c. A.D. 50) the Jewish thinker and exegete. Hegel discusses Philo's doctrines at some length in his 'History of Philosophy' (tr. Haldane and Simson, 3 vols. London, 1963) vol. II pp. 387–394. He evidently read him in an old seventeenth century edition: see 'Philonis Judaei Opera' (ed. A. Turnebo and D. Hoeschelio, Frankfurt, 1691); cf. 'Philonis Judaei opera Omnia, Graece et Latine' (ed. A. F. Pfeiffer, Erlangen, 1785).

H. A. Wolfson, in his 'Philo' (2 vols. Harvard Univ. Press, 1948) comments as follows upon the aspect of Philo's thought mentioned here by Hegel, 'It is because the Logos is conceived by Philo as both the totality of ideas and the totality of powers that sometimes as in the case of the ideas, he describes it as created. The Logos is thus spoken of as the eldest and most generic of created things, as "older than all things which were the objects of creation," as not being uncreated as God, though not created as human beings, as being the first-born son of God, the man of God, the image of God, second to God, a second God, and as being called a God by those who have an imperfect knowledge of the real God. An implication that the Logos is created is contained also in a passage where he says that "being the Logos of the Eternal (ἀιδίου) it is of necessity also itself incorruptible (ἄφθορτος)." Here, we take it, he uses the term "incorruptible" deliberately, in order to show that while God is "eternal", in the sense of being both ungenerated and incorruptible, the Logos is only "incorruptible" but not ungenerated.'

Cf. Philo's 'On Husbandry' (tr. Colson, Whitaker and Marcus, 12 vols Loeb, 1929–1962): J. Drummond 'Philo Judaeus' (2 vols. London, 1888): H. A. A. Kennedy 'Philo's Contribution to Religion' (London, 1919): E. R. Goodenough 'An Introduction to Philo Judaeus' (New Haven, Conn., 1940).

205, 31

This is almost certainly a reference to the whimsical speculations to be found in Kant's 'Allgemeine Naturgeschichte und Theorie des Himmels' (1755, 4th ed., Zeitz, 1808) pt. iii, 'The excellence of thinking natures, their quickness of apprehension, the clarity and vividness of their concepts, which come to them from impressions of the external world, their capacity to combine these concepts, and finally, their practical efficiency, in short the entire extent of their perfection, becomes higher and more complete in proportion to the remoteness of their dwelling place from the sun'.

Kant evidently speculated on the inhabitants of other planets on account of his having read Pope's 'Essay on Man' (epistle i); cf. Henry St. John Bolingbroke (1678–1751) 'Fragments' in 'Works' vol. VIII pp. 173 and 279. The origins of their ideas become apparent in the following passage from Addison's 'Spectator' (no. 621, Nov. 17, 1714), 'If the notion of a gradual rise in Beings from the meanest to the most High be not a vain imagination, it is not improbable that an Angel looks down upon a Man, as Man doth upon a Creature which approaches nearest to the rational Nature'. G. B. Shaw's 'Back to Methuselah' provides an instance of a fairly recent revival of similar imaginings.

206, 21

Schelling certainly makes remarks *resembling* this in his 'Ideen zu einer Philosophie der Natur' (1797, 2nd ed. 1803): 'Werke' ed. M. Schröter, vol. I pp. 653–723. See for example p. 717 ‚Die Natur, sofern sie als Natur, d.h. als diese besondere Einheit erscheint, ist demnach als solche schon außer dem Absoluten, nicht die Natur als der absolute Erkenntnißakt selbst (Natura naturans), sondern die Natur als der bloße Leib oder Symbol desselben (Natura naturata)'.

Cf. ‚Die Natur ist eine versteinerte Zauberstadt'.—Novalis 'Gesammelte Werke' (ed. C. Seelig, Zürich, 1946) vol. 4 p. 220.

209, 9

One of the clearest statements of this doctrine in classical literature is to be found in 'The Enneads' of *Plotinus* (tr. MacKenna and Page, 3rd ed. London, 1962) I 8, 7, III 6, 7: see especially the fourth tractate (II 4), 'The Matter in the Intellectual Realm is an Existent, for there is nothing previous to it except the Beyond-Existence; but what precedes the Matter of this sphere is Existence; by its alienism in regard to the beauty and good of Existence, Matter is therefore a non-existent'.

Cf. C. Baeumker 'Das Problem der Materie in der griechischen Philosophie' (Münster, 1890).

209, 18

Giulio Cesare Vanini (1584–1619) the Italian thinker. Hegel deals with his ideas at some length in his 'History of Philosophy' (3 vols. tr. Haldane and Simson, London, 1963) vol. III pp. 137–143. He was born at *Taurisano* in the kingdom of Naples, where his father managed the estates of the duke of that town. He was educated at the universities of Rome and Naples, where he studied mainly philosophy and theology, but where he also had a grounding in physics, astronomy and medicine. He was ordained priest at Padua.

Vanini's thinking was influenced by that of Ibn Averroes (1126–1198), Hieronymus Cardanus (1501–1576), Petrus Pomponatius (1462–1524) and Andreas Caesalpinus (1519–1603). Hegel notes that, 'he admires the living energy of Nature; his reasonings were not deep, but were more of the nature of fanciful ideas'. He developed a pantheistic view, regarding God as the infinite being which created the world, works within it, and is all in all. He tends to equate nature with God, while also regarding it as the *power* of God. He regards the world as being eternal, and matter as a unified and constant quantity.

He expressed his views, in the form of dialogues in two main works: 'Amphitheatrum aeternae providentiae divino-magicum' (Lyons, 1615), and 'De admirandis Naturae, reginae Deaque mortalium' (Paris, 1616). A French translation of these works was published by X. Rousselet in 1842, and there is an

Italian translation by L. Corvaglia 'Le opere di Giulio Cesare Vanini' (2 vols. Milan, 1933–1934).

He travelled widely in Europe, spreading his doctrines, and visited England in 1614, where he was imprisoned for 49 days: see E. Namer 'La Vita di Vanini in Inghilterra' (Lecce, 1933). He was eventually arrested in Toulouse in November 1618, brought before the Inquisition, condemned as an atheist on February 9, 1619, and executed ten days later.

Hegel is referring here to the account of a visit paid to Vanini by the president of the parliament of Toulouse while he was awaiting his execution: see Gabriel Bartholomi Grammond 'Historiarum Galliae ab excessu Henrici' (Toulouse, 1643) bk. III pp. 209–212, 'Lorsque Francon, homme de naissance et de probité, déposa que Vanini lui avait souvent nié l'existence de Dieu et s'était moqué en sa présence des mystères de la religion chrétienne. Vanini interrogé sur ce point répondit qu'il adorait avec l'Église un Dieu en trois personnes, et que la nature démonstrait evidemment l'existence de la Divinité. Ayant dans le même temps aperçu une paille qui était à ses pieds, il la prit, et fit un long discours sur la Providence en la construction de cette paille et en la production du blé, d'où il conclut que Dieu était le créature et l'auteur de tous les êtres. Mais, il disait cela plutôt par crainte que par une persuasion intérieur'.

Georg Gustav Fülleborn (1769–1803), in his 'Beyträge zur Geschichte der Philosophie' (12 pts. Züllichau and Freystadt, 1791–1799) pt. 5 (1795) pp. 1–31 translates some passages from Vanini's 'Amphiteatrum'. Fichte's being accused of atheism evidently motivated W. D. Fuhrmann into producing his excellent and scholarly, 'Leben und Schicksale, Geist, Character und Meynungen des Lucilio Vanini, eines angeblichen Atheisten im Siebzehnten Jahrhundert; nebst einer Untersuchung über die Frage: war derselbe ein Atheist oder nicht?' (Leipzig, 1800). The story concerning the straw is given on pp. 111–114 of this work. Cf. David Durand (1680–1763) 'The Life of Vanini, with an abstract of his writings' (London, 1730): John Owen 'The Skeptics of the Italian Renaissance' (London, 1893) pp. 345–419: E. Namer 'Documents sur la vie de Jules-César de Taurisano' (Bari, no date; published 1965).

210, 11

See the note III. 217.

210, 24

‚Der organiſche Körper iſt noch das Mannigfaltige, Außereinanderſeyende.'

211, 24

Jacob Boehme (1575–1624), the shoemaker of Görlitz. Hegel evidently has in mind the lengthy treatment of this subject in 'Aurora—the Day-Spring, or, the Dawning of the Day in the East; or, Morning-Redness in the Rising of the

Sun' (1612): see 'The Works of Jacob Behmen' (ed. Law, 4 vols. London, 1764–1781) vol. I pp. 1–269.

The relevant chapters are headed as follows: XII 'Of the Nativity and Life of the Holy Angels': XIII 'Of the terrible, doleful, and lamentable, miserable Fall of the Kingdom of Lucifer': XIV 'How Lucifer, who was the most beautiful Angel in Heaven, is become the most horrible Devil'. See ch. XII verse 129, 'Lucifer (was) created according to the Quality, Condition, and Beauty of God the Son, and was bound to and united with him in Love, as a dear Son or Heart, and his Heart also stood in the Center of Light, as if he had been God himself; and his Beauty or Brightness transcended all'. Cf. 'Mysterium Magnum' (1623) pt. I ch. XII verse 35 ('Works' III p. 54), 'And even then the Power of the expressed Word from the Light of the inward Nature did *pullulate*, and spring forth, through the external Nature, out of the Heaven through the *Earth*: (And so) now the Potentate, who was a King and a great Prince, has lost his Dominion; for the Essence of the *Wrath* was captivated in the Light of Nature, and he with it; and so he lies between Time and Eternity, imprisoned in the Darkness, till the Judgement of God'.

Similar passages are to be found in 'The Three Principles of the Divine Essence' (1619) ch. XII verses 25–30 ('Works' II p. 93) and 'The Threefold Life of Man' (1620) ch. IX verse 50.

In this connection it is interesting to remember that Hegel took *evil* to be 'nothing but the inadequacy of that which *is* to that which *should* be' ('Encyclopaedia' § 472, cf. §§ 23–35). see the note III. 330.

Cf. Jacob Böhme 'Sämtliche Schriften' (ed. Peuckert 11 vols. Stuttgart 1955–1961).

211, 31

Revelation I 8.

211, 37

See Hegel's 'Lectures on the Philosophy of Religion' (tr. Spiers and Sanderson, 3 vols. London, 1962) vol. I pp. 270–349, vol. II pp. 1–122.

212, 26

See the notes III. 229, 366.

213, 7

See the note III. 215.

213, 25

See the note II. 406.

214, 3

The central idea of emanation (Latin emanatio, from e-, out, manare, to flow), as Hegel notes, is that the universe of individuals consists of the involuntary outpourings of the ultimate divine essence. This essence is usually taken to be not only all-inclusive but also absolutely perfect, while the emanated individuals are regarded as degenerating in proportion to the degree of their 'distance' from it. In his 'Science of Logic' (tr. Johnston and Struthers, 2 vols. London, 1961) vol. II p. 170, Hegel treats the concept as a sub-category of actuality. For an account of its use in *European* thinking see R. Eisler 'Wörterbuch der Philosophischen Begriffe' (3 vols. Berlin, 1927–1930) vol. I pp. 321–322. As Hegel makes mention of 'fulgurations', particular attention, should perhaps be drawn to Leibniz's postulation of the 'prime monad' from which all created or derived productions appear, 'par des fulgurations continuelles de la Divinité de moment à moment, bornées par la réceptivité de la créature à laquelle il est essentiel d'être limitée': see 'The Monadology' (tr. Latta, Oxford, 1898) 47.

When he mentions the occurrence of emanation in *oriental* thinking, Hegel almost certainly has in mind the development of this doctrine in the 'Bhagavadgita': see S. Dasgupta 'A History of Indian Philosophy' (5 vols. Cambridge, 1922–1962) vol. II pp. 523–534: M. Hiriyanna 'Outlines of Indian Philosophy' (4th impression, London, 1958) ch. IV: Hegel's review 'Über die unter dem Namen Bhagavad-Gita bekannte Episode des Mahabharata; von Wilhelm von Humboldt' (1826), in 'Berliner Schriften 1818–1831' (ed. Hoffmeister, Hamburg, 1956) pp. 85–154.

Cf. F. von Schlegel 'Ueber die Sprache und Weisheit der Indier' (Heidelberg, 1808): E. Frauwallner 'Geschichte der indischen Philosophie' (2 vols. Salzburg, 1953–1956).

214, 40

Jacques Tissot quotes this axiom in his 'Discours véritable de la Vie . . . du Géant Theutobocus' (Lyons, 1613): this work is republished in E. Fournier's 'Variétés historiques et littéraires' (Paris, 1855–1863): see vol. 9 p. 247, 'Operatur natura quantum et quamdiu potest, sans neant moins faire aucum sault ab extremis ad extrema. Natura enim in operationibus suis non facit saltum'—Nature in her operations does not proceed by leaps. At almost the same time, Sir Edward Coke (1552–1634) applied it to the law: see 'The first part of the Institutes of the Lawes of England' (London, 1628) pp. 238b, 239, 'Natura non facit saltus, ita nec lex'.

Hegel probably came across the saying in the preface to Leibniz's 'Nouveaux Essais' (1704, ed. Boutroux, Paris, 1886) p. 135, 'C'est une de mes grandes maximes et des plus vérifiées, que la nature ne fait jamais des sauts'. Cf. Linnaeus 'Philosophia Botanica' (Stockholm, 1751) p. 27, Sect. 77. 'Primum et ultimum hoc in botanicis desideratum est, *Natura non facit saltus*'.

In the quantum theory and quantum mechanics of present day theoretical physics however, it is assumed that the elements only make *abrupt* and *discontinuous* transitions in passing from one state to another.

215, 10

F. Nicolin and O. Pöggeler in their edition of the 'Enzyklopädie' (Hamburg, 1959) omit the word ,individuellen' at this juncture (p. 203).

215, 30

In a footnote here, Hegel refers to Wilhelm Traugott Krug (1770–1842), 'This is what Mr. *Krug* did, in what was at the same time a wholly naïve request, when he set the philosophy of nature the *modest* task of deducing his quill. If it were possible that the time should come when science should be so advanced and perfected in all the more important matters of heaven and earth, the present and the past, that there should be nothing more important to be explained, then one might have been able to offer him hope with regard to the accomplishment of this undertaking and the proper glorification of *his* quill'.

Hegel deals very shortly with Krug's ideas in the 'History of Philosophy' (tr. Haldane and Simson, 3 vols. London, 1963) vol. III p. 511–512. His main treatment of him is to be found in a hard-hitting article published in the 'Critical Journal of Philosophy' (vol. I art. i, 1802): cf. 'Aufsätze aus dem kritischen Journal der Philosophie' (ed. Glockner, Stuttgart, 1958) pp. 193–212: 'Wie der gemeine Menschenverstand die Philosophie nehme'. In this work he singles out Krug's 'Briefe über die Wissenschaftslehre' (Leipzig, 1800) 'Briefe über den neuesten Idealism' (Leipzig, 1801), and 'Entwurf eines neuen Organons der Philosophie' (Meissen and Lübben, 1801). W. T. Stace, in 'The Philosophy of Hegel' (Dover ed. 1955) thinks that Krug may well have made an important point here, but these lectures should have clarified the issue for him. Hegel is surely justified in concentrating upon assessments of the *generalized* subject-matter of the natural sciences rather than *particularities*. Particular phenomena certainly provide an essential foundation for these generalizations, but it is the *generalizations* which make *further* particularities *intelligible*, and not vice versa.

Krug studied at Wittenberg, Jena and Göttingen, and habilitated as a university teacher at Wittenberg in 1794 with a dissertation, 'De pace inter philosophos'. In 1800 he published 'Philosophie der Ehe' and in 1802 replied to Hegel's attacks in two pamphlets, 'Wie der ungemeine Menschenverstand die Philosophie nehme', and 'Der Widerstreit der Vernunft mit sich selbst'. He married the daughter of a major general in 1803, and ten years later volunteered for the army. In 1815 he published 'System der Kriegswissenschaft'.

He succeeded Kant as professor of philosophy at Königsberg in 1804, and in 1809 gained an appointment at Leipzig, where he remained for the rest of his life, becoming 'Rektor' of the university there in 1830. In all, he published no less than 189 works, and towards the close of his life attempted various syntheses of knowledge, *alphabetical* in 'Allgemeines Handwörterbuch der philosophischen Wissenschaften' (4 vols. Leipzig, 1827–1829), and *co-educational* in 'Universalphilosophische Vorlesungen für Gebildete beiderlei Geschlechts' (Neustadt, 1831). He first published his autobiography in 1825, and re-issued it with supplementary information during the railway boom seventeen years later: see his 'Lebensreise in 6 Stazionen von ihm selbst beschrieben' (Leipzig, 1842). On his *political* views see Alfred Fiedler 'Die staatswissenschaftliche Anschauung und die politisch-publizistische Tätigkeit des Nachkantianers W. T. Krug' (Dissertation, Leipzig, 1933); 'Krug's Gesammelte Schriften' (12 vols. Brunswick, 1830–1841).

216, 30

See Robert Southey (1774–1843) 'The Poet's Pilgrimage to Waterloo' (1816) pt. II ii 20:—

'The winds which have in viewless heaven their birth,
The waves which in their fury meet the clouds,
The central storms which shake the solid earth,
And from volcanoes burst in fiery floods,
Are not more vague and purportless and blind,
Than is the course of things among mankind.'

217, 32

The lay-out of this § adopted by F. Nicolin and O. Pöggeler in their edition of the 'Enzyklopädie' (Hamburg, 1959) has been reproduced in this translation.

218, 36

'nicht mit der wahrhaften Sphäre'.

221, 12

For a criticism of the term 'mechanics', and the general background to the Newtonian world-picture, see E. J. Dijksterhuis 'The Mechanization of the World Picture' (Oxford, 1961). For a recent general history of mechanics see R. Dugas 'A History of Mechanics' (tr. Maddox, London, 1957).

223, 8

See J. T. Baker 'An historical and critical examination of English space and time theories' (New York, 1930). M. Jammer 'Concepts of Space' (New York, 1960): A. Grünbaum 'Philosophical Problems of Space and Time' (New York, 1963).

J. J. C. Smart has made an interesting collection of passages and papers on the subject in his 'Problems of Space and Time' (London, 1964).

223, 10

Kant's views on space underwent considerable development: see C. B. Garnett 'The Kantian Philosophy of Space' (New York, 1939). Hegel is evidently referring to the mature exposition of them in the 'Critique of Pure Reason'. See J. J. C. Smart 'Problems of Space and Time' (London, 1964) pp. 104–125.

Kant denied that space is an empirical concept derived from experiences of objective phenomena, because he took it to be a necessary *presupposition* of these experiences. He therefore regarded it as an *a priori* representation underlying all our intuitions of the external world. As he took it to *underlie* them, he regarded it not as a general concept arising from the relations of things in general, but as a *pure intuition*, which is essentially one.

From this line of reasoning he concluded: (*a*) That space represents neither any property of things in themselves, nor any relation between them. (*b*) That space is nothing but the *subjective* condition of sensibility, under which alone intuition of objectivity is possible for us.

Cf. B. Russell's critical analysis of Kant's theory of space and its bearing upon the distinction between logic, and mathematics in 'The Principles of Mathematics' (7th impression, London, 1956).

223, 24

'The Logic of Hegel' (tr. Wallace, Oxford, 1963) pp. 189–190.

224, 5

Cf. 'The Logic' §§ 84–86. Just as Being is the most comprehensive and primary *category* of the logic, so space is the most comprehensive and primary *stage* of nature. This observation underlines the fact that Hegel regarded the overall structure of the philosophy of nature as a reformation in natural *phenomena* of the *logical* pattern exhibited in the first part of the 'Encyclopaedia'.

224, 23

See John Keill (1671–1721) 'An introduction to natural philosophy' (4th ed. London, 1745) p. 15, 'We conceive space to be that, wherein all Bodies are placed, or, to speak with the Schools, have their Ubi; that it is altogether penetrable, receiving all Bodies into itself, and refusing ingress to nothing whatsoever; that it is immovably fixed, capable of no Action, Form or Quality; whose Parts it is impossible to separate from each other, by any Force however great; but the space itself remaining immovable, receives the Successions of things in Motion, determines the velocities of their Motions, and measures the distances of the things themselves'.

224, 29

See Euclid's definition of a point as, 'that which has no part': T. L. Heath 'The Thirteen Books of Euclid's Elements' (3 vols. Cambridge, 1908) vol. I p. 153. Heath discusses the difficulties Aristotle encountered in dealing with similar definitions, see his 'Mathematics in Aristotle' (Oxford, 1949) pp. 89–90. Cf. B. Russell 'The Principles of Mathematics' (7th impression, London, 1956) pp. 445–455. Hegel's statement that there can *be* no such thing as a point accords well with subsequent views on the subject. Cf. H. M. Weber and J. Wellstein 'Encyclopädie der elementaren Mathematik' (Leipzig and Berlin, 1905) vol. II p. 9, 'This notion (the point) is evolved from the notion of the real or supposed *material* point by the process of limits, i.e. by an act of the mind which sets a term to a series of presentations in itself unlimited. Suppose a grain of sand or a mote in a sunbeam, which continually becomes smaller and smaller. In this way vanishes more and more the possibility of determining still smaller atoms in the grain of sand, and there is evolved, so we say, with growing certainty, the presentation of the point as a definite position in space which is one and is incapable of further division. But this view is untenable; we have, it is true, some idea how the grain of sand gets smaller and smaller, but only so long as it remains just visible; after that we are completely in the dark, and we cannot see or imagine the further diminution. That this procedure comes to an end is unthinkable; that nevertheless there exists a term beyond which it cannot go, we must believe or postulate without ever reaching it . . . It is a pure act of *will*, not of the understanding'. Cf. Max Simon 'Euklid und die sechs planimetrischen Bücher' (Leipzig, 1901).

Hegel's dialectical assessment of the point throws light on the nature of this 'act of will'. What is more, the problem of the point as stated by Weber, Wellstein and Simon, tends to confirm the validity of Hegel's transition from the being-for-self of the Idea (§ 244), to space as implicitly three-dimensional. i.e. Notional (§ 255), and of his characterisation of space as 'a non-sensuous sensibility' (i.e. its *natural* aspect), and a 'sensuous insensibility' (i.e. its *logical* aspect).

See F. Robartes 'On the proportion of mathematical points to each other' ('Phil. Trans. Roy. Soc.' vol. 27 p. 470). In the light of Hegel's subsequent analysis of the point, the line and the plane it may be of interest to note that Roberts regards the point of contact between a sphere and a plane as being infinitely greater than that between a circle and a line. Cf. Andrzej Grzegorczyk 'Axiomatizability of geometry without points' in 'The Concept and Role of the Model in Mathematics' (ed. Kazemier, Dordrecht, 1961).

224, 31

'die Welt ist nirgends mit Brettern zugenagelt.' See K. Simrock 'Die deutschen Sprichwörter' (Frankfurt-on-Main, 1845) no. 1297: K. F. W. Wander 'Deutsches Sprichwörter-Lexikon' (5 vols. 1867–1880) vol. V col. 166. The *pro-*

verb is usually explained as meaning that a capable person will get on anywhere, but in German *folklore* the remark seems to have had another significance.

Johann *Sommer* (1559–1622) 'Olorinus' or 'Variscus' as he sometimes called himself, the protestant botanist, translator, folklorist, satirist, tragedian and theologian from Zwickau, in his 'Ethnographia Mundi. Lustige, Artige, und Kurtzweilige, jedoch Warhafftige und Glaubwirdige Beschreibung der heutigen Newen Welt' (Magdeburg, 1609) p. 17 makes mention of a traveller who has been to the end of the world and found it boarded up. There is also a folk-tale from *Ditmarsh* according to which, 'The world beyond Husum is in fact boarded up. A giant sits there at the furthest end of it, and has the sun on a rope. Every morning he winds it up, and in the evening lets it down again'. See Carl Müllenhof 'Sagen, Märchen, und Lieder der Herzogthümer Schleswig-Holstein und Lauenburg' (Kiel, 1845) no. 1921 p. 378.

225, 11

In Hegel's day it was usual to overcome this problem simply by following Newton and distinguishing between *absolute* and *relative* space: see 'Mathematical Principles' (ed. Cajori, Berkeley, 1947), the scholium following the initial definitions, 'Absolute space, in its own nature, without relation to anything external, remains always similar and immovable. Relative space is some movable dimension or measure of the absolute spaces: which our senses determine by its position to bodies; and which is commonly taken for immovable space; such is the dimension of a subterraneous, an aerial, or celestial space, determined by its position in respect of the earth. Absolute and relative space are the same in figure and magnitude; but they do not remain always numerically the same'. Cf. Charles Hutton (1737–1823) 'A Philosophical and Mathematical Dictionary' (2 vols. London, 1815) vol. II pp. 416–417.

Hegel is therefore attempting to assess what was usually referred to as absolute space, in its relation not to 'bodies', but to the concepts of Euclidean geometry. Kant (see notes pp. 306 and 309) has clearly influenced his formulation of this transition.

Cf. Bishop Berkeley's objections to absolute space in his 'Principles of Human Knowledge' (1710) and 'The Analyst' (Dublin, 1734), and the note by Cajori (op. cit. pp. 639–644).

225, 12

,Er ist also eine unsinnliche Sinnlichkeit, und eine sinnliche Unsinnlichkeit.' See the note on p. 307. The 'non-sensuous sensibility' of space is its *natural* aspect, its 'sensuous insensibility' is its *logical* aspect. It is this, its dual nature, which gave rise to Hegel's making use of it in the transition from logic to nature. Cf. G. J. Whitrow 'Why physical space has three dimensions' ('British Journal for the Philosophy of Science' vol. 6 pp. 13–31, 1955).

225, 17

Leibniz treats this subject most extensively in his correspondence with Samuel Clarke (1675–1729): see 'A collection of papers, which passed between the late learned Mr. Leibniz and Dr. Clarke in the years 1715 and 1716 relating to the principles of natural philosophy and religion' (London, 1717, ed. H. G. Alexander, Manchester, 1956) paper III sects. 3–6, paper V sects. 32–124. See also his 'Mathematische Schriften' (ed. C. I. Gerhardt, 7 vols. Berlin and Halle, 1849–1863; reprinted Hildesheim, 1962) vol. VII p. 17 ff.: 'Hauptschriften zur Grundlegung der Philosophie' (5 vols. Leipzig, 1904–1906) vol. I p. 53 ff. 'Nouveaux Essais sur l'entendement humain' (Eng. tr. A. G. Langley, Chicago, 1949) II ch. 13 § 17.

As against Descartes, Leibniz held a *relational* theory of space, whereby space is in no sense a materiality, but merely a system of relations dependent upon the relationships between the indivisible substances or 'monads.'

225, 28

Cf. the treatment of space in Kant's 'Critique of Pure Reason' (note p. 306) § 3, 'Geometry is a science which determines the properties of space synthetically, and yet *a priori*. What, then, must be our representation of space, in order that such knowledge of it may be possible? It must in its origin be intuition; for from a mere concept no propositions can be obtained which go beyond the concept—as happens in geometry . . . Further, this intuition must be *a priori*, that is, it must be found in us prior to any perception of an object, and must therefore be pure, not empirical, intuition. For geometrical propositions are one and all apodeictic, that is, are bound up with the consciousness of their necessity; for instance, that space has only three dimensions. Such propositions cannot be empirical or, in other words, judgements of experience, nor can they be derived from any such judgements . . .

How, then can there exist in the mind an outer intuition which precedes the objects themselves, and in which the concept of these objects can be determined *a priori*? Manifestly, not otherwise than in so far as the intuition has its seat in the subject only, as the formal character of the subject in virtue of which, in being affected by objects, it obtains *immediate representation*, that is, *intuition* of them; and only in so far, therefore, as it is merely the form of outer sense in general.

Our explanation is thus the only explanation that makes intelligible the *possibility* of geometry, as a body of *a priori* synthetic knowledge.'

When B. Russell (note p. 306) criticizes Kant for distinguishing between logic and mathematics in this way, he has some common ground with Hegel, who is here indicating the *logical antecedent* of the three dimensions of classical geometry.

When he sketches the extent to which he regards geometry as being susceptible to dialectical assessment (§ 256), Hegel refers to Euclid. He refuses however to treat Euclidean geometry as being rigorously philosophical, despite his having dialectically assessed several of its axioms. This is almost certainly due to the developments then taking place in non-Euclidean geometry. See the letter written by K. F. Gauss (1777–1855) to his friend H.W. M. Olbers (1758–1840) in 1817, 'I become more and more convinced that our geometry cannot be demonstrated, at least neither by, nor for, the human intellect. In some future life, perhaps, we may have other ideas about the nature of space which, at present, are inaccessible to use. Geometry therefore, has to be ranked until such time not with arithmetic, which is of a purely aprioristic nature, but with mechanics': Gauss's 'Werke' (Leipzig, 1863–1903) vol. VIII p. 177. Cf. A. Vucinich 'Nikolai Ivanovich Lobachevskii: the man behind the first non-Euclidean geometry' ('Isis' 1962 pp. 465–481).

The validity of Euclid's fifth axiom, 'That if a straight line falling on two other straight lines make the alternate angles equal to one another, the two straight lines shall be parallel to one another' was defended by Girolamo Saccheri (1667–1733) in his 'Euclidis ab omni naevo vindicatus' (Milan, 1733), but this work merely initiated a widespread questioning of the demonstrability of the postulate, which by the early decades of the last century had already given rise to an extensive literature: see G. S. Klügel (1739–1812) 'Conatuum praecipuorum theoriam parallelarum demonstrandi recensio' (Göttingen, 1763), J. H. Lambert (1728–1777) 'Zur Theorie der Parallellinien' (Leipzig, 1786): G. S. Klügel 'Mathematisches Wörterbuch' (7 vols. Leipzig, 1803–1836) vol. III pp. 727–739: J. W. Müller 'Auserlesene mathematische Bibliothek' (Nuremberg, 1829): F. Engel and P. Stäckel 'Theorie der Parallellinien von Euclid bis Gauss' (Leipzig, 1895): D. M. Y. Somerville 'Bibliography of Non-Euclidean Geometry' (St. Andrews, 1911): R. Bonola 'Non Euclidean Geometry' (Chicago, 1912).

226, 18

This definition of the line overcomes the objection Aristotle raised against Euclid's Platonic definition of it as 'breadthless length': 'The Thirteen Books of Euclid's Elements' (3 vols. Cambridge, 1908) vol. I pp. 153–165. See Aristotle's 'Topics' VI. 6. 143^{b}–144^{a}4, 'Again there is the case where one divides the genus by negation, as those do who define a line as "breadthless length". This signifies nothing except that it has not any breadth. The effect in this case will be that the genus will partake of the species; for every length is either breadthless or possessed of breadth, because either an affirmation or the corresponding negation is true of anything whatever . . . This commonplace rule is of service in arguing with those who assume the existence of "Forms".'

Aristotle's conception of the line ('Metaphysics' 1016^{b}25–27) is closer to Hegel's in that he regards it as a magnitude 'divisible in one way only', in contrast to a magnitude divisible in two ways (a surface), and a magnitude divisible 'in all or three ways' (a body).

See T. L. Heath 'Mathematics in Aristotle' (Oxford, 1949) pp. 88–91.

226, 26

Cf. T. L. Heath op. cit. I pp. 169–176. Hegel is here reconstructing the following of Euclid's definitions:—

no. 5 'A surface is that which has length and breadth only'.

no. 6 'The extremities of a surface are lines'.

no. 7 'A plane surface is a surface which lies evenly with the straight lines on itself'.

For an almost contemporary discussion of the evolution of the properties of the plane, see A. L. Crelle (1780–1855) 'Zur Theorie der Ebene' ('Abhandlugen der Königlichen Akademie der Wissenschaften zu Berlin' 1834 pp. 23–64).

227, 9

See Aristotle 'De Anima' I. 4, 409 a 4, 'They say that a line by its motion produces a surface and a point by its motion a line'.

Proclus (410–485) defines the line as the 'flux of a point' (ῥύσις σημείου), i.e. the path of a point when *moved*. See Thomas Taylor (1758–1835) 'The Philosophical and Mathematical Commentaries of Proclus on the first Book of Euclid's Elements' (London, 1792).

227, 23

In the 'Critique of Pure Reason' (Introduction), Kant defines analytical judgements as being those in which the connection of the predicate with the subject is cogitated through identity, and synthetical judgements as being those in which this connection is cogitated without identity. He therefore takes the intuition to be an essential factor in the formation of synthetical judgements. Cf. H. Feigl 'Some Major Issues and developments in the philosophy of science and logical empiricism.' ('Minnesota Studies in the Philosophy of Science' 3 vols. Minneapolis, 1962) I pp. 3–37: cf. III pp. 357–397.

Hegel is referring to the following passage (op. cit. Introduction V i), 'A straight line between two points is the shortest', is a synthetical proposition. For my conception of *straight* contains no notion of *quantity*, but is merely *qualitative*. The conception of the *shortest* is therefore wholly an addition, and by no analysis can it be extracted from our conception of a straight line. Intuition must therefore here lend its aid, by means of which and thus only, our synthesis is possible.'

Kant may also have been led to regard this as a synthetical proposition involving intuition on account of his having entertained the possibility of there being different *kinds of space*, arising out of different *gravitational relationships*: see N. K. Smith 'A Commentary to Kant's 'Critique of Pure Reason'. (London, 1918) pp. 117 ff, 128 ff. For an exhaustive treatment of the subject, see C. B. Garnett 'The Kantian Philosophy of Space' (New York, 1939).

227, 27

'The Logic of Hegel' (tr. Wallace, Oxford, 1963) pp. 366–367.

228, 2

,denn zum Zweiten gehören ebenso gut zwei, als zur Zwei'.

228, 16

This is a reference to Euclid's 'Elements' bk. I prop. 4, 'If two triangles have two sides of the one equal to two sides of the other, each to each, and have also the angles contained by those sides equal to one another, they shall also have their bases or third sides equal; and the two triangles shall be equal; and their other angles shall be equal, each to each, namely, those to which the equal sides are opposite.'

Euclid proves this by *superposition*, a method which he evidently disliked. The first triangle is taken up and *placed on* the second, so that the parts of the triangles which are known to be equal *fall upon* each other. Jacques Peletier (1517–1582) was one of the first to point out that the mere superpositing of lines and figures does not constitute a geometrical proof: see his note on this proposition in his 'In Euclidis Elementa geometrica demonstrationum libri sex' (Lugduni, 1557).

Although John Playfair (1748–1819), in his 'Elements of geometry' (Edinburgh, 1826) pp. 427–429 defends the 'purity' of Euclid's reasoning at this juncture, by Hegel's day it was usual to say that this proof is unsatisfactory because it introduces *motion* into geometry, and presupposes the axiom that figures may be *moved* without change of shape or size. Hegel's assessment of the matter is surely more to the point, and is in substantial agreement with D. Hilbert's statement that Euclid would have done better to assume this proposition as an axiom: see 'Grundlagen der Geometrie' (Leipzig, 1899) p. 12: Eng. tr. by Townsend 'The Foundations of Geometry' (London, 1902) p. 9.

Cf. Moritz Pasch 'Vorlesungen über neuere Geometrie' (Leipzig, 1882) § 13, Grundsatz ix: B. Russell 'The Principles of Mathematics' (7th impression, London, 1956) pp. 404–407. Russell follows Pasch and Hilbert, and gives a brilliant and colourful exposition of the subject. A manuscript of Hegel's, dated Mainz, 23rd Sept. 1800, and now in the Harvard University Library, shows the care with which he considered this and related problems: Johannes Hoffmeister 'Dokumente zu Hegels Entwicklung' (Stuttgart, 1936) pp. 288–300, 470–473.

228, 29

Euclid's 'Elements' bk. I prop. 47, 'In right-angled triangles the square on the side subtending the right angle is equal to the squares on the sides containing the right angle.' See the detailed account of the ways in which Pythagoras may have discovered this theorem in T. L. Heath 'The Thirteen Books of Euclid's Elements' (3 vols. Cambridge, 1918) vol. I pp. 349–368.

In Hegel's day the standard German edition of Euclid was that of J. F. Lorenz

(1738–1807) 'Euclid's Elemente, fünfzehn Bücher aus dem Griechischen übersetzt' (3rd edition ed. K. Mollweide, Halle, 1809).

228, 35

For the definition of the circle based on the equality of the radii see Euclid's 'Elements' bk. I def. 15.

The 'higher definition of the circle' mentioned here by Hegel is the standard definition of analytical geometry, employing Cartesian co-ordinates: see R. Descartes 'Geometry' (tr. Smith and Latham, La Salle, 1924). For every point of the circumference of a circle with the origin of the co-ordinate-system as centre, we have from Pythagoras's theorem the equation

$$x^2 + y^2 = r^2$$

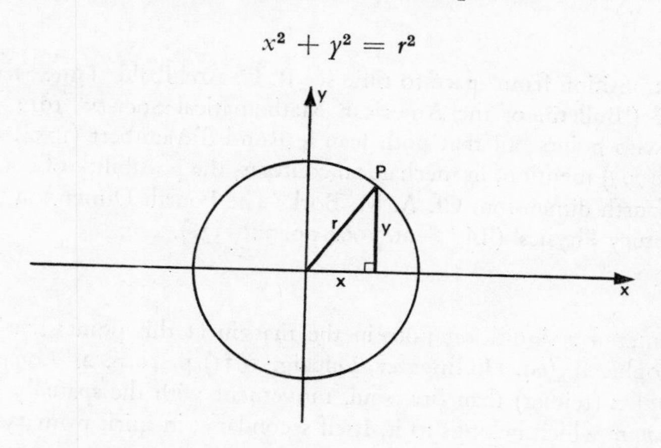

Cf. Gaspard Monge (1746–1818) 'Feuilles d'analyse appliquée à la Géométrie' (Paris, 1801): T. L. Heath 'A Manual of Greek Mathematics' (Oxford, 1931) p. 96: C. B. Boyer 'A History of Analytical Geometry' (New York, 1957): H. Eves 'An introduction to the history of mathematics' (New York, 1953) ch. X.

228, 40

This is not quite accurate. The concluding proposition of bk. I is *no. 48*, 'If in a triangle the square on one of the sides be equal to the squares on the remaining two sides of the triangle, the angle contained by the remaining two sides of the triangle is right.' Pythagoras's theorem is presented by Euclid as no. 47. The concluding proposition of bk. II (no. 14) is, 'To construct a square equal to a given rectilineal figure.' T. L. Heath 'The Thirteen Books of Euclid's Elements' (3 vols. Cambridge, 1908) vol. I.

229,4

Johann Karl Friedrich Rosenkranz (1805–1879), in his 'Kritische Erläuterungen des Hegel'schen Systems' (Königsberg, 1840), puts forward a 'Probe eines Commentar's zu Hegels Lehre von Raum und Zeit' (1835), in which he attempts to develop geometry dialectically. He points out that there are right-angles, acute and obtuse *angles*, equilateral, scalene and isosceles *triangles*, that *four-sided plane figures* are either squares, parallelograms or trapeziums, and that the relation of all straight-lined figurations within the *circle* might be used to round off such an exposition.

The *triadic* nature of such a geometry is clear enough, but it can hardly be regarded as *dialectical*.

Cf. Erwin Metzke 'Karl Rosenkranz und Hegel' (Leipzig, 1929): Hermann Lübbe 'Die Hegelsche Rechte' (Stuttgart and Bad Cannstadt, 1962).

229, 12

On this transition from space to time see R. C. Archibald 'Time as a Fourth Dimension' ('Bulletin of the American Mathematical Society' 1914, 20: pp. 409–412), who points out that both Jean le Rond d'Alembert (1754) and J. L. Lagrange (1797) mention, in mechanical contexts, the possibility of considering time as a fourth dimension. Cf. A. M. Bork 'The Fourth Dimension in Nineteenth-Century Physics' ('Isis' Sept. 1964 pp. 326–338).

229, 17

Hegel entered a significant note in the margin at this point: see 'Jenenser Realphilosophie II' (ed. Hoffmeister, Leipzig, 1931) p. 10 n. 2, '*Leaping point*-more complex (reicher) than fire, soul, movement with the spatially involved *power* of *nature* which belongs to it. Itself secondary; in spirit primary.' Cf. the note III. 315.

229, 30

Cf. Aristotle's comparison of the 'now' in time and the point in space ('Physics' IV. 10. 218 a 6–8; II. 219^{b} 11–15; 220 a 4–13, 18–21). This is discussed by T. L. Heath in his 'Mathematics in Aristotle' (Oxford, 1949) pp. 120–121.

230, 5

Cf. Kant's 'Critique of Pure Reason' sect. II § 4, 'Time is a necessary representation that underlies all intuitions. We cannot, in respect of appearances in general, remove time itself, though we can quite well think time as void of appearances. Time is, therefore, given *a priori*. In it alone is actuality of appearances possible at all. Appearances may, one and all, vanish; but time (as the univeral condition of their possibility) cannot itself be removed.'

230, 12

See Robert Adamson 'Fichte' (London, 1881) p. 145 ff. Cf. the note III. 301.

230, 14

Cf. 'The Logic of Hegel' (tr. Wallace, Oxford, 1963) § 88. The position of 'becoming' in the logic, corresponds to that of time in the philosophy of nature.

230, 17

,die abstrakt sich auf sich beziehende'. In the 1817 edition of the 'Encyclopaedia' this phrase occurs as 'abstrakte sich auf sich beziehende'.

230, 27

Cronos (time) was originally a harvest god, and presided over the Golden Age of the world, when the earth brought forth of its own accord, and all men lived in peace and charity. He was one of the Titans, son of Uranus (the sky) and Gaea (the earth), and came to rule the world by overthrowing his father with the aid of his mother.

He married his sister Rhea (Cybele, the power of nature), and became the father of Hestia (the family), Demeter (agriculture), Hera (wifehood), Poseidon (the sea), Hades (wealth), and Zeus (supreme brightness). Fearing the prophecy that he also would be overthrown by his own offspring, he swallowed his children as soon as they were born. Rhea saved Zeus however, and when the boy had grown to maturity, he forced his father to disgorge his brothers and sisters. The subsequent war of the Titans against the gods resulted in the overthrow of Cronos and his confinement in Tartarus.

See Hesiod 'Theogony' 167 ff; 485 ff; 617 ff; 'Works and Days' 169 ff: 'Paulys Real-Encylopädie der Classischen Altertumswissenschaft' (ed. Wissowa and Kroll, Stuttgart, 1922) vol. XI cols. 1982–2018.

232, 12

See Goethe and Schiller 'Xenien' (note p. 293):

> ,Warum bin ich vergänglich, o Zeus?' fragte die Schönheit.
> ,Macht' ich doch' sagte der Gott, ,nur das Vergängliche schön'.

Cf. Ben Jonson's 'Ode Pindaric to the immortal Memory' etc. in his 'Underwoods':

> 'It is not growing like a tree
> In bulk, doth make men better be.' etc.

232, 37

The general lay-out of the Hegelian system has to be borne in mind if this exposition of time is to be fully intelligible. The *Logic* does not involve time, and so endures on account of the imperfection of its abstract universality. The things of *Nature* give rise to the process of time through the restlessness and contradiction of their externality and finitude. *Spirit* is above time in that the universality of the Idea is realized within it. This realization involves eliciting the *Notion* of time, which is what Hegel is attempting to do in these paragraphs.

It was evidently Kant's characterization of time as a pure form of intuition, which helped to form the distinctive features of Hegel's thinking at this juncture, although he rejects Kant's assertion that time involves the difference between objectivity and a distinct subjective consciousness.

Kant's work is to be seen against the background of early eighteenth century thinking on this subject. Newton for example distinguished between *absolute* and *relative* time, 'Absolute, true, and mathematical time, of itself, and from its own nature, flows equably without relation to anything external, and by another name is called duration: relative, apparent, and common time, is some sensible and external (whether accurate or unequable) measure of duration by the means of motion, which is commonly used instead of true time; such as an hour, a day, a month, a year.'—'Mathematical Principles' (ed. Cajori, Berkeley, 1947), the scholium following the initial definitions. Ernst Mach (1838–1916) 'The Science of Mechanics' (tr. Mc. Cormack, Chicago and London, 1919) II vi, 2 and Cajori (op. cit. pp. 640–641) both criticize Newton for postulating an abstract absolute time, 'since our knowledge of time can only be based upon our observation of the changes of things'. Kant took a step forward here in that he showed that knowledge of these things would be impossible without the *presupposition* of time. Hegel disregarded Kant's peculiar epistemological considerations, and simply treated time as the sequence of space and the antecedent of motion, that is to say, as a necessary presupposition not only of experience, but also of the things of nature.

The dialectical assessment involved in this treatment constitutes the *Notion* of time; the construing of time at this juncture in the dialectical progression certainly has advantages in any attempt to expound the phenomena of mechanics in a rational sequence. The geometry assessed in § 256 does not involve time, whereas the motion, impact, fall etc. assessed in § 260 et. seq. do. However, taking time to be the abstract *presupposition* or *antecedent* of the things of nature involved a distinction closely resembling Newton's. While emphasizing the prime importance of the Notion of time, Hegel therefore distinguishes between *eternity* or absolute timelessness, *duration* or the relative sublation of time, and *natural time* or the easily observable *becoming* involved in the arising and passing away of the finite things of nature.

When he observes that eternity is not relative to time, but that like the Notion of time itself, constitutes the absolute present, Hegel is redefining Newton's 'absolute time' in a way which overcomes the objections raised against it by Mach and Cajori. Newton was quite clearly not justified in attributing an 'equable flow' to absolute time, although his (religious?) instinct was right when it told him that time is not simply a 'measure of duration by means of motion':

see E. A. Burtt 'The Metaphysical Foundations of Modern Physical Science' (London, 1925) pp. 243–263.

Cf. Samuel Vince (1749–1821) 'A Complete System of Astronomy' (3 vols. London, 1814–1823) vol. I pp. 562–568 on relative time: J. M. E. Mc Taggart 'The Nature of Existence' (Cambridge, 1927) vol. II, 'Philosophical Studies' (ed. Keeling, London, 1934) pp. 110–155, where the Notion of time is confused with natural time: C. D. Broad 'Examination of Mc Taggart's Philosophy' (Cambridge, 1938) vol. II, pt. i p. 316, D. N. Sanford 'McTaggart on Time' ('Philosophy' Oct: 1968); G. J. Whitrow 'The Natural Philosophy of Time' (London, 1961); Helmut Kobligk 'Denken und Zeit. Beiträge zu einer Interpretation des Hegelschen Zeitbegriffes' (Dissertation, Univ. of Kiel, January 21, 1952); Norbert Altwicker 'Der Begriff der Zeit im philosophischen System Hegels' (Dissertation, Univ. of Frankfurt-on-Main, July 25, 1951).

233, 31

Kant's 'Critique of Pure Reason' sect. II § 4, 'Time is not an empirical concept that has been derived from any experience. For neither coexistence nor succession would ever come within our perception, if the representation of time were not presupposed as underlying them *a priori*. Only on the presupposition of time can we represent to ourselves a number of things as existing at one and the same time (simultaneously) or at different times (successively).'

Georg Simon Klügel (1739–1812), in his extremely valuable 'Mathematisches Wörterbuch' (7 vols. Leipzig, 1803–1836) vol. V pp. 1053–4 has the following to say about number, 'The general origin of the notion of number is the concept of a *multiplicity* of *things*, which are either really and completely *similar* and *homogeneous*, or which have at least a variety that is ignored in so far as they are regarded as being *united* in a number. It might well be said therefore that its origin is the concept of the *repetition* or *duplication* of *one and the same thing*, indicated in general by A.' The same dictionary (vol. III pp. 602–613) contains an interesting account of the basic concepts of 'pure' mathematics, i.e. multiplicity, dimension, location, ratio etc.

B. M. Stewart, opens his 'Theory of Numbers' (New York, 1964) by quoting the remark made by Leopold Kronecker (1823–1891), 'God made the integers, all else is the work of man.' The recent attempts to treat embryology and cytology *mathematically* provide a good example of the involvement of time in any definition of a unit and a number. The cells or nuclei submitted to this treatment cannot of course be regarded as the merely *spatial* units which may be seen on a fixed microscope slide. They are therefore regarded as having their temporal *beginning* in division or fusion, and their temporal *end* in division, fusion or death: see J. H. Woodger 'The Axiomatic Method in Biology' (Cambridge, 1937) 'Problems arising from the application of mathematical logic to biology in "Actes de 2ième Colloque Internationale de Logique Mathematique"' (Paris, 1954).

234, 11

'The Logic of Hegel' (tr. Wallace, Oxford, 1963) pp. 190–192. Hegel treats *number* as a sub-category of quantum.

234, 21

Hegel is referring here to Aristotle's 'Metaphysics' 1092a 21– 1093b 29, and is evidently in substantial agreement with Aristotle's criticism of the Pythagorean doctrine of numbers, 'Those who derive existing things from elements and hold that the primary entities are the numbers, should have distinguished the senses in which one thing is said to come from another, and should then have explained in which of these senses number is derived from its elements . . . It has yet to be explained *how* numbers are the causes of substances and of being; whether (i) as boundaries, as points are of spatial magnitudes, or as Eurytus determined the number of each living thing (e.g. man or horse) by counting the number of pebbles he used in tracing its outline (in the way that some people reduce numbers to the forms of triangles or squares); or (ii) because harmony, man, and everything else is a ratio of numbers.

But how can attributes like white, sweet, hot, be numbers? . . . Number in general, then, or the number which consists of abstract units is neither the efficient, material, formal, nor of course the final cause of things'.

See the brilliant exposition of the Pythagorean philosophy in Hegel's 'Lectures on the History of Philosophy' (tr. Haldane and Simson, 3 vols. London, 1963) vol. I pp. 208–239. Cf. F. M. Cornford 'Mysticism and Science in the Pythagorean Tradition' ("The Classical Quarterly' 1922 and 1923: vol. XVI pp. 137–150, vol. XVII pp. 1–12). Cf. J. E. Raven 'Pythagoreans and Eleatics' (Cambridge, 1948) ch. X: P. H. Michel 'De Pythagore à Euclide' (Paris, 1950): R. Harré 'The Anticipation of Nature' (London, 1965) ch. 4: Sir William Hamilton's famous attack upon the study of mathematics as a training of the mind. which appeared in the 'Edinburgh Review' of 1836.

235, 9

Cf. Charles Hutton (1737–1823) 'A Philosophical and Mathematical Dictionary' (2 vols. London, 1815) vol. II p. 23, '*Mathematics*, the science of quantity; or a science that considers magnitudes either as computable or measurable. The word in its original μαθησις, mathesis, signifies Discipline or Science in general; and, it seems, has been applied to the doctrine of quantity, either by way of eminence, or because, this being the first of all other sciences, the rest took their common name from it.'

Leibniz and J. H. Lambert (1728–1777) had both attempted, not very successfully, to develop systems of mathematical logic. In Hegel's day the distinction between 'pure' and applied mathematics was certainly drawn, but an examination of the axioms on which 'pure' mathematics was then supposed to rest, makes it abundantly clear that a radical reassessment of them was necessary:

see for example G. S. Klügel's 'Mathematisches Wörterbuch' (7 vols. Leipzig, 1803–1836) vol. III pp. 602–613. Hegel was certainly justified in arguing that since it involved the *presupposition* of certain axioms, capable of philosophical assessment, but in fact taken up more or less at random from 'concrete nature', the mathematics of his day was not pure in any rigorous or truly philosophical sense. George Boole (1815–1864), in his 'An Investigation of the Laws of Thought' (London, 1854) was the first to develop mathematics as a truly philosophical science, and his work led on to the founding of mathematical logic by F. L. G. Frege (1848–1925), Louis Couturat (1868–1914), and Bertrand Russell.

For Hegel, philosophical mathematics would simply involve a *dialectical assessment* of the concepts involved in dealing with figurations of space (geometry) and time (the unit, arithmetic), and would *include* the distinction between the 'pure' and applied levels of the subject.

See G. T. Kneebone 'Mathematical Logic and the foundation of mathematics' (London, 1963), E. Carruccio 'Mathematics and Logic' (tr. Quigly, London, 1964): L. O. Kattsoff 'A Philosophy of Mathematics' (Iowa, 1949).

235, 19

Hades was the son of Cronos and Rhea (see note p. 315). When he was overthrown by Zeus a threefold division of the world took place: Zeus ruled heaven and earth, Poseidon the waters, and Hades the underworld, the regions of the dead.

See the 'Iliad' IV, 59: V, 395 ff; IX, 569 ff; XV, 187 ff, XX, 61 ff: Hesiod 'Theogony' 311; 455; 768; 774; 850: 'Works and Days' 153.

236, 29

‚als Totalität aller Dimensionen.' see 'Jenenser Realphilosophie II' (ed. Hoffmeister, Leipzig, 1931) p. 14. Michelet's version read ‚als Totalität der Dimensionen'.

238, 7

See Newton 'Opticks' (3rd ed. London, 1721) pp. 375–376: 'It seems probable, God, in the beginning, formed matter in solid, massy, hard, impenetrable, movable particles, of such sizes, figures, and with such other properties, and in such proportion to space, as most conduced to the end for which he formed them . . . While the particles continue entire, they may compose bodies of one and the same nature and texture in all ages'. Cf. his 'Mathematical Principles' (ed. Cajori, Berkeley, 1947) Bk. III Prop. VI, Cor. IV: A. R. and M. B. Hall 'Newton's Theory of Matter' ('Isis' 1960 pp. 131–144).

R. J. Boscovich (1711–1787), in his 'Theoria Philosophiae Naturalis' (Venice, 1763, Eng. tr. J. M. Child, London, 1922) criticizes the theory that matter is impenetrable, and puts forward the view that it consists only of physical points endued with powers of attraction and repulsion. Cf. J. Priestley (1733–1804)

'History and Present State of Discoveries relating to Vision, Light, and Colours' (2 vols. London, 1772) p. 390.

For late eighteenth century objections to the theory of the penetrability of matter, see Richard Price (1723–1791) 'A Free Discussion of the doctrines of Materialism and Philosophical Necessity' (London, 1778). Price's argument rests upon the axiom that, 'nothing can act where it is not'. Cf. A. E. Woodruff 'Action at a distance in Nineteenth Century Electrodynamics' ('Isis' 1962 pp. 439–459).

239, 2

‚Dieser Ort weist nicht nur auf einen andern hin, son(dern) hebt sich selbst auf, wird anders': see 'Jenenser Realphilosophie II' (ed. Hoffmeister, Leipzig, 1931) p. 15. Michelet's version is as follows, ‚Ein Ort weist nur auf einen anderen hin, hebt so sich selbst auf und wird ein anderer'.

239, 4

‚oder der Ort ist das schlechthin vermittelte Hier': see 'Jenenser Realphilosophie II' p. 15. Michelet substituted ‚allgemeine' (universal) for ‚vermittelte'.

239, 8

The Greek fragments relating to Zeno's views on motion are to be found in H. D. P. Lee's 'Zeno of Elea' (Cambridge, 1936) pt. III. Here, Hegel is evidently referring to Aristotle's 'Physics' bk. IV ch. 9, where Zeno's four celebrated dilemmas are dealt with. Zeno argued that a flying arrow cannot move because at any given moment it always occupies a space equal to itself, and everything which does this must be at rest. Aristotle points out (op. cit. 239b 31–34) that this argument rests upon the assumption that time consists of 'nows', and that this is a questionable proposition.

This subject has recently attracted a great deal of attention: see Gilbert Ryle 'Dilemmas' (Cambridge, 1954); V. C. Chappell 'Time and Zeno's Arrow' in 'Journal of Philosophy' vol. 59 pp. 197–213 (1962); H. N. Lee 'Are Zeno's arguments based on a mistake?' in 'Mind vol. 14 pp. 563–590 (Oct. 1965); Adolf Grünbaum 'Modern Science and Zeno's Paradoxes' (Middletown Conn., 1967): F. Cajori 'History of Zeno's arguments on motion' ('American Mathematical Monthly' 1922 vol. 22 p. 114).

239, 23

The original form of this phrase differs from Michelet's version of it, which is translated here. See 'Jenenser Realphilosophie II' pp. 16–17, ‚Wie die Zeit die einfache Seele, so ist sie der Begriff der wahren Seele, der Welt.'

In the margin, Hegel wrote, 'Moments of Quantity, formerly pure being and not-being, here reality, or determinate being, i.e. space in its indifference and time in its otherness'.

239, 25

Newton 'Opticks' (4th ed. London, 1730) bk. III pt. i query 28, 'And these things being rightly dispatch'd, does it not appear from the Phaenomena that there is a Being incorporeal, living, intelligent, omnipresent, who in infinite Space, as it were in his Sensory, sees the things themselves intimately, and throughly perceives them, and comprehends them wholly by their immediate presence to himself.' Cf. op. cit. query 31, where Newton speaks of God, 'who being in all places, is able by his will to move bodies within his boundless uniform sensorium'.

Addison, in the 'Spectator' (no. 565, July 1714) brings out the point of Newton's remark, 'Others have considered infinite space as the Receptacle, or rather the Habitation of the Almighty: but the noblest and most exalted way of considering this infinite Space, is that of Sir Isaac Newton, who calls it the *Sensorium* of the Godhead. Brutes and Men have their Sensoriola, or little *Sensoriums*, by which they apprehend the Presence, and perceive the Actions, of a few Objects that lie contiguous to them. Their Knowledge and Observation turn within a very narrow Circle. But as God Almighty cannot but perceive and know everything in which he resides, infinite Space gives Room to infinite Knowledge, and is, as it were, an Organ to Omniscience.'

This observation of Newton's played an important part in the Leibniz-Clarke correspondence: see 'The Leibniz-Clarke Correspondence' (ed. H. G. Alexander, Manchester, 1956).

239, 35

‚Diese Rückkehr als der Linie ist die Kreislinie': 'Jenenser Realphilosophie II' p. 19. Michelet omitted ‚als'. In the margin Hegel wrote, 'The self-moving point, *the quiescent unit*.'

240, 34

This presentation of matter as the 'quiescent identity' of space, time and motion is evidently meant to replace Newton's corpuscular theory (see note p. 319), and is an interesting anticipation of the corresponding dynamical concepts of modern physics: see Max Jammer 'Concepts of Mass' (New York, 1964): B. Russell 'The Principles of Mathematics' (7th imp.) London, 1956 §§ 437–441.

Newton does not define density. He begins his 'Mathematical Principles' with a definition of mass, 'The quantity of matter is the measure of the same arising from its density and bulk conjointly . . . It is this quantity that I mean hereafter everywhere under the name of body or mass. And the same is known by the weight of each body, for it is proportional to the weight, as I have found by experiments on pendulums . . .' Ernst Mach (1838–1916), in 'The Science of Mechanics (Chicago, 1919) ch. II iii points out that as density can only be defined as the mass of unit volume, Newton's use of the concept in a definition of mass involves him in a circular argument. For a somewhat unconvincing defence of Newton on this point see H. Crew 'The Rise of Modern Physics' (Baltimore, 1928) p. 134.

Cf. Newton's 'Mathematical Principles' (ed. Cajori, Berkeley, 1947) pp. 638–639: E. McMullin 'From Matter to Mass' in 'Boston Studies in the Philosophy of Science' (New York, 1965) vol. II pp. 25–53. For a recent treatment of the subject involving *physical* factors see A. H. Cottrell 'The Mechanical Properties of Matter' (London, 1964).

241, 17

Kant 'Metaphysische Anfangsgründe der Naturwissenschaft' (Riga, 1786). Hegel is evidently referring to the second main part of this work 'Metaphysische Anfangsgründe der Dynamik'. See 'Immanuel Kant. Werke' (ed. W. Weischedel, 6 vols. Wiesbaden, 1960) vol. V pp. 7–135. Cf. G. Martin 'Kant's Metaphysics and Theory of Science' (tr. Lucas, Manchester, 1951).

241, 24

In his 'Science of Logic' (tr. Johnston and Struthers, 2 vols. London, 1961) vol. I pp. 192–197, Hegel treats the Kantian exposition of attraction and repulsion in an observation on a sub-category of Being-for-Self.

242, 12

In the second edition of the 'Encyclopaedia' (1827) Hegel added here 'the being-for-self as universal'.

242, 34

See Newton's 'Mathematical Principles' (ed. Cajori, Berkeley, 1947) bk. I sect. xi, 'I have hitherto been treating of the attraction of bodies towards an immovable centre; though very probably there is no such thing existent in nature. For attractions are made towards bodies, and the actions of the bodies attracted and attracting are always reciprocal and equal, by Law III; so that if there are two bodies neither the attracted nor the attracting body is truly at rest, but both (by Cor. IV of the Laws of Motion), being as it were mutually attracted, revolve about a common centre of gravity.'

The two references in this extract throw more light upon Hegel's statement.

'Law III. To every action there is always opposed an equal reaction: or, the mutual actions of two bodies upon each other are always equal, and directed to contrary parts.'

'Corollary IV. The common centre of gravity of two or more bodies does not alter its state of motion or rest by the actions of the bodies among themselves; and therefore the common centre of gravity of all bodies acting upon each other (excluding external actions and impediments) is either at rest, or moves uniformly in a right line.'

In the scholium which concludes bk. I sect. xi Newton defines *attraction* more closely. However, a letter he wrote to Cotes (28.iii.1713) makes it seem probable that he would have countenanced the use of the word 'attraction' in Motte's translation of the 'Principia' (2 vols. London, 1729), despite the fact that the distinction between the centripetal forces by which bodies tend (petunt) towards each other and mere attraction is not so clearly apparent in Motte's English as it is in the orginal Latin. Newton uses the concrete Keplerian term 'tractio' for the former, and gives 'attractio' a more passive meaning. In Newton's Latin therefore, bodies 'trahunt' each other, but are 'attracta'. Hegel, using the Latin version, grasped this distinction rather better than some of his English contemporaries. See Alexandre Koyré 'Newtonian Studies' (London, 1965) appendices A, B, C. H. Metzger 'Attraction universelle et religion naturelle chez quelques commentateurs anglais de Newton' (Paris, 1937).

Cf. I. B. Cohen 'Pemberton's Translation of Newton's Principia, with notes on Motte's Translation' ('Isis' 1963 pp. 319–351): A. E. Short 'Elementary Statics' (Oxford, 1955) ch. 9: J. Edelston 'Correspondence of Newton' (London, 1850), p. 154

243, 2

Newton op. cit. bk. iii prop. 7, 'That there is a power of gravity pertaining to all bodies, proportional to the several quantities of matter which they contain.'

234, 6

‚Die Vereinzelten, welche von einander repellirt werden, ſind aber alle nur Eins, viele Eins.‚

243, 18

‚ſo iſt ſie nicht ſo dumm, als die Philoſophen . . .' Cf. 'The Logic of Hegel' (tr. Wallace, Oxford, 1963) §§ 96–98.

243, 27

See G. S. Klügel 'Mathematisches Wörterbuch' (Leipzig, 1803–1836) pt. iii pp. 402–429. Cf. Newton 'Mathematical Principles' bk. i sect. 12, 'The attractive forces of spherical bodies.'

244, 20

‚Nach der Raumbeſtimmung, in welcher die Zeit aufgehoben iſt.‚ In the 1817 and 1827 editions of the 'Encyclopaedia', this read, ‚Nach dem Raum, in welchem.‚

244, 27

Galileo was the first to discover the so-called law of inertia: see his 'Discorsi demostrazioni matematiche' (Leyden, 1638, Eng. tr. Crew, New York, 1914), by considering a body falling down an inclined plane and then ascending a second plane with the velocity so acquired. He observed that the nearer the second plane approaches the horizontal, the less will be the retardation of the body, and that if it is horizontal, the body would continue to move indefinitely with a constant velocity if air resistance and friction could be removed.

This law reappears in Newton's 'Mathematical Principles' (ed. Cajori, Berkeley, 1947) definition iii, 'The vis insita, or innate force of matter, is a power of resisting, by which every body, as much as in it lies, continues in its present state, whether it be of rest, or of moving uniformly forwards in a right line.'

Ernst Mach (1838–1916), in 'The Science of Mechanics', points out that it was Galileo's successors who developed a *theory* of inertia out of his *description* of this situation, and that Newton's third definition is rendered superfluous by his subsequent definitions (iv–viii) of force, inertia being included and given in the fact that forces are accelerative.

Hegel avoids this fault in the traditional treatment of inertia, by taking it to involve a body's having motion *external* to it. He would therefore have denied that a body's 'moving uniformly forwards in a right line' is an example of inertia. He may have been influenced by Kant and Euler's questioning of the concept: see 'Neuer Lehrbegriff der Bewegung und Ruhe' (1758, ed. O. Bük, Leipzig, 1907). Cf. Max Jammer 'Concepts of Mass' (New York, 1964); P. Frank 'Foundations of Physics' ('International Encyclopedia of Unified Science' vol. i, part 2, iii 10, Chicago, 1955).

245, 8

Newton, 'Mathematical Principles' (ed. Cajori, Berkeley, 1947), 'Axioms, or Laws of Motion. Law 1. Every body continues in its state of rest, or of uniform motion in a right line, unless it is compelled to change that state by forces impressed upon it.'

245, 23

‚Die Masse, in diesem Sinne fixirt, heißt träge: es ist aber nicht so, daß das Ruhen damit ausgedrückt würde.' Hoffmeister ('Jenenser Realphilosophie' II p. 21) suggests this version of the sentence. *Hegel's* punctuation of the following sentences differs considerably from Michelet's.

245, 32

Jean Bernoulli (1667–1748) was the first to observe that as the *same* body can receive different gravitational accelerations, a distinction should be made between *mass* and *weight*: see his 'Meditatio de Natura Centri Oscillationis' (1714); 'Opera Omnia' (4 vols. Lausanne and Geneva, 1742) vol. ii p. 168. It was the observations on the pendulum made between 1671 and 1673 by Jean Richer (d. 1696), which led him to make this distinction: see 'Observations astronomiques et physiques faites en l'îsle de Cayenne' (Paris, 1679); J. W. Olmsted 'The Scientific Expedition of Jean Richer to Cayenne, 1672–1673' ('Isis' 1942 pp. 117–128). Cf. Newton's proof of the proportionality of mass and weight on the same spot of the earth, by observations on pendulums of different materials: 'Mathematical Principles' bk. ii sect. 6. On Newton's subsequent definition of mass see the note on p. 321.

Ernst Mach (1838–1916) criticized Newton's definition of mass in that it involves a circular argument and the obscure concept of a 'quantity of matter'. Hegel's definition of mass as 'the unity of the moments of rest and motion' etc. accords rather well with Mach's definition of equal masses, 'All those bodies are of equal mass, which, mutually acting on each other, produce in each other equal and opposite accelerations.'—'The Science of Mechanics' II v.

245, 34

In the margin at this juncture, Hegel wrote, ,Reibung, Widerstand der Luft; Pendel fortschwingen — losgeschossene Kugel zufällig.' 'Jenenser Realphilosophie' II p. 22 n. 1.

246, 4

See Hegel's 'Philosophy of Right' (tr. Knox, Oxford, 1962) §§ 103–104.

246, 12

See Lazare Nicholas Marguerite Carnot (1753–1823), 'Essai sur les machines en général' (Paris, 1783), and the extension of this work in, 'Principes fondamentaux de l'équilibre et du mouvement' (Paris, 1803).

Carnot regards the action of a continuous force such as gravity as a series of infinitely small impacts. In his studies on the mechanics of systems he introduces the concept of *geometrical motions*, that is to say, motions that have no effect on the actions which are exerted between the bodies of a system, but depend only upon the conditions of constraint between the parts of the system. This led him to establish his theorem of the impact of 'hard bodies', 'In the impact of hard bodies, the sum of living forces before the impact is always equal to the sum of the living forces after the impact together with the sum of the living forces that each of these bodies would have if it moved freely with only the velocity which it lost in the impact.'

Cf. René Dugas 'A History of Mechanics' (tr. Maddox, London, 1957) ch. 10.

246, 27

Cf. Newton 'Mathematical Principles' def. ii, 'The quantity of motion is the measure of the same, arising from the velocity and quantity of matter conjointly.' In more modern mechanics this 'quantitas motus' as it is called by Newton throughout the 'Principia', is known as *momentum*, and is measured by the product of *mass* and velocity.

For the *history* of the concept see Ernst Mach (1838–1916) 'The Science of Mechanics' III ii 3–4.

247, 14

See John Wallis (1616–1703) 'Mechanica sive de Motu' (3 pts., London, 1670–1671). Wallis observed that if a body is rotating about an axis, and its motion is suddenly checked by the retention of one of its points, the force of the percussion will vary with the distance of this point from the axis. This observation led him into investigations of what he called the *centre of percussion*, i.e. the *point* at which the intensity of impact is greatest.

247, 25

,Aber sein Ganzes verlassend, ist er um ebenso intensiveres Eins.' The text of the manuscript is clearly corrupt at this juncture, and Hoffmeister amends it as follows, ,sein Ganzes verlassend ist (er ein) um so (Hegel — ebenso) intensiveres Eins'. See 'Jenenser Realphilosophie II' p. 42.

247, 28

See I. Todhunter 'A History of Elasticity' (2 vols., Cambridge, 1886–1893): A. H. Cottrell 'The Mechanical Properties of Matter' (London, 1964) pp. 82–155: S. Timoshenko and J. N. Goodier 'Theory of Elasticity' (New York, 1951): A. E. Green and W. Zerna 'Theoretical Elasticity' (Oxford, 1954).

247, 38

See Newton's parallelogram of forces and the second of his laws of motion (note p. 358).

248, 1

In 1666 the Royal Society set certain of its members, including Huyghens, Wallis and Wren, the problem of investigating the laws of impact. Their papers were communicated between November 26, 1668 and January 4, 1669, and constituted the first systematic treatment of the subject: see Newton 'Mathematical Principles', the scholium to the initial axioms.

According to Wallis, the decisive factor in impact is momentum, or the product of the mass (pondus) into velocity. All his theorems may be brought together in the formula $u=(mv+m'v')/(m+m')$, in which m,m' denote the masses, v,v' the velocities before impact, and u the velocity after impact. See his 'Mechanica sive de Motu' (3 pts., London, 1670–1671).

For Huyghens' mature views see his 'Opuscula posthuma': 'De Motu Corporum ex Percussione' (Leyden, 1703). For a survey of eighteenth century views on the subject see Ernst Mach (1838–1916) 'The Science of Mechanics' iii 4, 4–10: W. L. Scott 'The Significance of "Hard Bodies" in the history of scientific thought' ('Isis' 1959 pp. 199–210).

248, 5

Newton's 'Mathematical Principles' law iii, 'To every action there is always opposed an equal reaction: or, the mutual actions of two bodies upon each other are always equal, and directed to contrary parts.' Cf. V. F. Lenzen 'Newton's Third Law of Motion' ('Isis' 1937 pp. 258–260); A. E. Short 'Elementary Statics' (Oxford, 1955) ch. 6.

248, 19

It has often been said for example, that the principle enunciated by Jean le Rond d'Alembert (1717–1783), see his 'Traité de dynamique' (Paris, 1743), that the internal forces in an assemblage of particles constituting a material body form a system in equilibrium, reduces all dynamics to statics. For a concise survey of theories relating to force from Descartes to Lagrange, see A. Wolf 'A History of Science, Technology, and Philosophy in the Eighteenth Century' (London, 1938) pp. 61–71: Charles Hutton 'A Philosophical and Mathematical Dictionary' (2 vols., London, 1815) vol. i pp. 533–538. Forces were defined as being motive, accelerative, retardive, constant, variable etc., and the general conception of the subject had changed very little by the end of the 1820's: see Neil Arnott (1788–1874) 'Elements of Physics' (3rd. ed. London, 1828) vol. i pp. 45–110.

On the new critical attitude of the mid-nineteenth century, anticipated here by Hegel, see Max Jammer 'Concepts of Force' (Cambridge, Mass., 1957).

248, 28

'Hypomochlium', i.e. the fulcrum: see Archimedes' proof of the law of the lever, which depends fundamentally on the extension of two ideas: (i) that equal weights at equal distances from the fulcrum are in equilibrium, and (ii) that the centre of gravity of two equal weights not having the same centre of gravity is at the middle point of the line connecting their individual centres of gravity.

Archimedes 'De Planorum Aequilibriis' props. vi and vii: see 'The Works of Archimedes' (ed. Heath, 2 pts. Cambridge, 1897, 1912); 'Des unvergleichlichen Archimedis Kunst-Bücher' (ed. Sturm, 2 pts. Nuremberg, 1670); 'Archimedes von Syrakus vorhandene Werke' (tr. and ed. Nizze, Stralsund, 1824).

Cf. John Playfair (1748–1819) 'Outlines of Natural Philosophy' (2 vols., Edinburgh, 1812); Ernst Mach's criticism that in this exposition Archimedes presupposed everything he wished to prove: 'The Science of Mechanics'; J. M. Child 'Archimedes' principle of the balance and some criticisms upon it' in C. Singer 'Studies in the history and method of science' (2 vols., Oxford, 1917, 1921).

248, 37

See Newton's law of the conservation of the centre of gravity: 'Mathematical Principles' bk. i prop. lxi theorem 24.

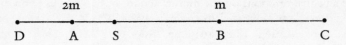

Imagine in A and B two masses, 2m and m, in mutual action, say that of electrical repulsion; their centre of gravity is situated at S, where BS=2AS. The accelerations they impart to each other are oppositely directed and in the inverse proportion of the masses. If, then, in consequence of the mutual action, 2m describes a distance AD, m will necessarily describe a distance BC=2AD. The point S will still remain the position of the centre of gravity, as CS=2DS. Therefore, two masses cannot, by *mutual action*, displace their common centre of gravity.

Cf. Daniel Bernoulli (1700–1782), 'Hydrodynamica, seu de Viribus et Motibus Fluidorum Commentarii' (Strassburg, 1738), in which the attempt is made to apply the idea that when a liquid sinks, the space through which its centre of gravity actually descends is equal to the space through which the centre of gravity of the separated parts affected with the velocities acquired in the fall can ascend.

249, 13

Newton 'Mathematical Principles' law i, 'Every body continues in its state of rest, or of uniform motion in a right line, unless it is compelled to change that state by forces impressed upon it.'

249, 17

In the second edition of the 'Encyclopaedia' (1827), Hegel added the following remark here, 'Descartes' proposition that the universe always contains the same amount of motion, is of this kind.'

See 'The Philosophical Works of Descartes' (tr. Haldane and Ross, 2 vols., Cambridge, 1911) vol. 1 p. 267. Hegel is evidently referring to the 'Principles of Philosophy' pt. II princ. 36, 'That God is the First Cause of movement and that He always preserves an equal amount of movement in the universe.' Descartes distinguishes between the vulgar conception of motion as the passing of a body from one place to another, and the 'true or scientific' conception of it as the transfer of matter from the vicinity of those bodies with which it was in immediate contact into the vicinity of other bodies.

Leibniz questioned this Cartesian tenet in 'A short demonstration of the remarkable error of Descartes and others, concerning the natural law by which they think that the Creator always preserves the same quantity of motion.' ('Acta Eruditorum' 1686.) Cf. J. L. R. D'Alembert (1717–1783) 'Traité de dynamique' (Paris, 1743); E. Mach 'The Science of Mechanics' III iii 4. On the loss of kinetic energy in collisions see L. N. M. Carnot (1753–1823) 'Essais sur les machines en général' (Paris, 1783).

249, 20

In Hegel's day, a distinction was drawn between the *relatively* perpetual motion of, for example, electricity and the expansion and contraction of metal rods brought about by changes of temperature (perpetuum mobile electricum et physicum), and *absolute* 'perpetuum mobile *mechanicum*'. It is clearly the second of these that Hegel has in mind.

See C. G. Kratzenstein (1723–1795), 'De horologio perpetuo mobili' ('Novi Commentarii Academiae Petropolitanae' II 1751 p. 222). In 1775 the French Academy decided to consider no further claims that perpetual motion machines had been constructed, 'Mémoires de l'Academie' 1775 p. 65. Cf. L. N. M. Carnot (1753–1823), 'Principes fondamentaux de l'équilibre et du mouvement' (Paris, 1803) 8. § 281; Thomas Young (1772–1829) 'Lectures on Natural Philosophy' (2 vols. London, 1807) vol. 1 p. 91, where the possibility of a 'perpetuum mobile mechanicum' is ruled out.

249, 32

Newton 'Mathematical Principles of Natural Philosophy' (tr. A. Motte, ed. F. Cajori, Berkeley, 1947): 'A stone, whirled about in a sling, endeavours to recede from the hand that turns it; and by that endeavour, distends the sling, and that with so much the greater force, as it is revolved with greater velocity, and as soon as it is let go, flies away.'

250, 1

Newton loc. cit., 'If a leaden ball, projected from the top of a mountain by the force of gunpowder, with a given velocity, and in a direction parallel to the horizon, is carried in a curved line to the distance of two miles before it falls to the ground; the same, if the resistance of the air were taken away, with a double or decuple velocity, would fly twice or ten times as far. And by increasing the velocity, we may at pleasure increase the distance to which it might be projected; . . . so that . . . lastly . . . it might never fall to earth, but go forwards into the celestial spaces, and proceed in its motion *in infinitum*.'

250, 6

Hegel inserts a foot-note here in which he quotes again from the *Latin* version of the 'Mathematical Principles' giving the following emphasis, 'Newton (ibid. Defin. viii.) says expressly, 'I likewise call attractions and impulses, in the same sense, accelerative, and motive; and use the words attraction, impulse or propensity of any sort towards a centre, promiscuously, and indifferently, one for another; considering those forces *not physically*, but *mathematically*: wherefore the reader is *not* to *imagine* that by those words I anywhere take upon me to define the *kind*, or the *manner* of any action, the causes or the *physical reason* thereof, or that I attribute forces, in a *true* or *physical* sense, to certain centres (which are only mathematical points); when at any time I happen to speak of centres as attracting, or as endued with attractive powers." Merely by introducing the concept of forces, *Newton* wrenched the determinations out of physical reality, and made them *essentially* independent. At the same time he continued consistently to treat these representations as physical objects. Yet in the professedly purely *physical* and supposedly unmetaphysical expositions of what he called the system of the world, he spoke of such *mutually independent* and distinct forces, as well as their attractions, impacts and suchlike, as if they were physical existences, and treated them according to the principle of identity.'

Hegel is right when he points out that although Newton expressly (and repeatedly) makes the distinction between the mathematical representations of the problems he is dealing with and the physical reality of the situations he is describing, it often appears to be absent from his expositions. Nevertheless, it is quite certain that the passage quoted here by Hegel expresses his opinion on the matter, and that the attribution of distinctness and physical reality to the forces mentioned in the 'Principia' is due mainly to his interpreters, and not to Newton himself.

Newton frequently stated for example, that he was ignorant of the *physical nature* of gravity; see his letter to Bentley of January 17, 1693, 'You some times speak of gravity as essential and inherent to matter. Pray, do ascribe that notion to me; for the cause of gravity is what I do not pretend to know, and therefore would take more time to consider of it.' Alexandre Koyré, 'Newtonian Studies' (London, 1965) p. 163, remarks that by ignoring Newton's distinction between the mathematical and physical aspects of his expositions, 'the eighteenth century, with very few exceptions, became reconciled to the ununderstandable.'

Cf. 'Four Letters from Sir Isaac Newton to Doctor Bentley' (London, 1756); Ernst Mach 'The Science of Mechanics' II iii 6; Newton 'Mathematical Principles' (ed. Cajori, Berkeley, 1947) pp. 632–635; A. E. Heath 'Newton's influence on method in the physical sciences' in W. J. Greenstreet 'Isaac Newton 1642–1727' (London, 1927) pp. 130–133; A. J. Snow 'Matter and Gravity in Newton's Physical Philosophy' (Oxford, 1926); C. Isenkrahe 'Das Räthsel von der Schwerkraft' (Brunswick, 1879).

The slight inaccuracies which have been discovered of recent years in Newton's laws, only become apparent in astronomy or nuclear physics, when very large or very small measurements are being made. Newtonian mechanics still provides the broad basis of the great bulk of the work being done in engineering and general physics: see for example A. S. Ramsey 'An Introduction to the theory of Newtonian attraction' (Cambridge, 1940). Cf. P. Frank 'Foundations of Physics' in 'International Encyclopedia of Unified Science' (Chicago, 1955) vol. 1 pp. 423–504.

251, 9

The following lines are condensed by Michelet from a passage roughly four times as long: see 'Jenenser Realphilosophie II' pp. 40–41.

251, 15

At this juncture, Hegel entered the following note in the margin: see 'Jenenser Realphilosophie II' p. 107, 'In the pulley, lever and centre; friction on the pulley, so that a weight on one side, quickly released, *tears* the rope and does not pull the other after it, see Kästner—or friction becomes pure intensity, which is free from gravity, as is even the point of the lever. *Individuality* which has weight.

That which exhibits itself here in dimensions, is immediately one—or the centre of gravity makes itself in this way into the whole individual body.'

See Abraham Gotthelf Kästner (1719–1800) 'Anfangsgründe der höheren Mechanik' (Leipzig, 1765, 2nd ed. Leipzig, 1793).

251, 17

‚der Schwerpunkt'. Michelet changed this to ‚die Schwere' (gravity).

252, 8

See the note on p. 329. Certain papers on this subject by the severely practical and military Newtonian Benjamin Robins (1707–1751), were collected and published as the famous 'New Principles of Gunnery' (London, 1742). Euler translated the work into German, 'Neue Grundsätze der Artillerie' (Berlin, 1745), supplying it with an immense commentary, and Charles Hutton (1737–1823) brought out a new edition of it as late as 1805. Robins makes much of the importance of air resistance in ballistics. Cf. A. Wolf 'A History of Science . . . in the Eighteenth Century' (London, 1938) pp. 72–73.

252, 20

See Charles Hutton (1737–1823) 'A Philosophical and Mathematical Dictionary' (2 vols. London, 1815) vol. II p. 163, 'A pendulum raised to B, through the arc of the circle AB, will fall, and rise again, through an equal arc, to a point equally high, as D; and thence will fall to A, and again rise to B; and thus continue rising and falling perpetually, supposing neither friction nor resistance.'

This doctrine originated in the work of Christian Huyghens (1629–1695), who was the first to investigate the principles and properties of pendulums in a successful manner. He maintained that if the centre of motion is fixed and all resistance is removed, a pendulum will continue to oscillate indefinitely, that all its vibrations will be perfectly isochronal, and that its arc of vibration will remain constant: see his 'Horologium Oscillatorium' (Paris, 1673 Germ. tr. Heckscher and Oettingen, Ostwalds Klassiker no. 192); A. H. Bell 'Christian Huygens' (London, 1947).

For Newton's treatment of the pendulum see 'Mathematical Principles' bk. I sect. 10; bk. II sect. 6. Cf. John Playfair (1749–1819) 'Outlines of Natural Philosophy' vol. I pp. 120–128 (Edinburgh, 1812); Thomas Reid 'Treatise on

Clock and Watch Making' (Edinburgh, 1826); A. Wolf 'A History of Science, Technology and Philosophy in the Eighteenth Century' (London, 1938) pp. 75–81.

252, 28

Louis-Benjamin Francoeur (1773–1849) came of a musical family. His father, Louis-Joseph (1738–1804) was employed at the French court as a musician and wrote some valuable works on musical theory.

Louis-Benjamin was born in Paris, and lived the whole of his life there. He was not educated for an academic career, but in 1795, when he was already married, he entered the newly founded Paris Polytechnic, and soon discovered his flare for mathematics. He then taught the subject at a central school in Paris for some years. In 1798 he gained a minor teaching post at the Polytechnic, and when he finally left this institution in 1804, continued to examine there. In 1805 he was appointed teacher of differential and integral calculus (mathématiques transcendantes) at a Paris Grammar School, and in 1809 professor of higher algebra at the Sorbonne. He taught in the Science Faculty of the University, mainly algebra, geodesy and the theory of probabilities.

As his loyalty to the royalist cause was suspect, he was penalized in 1815, and although he kept his position at the Sorbonne, he was not allowed to examine. In 1842 he was elected a member of the Academy of Sciences: see I. Francoeur 'Notice sur la vie et les ouvrages de M. L. B. Francoeur' (Paris, 1853); 'Nouvelle Biographie générale' (ed. Höfer, 41 vols. Paris, 1855–1862); E. G. Gersdorf 'Leipziger Repertorium' (72 vols. Leipzig, 1843–1860) 1850.

Francoeur's works on pure and applied mathematics are distinguished by their accuracy, orderliness and clarity of exposition. Several of them were translated into English: see 'Cours complet de Mathématique pures' (2 vols. Paris, 1809), 'A complete course of Pure Mathematics' (tr. R. Blakelock, 2 vols. Cambridge and London, 1830); 'Le Dessin linéaire' (Paris, 1819), 'Lineal Drawing' (London, 1824). His works on *applied mathematics* proved to be particularly popular: 'Uranographie, ou traité élémentaire d'Astronomie' (Paris, 1812) reached a fifth edition by 1853, and 'Géodesie ou traité de la figure de la Terre' (Paris, 1835) an eighth edition by 1895. See also his 'Éléments de Statique' (Paris, 1810) and 'Astronomie pratique' (Paris, 1830).

Hegel is referring here to his 'Traité élémentaire de Mécanique, adopté dans l'instruction publique' (Paris, 1801), which reached a fifth edition by 1825. The book begins with a series of definitions, and then falls into four main sections: (i) *Statics*, dealing with forces, gravity, machines and obstacles (the section quoted by Hegel); (ii) *Dynamics*, dealing with movement in lines, curves and systems; (iii) *Hydrostatics*, dealing with equilibrium, pressures and density; and (iv) *Hydrodynamics*, dealing with the movements of fluids. The work probably interested Hegel on account of the potentially 'speculative' nature of this arrangement.

Francoeur deals with friction on pp. 174–184, and Hegel is referring to the following passages:

'4° *Le frottement ne dépend pas de l'étendue des surfaces en contact, le poids du corps restant la meme.* Ce principe, attesté par l'expérience, paroît d'abord singulier; cependant on peut observer que, suivant qu'on fait frotter un parallelipipède sur l'une ou l'autre de ses faces, les points de contact sont plus ou moins nombreux, mais que chacun d'eux porte un poids moins ou plus considérable, et il paroît qu'il y a compensation entre ces deux effets. Cependant si les corps frottant étoit terminé par une pointe, comme ce corps traceroit par son poids un sillon sur la surface frottée, ce cas doit être excepté de la règle.

5° *Le frottement est proportionnel à la pression*, toutes choses égales d'ailleurs; c'est-à-dire qu'on éprouve une résistance d'autant plus grande que le corps presse davantage. Voici comment on doit entendre cette proposition, qui va servir de fondement à tout ce que nous aurons à dire.'

252, 40

This analysis of dry friction accords fairly well with the classical view of the subject as established by C. A. Coulomb (1736–1806) in 'Théorie des machines simples, en ayant regard au frottement de leurs parties et à la roideur des cordages' (Paris, 1779, new ed. 1820), Samuel Vince (1749–1821) in 'On the motion of bodies affected by friction' ('Phil. Trans. Roy. Soc.' 1785 p. 165), and A. J. Morin (1795–1880) in 'Notions fondamentales de mécanique' (Paris, 1855, Eng. tr. New York, 1860). G. Amontons (1663–1705) was the first to maintain that the magnitude of friction depends upon the force with which the surfaces press each other, and not upon the *extent* of these surfaces: see 'Sur la résistance causée dans les machines par le frottement et par le roideur des cordes.' ('Mém. de l'Acad. de Paris' 1699); cf. J. H. Lambert (1728–1777) 'Sur le frottement' ('Mém. de l'Acad. de Berlin' 1772 and 1776), where this thesis is questioned.

The 'laws of friction, which are simply empirical and not strictly accurate, are generally formated as follows:

(i) The friction is just sufficient to prevent sliding provided the friction required to do so is not greater than a certain fraction of the normal reaction.

(ii) The value μ of this fraction is constant for any two materials in contact. It is called the *coefficient of friction.*

(iii) When sliding is taking place the friction opposes the motion and assumes its maximum value, which is μ times the normal reaction. See D. E. Rutherford 'Classical Mechanics' (Edinburgh, 1964) p. 41.

During Hegel's lifetime, most of the research into this subject was concerned with the relation between friction and pressure, and special attention was paid to the specific *substances* and *conditions* under observation. Very few *general* laws were confidently enunciated: see for example George Rennie (1791–1866) 'Experiments on the friction and abrasion of surfaces and solids.' ('Phil. Trans. Roy. Soc.' 1829 pp. 143–170). This caution was justified, for apart from the distinctions between dry, fluid, internal and external friction, a *comprehensive* theory of the dry friction mentioned here by Hegel has yet to be worked out. It would involve a consideration of the influence of molecular attraction under conditions where the mating surfaces are in very intimate contact, of the deformation and tearing of surface irregularities, the generation of high local temperatures and adhesion at contact points, the relative hardness of mating surfaces, and the presence of thin surface films of oxide, oil, dirt, or other substances. It would in fact be a *physical* as much as a mechanical matter: see F. P. Bowden and D. Tabor 'The Friction and Lubrication of Solids' (2 vols. Oxford, 1950, 1964); Robert Davies 'Friction and Wear' (Amsterdam, 1959); M. Lavik 'Mechanisms of Solid Friction' (Amsterdam, 1964).

253, 11

‚er geht aber aus von der beſtimmten.' Michelet substitutes ‚dabei' for ‚aber', and Hoffmeister suggests ‚zwar': 'Jenenser Realphilosophie II' p. 39.

253, 12

The motion of anything but a vertically trajected projectile, even if air resistance and the motion of the earth are not taken into consideration, is a parabola, and never becomes 'simple fall'. See Thomas Rutherforth (1712–1771) 'A System of Natural Philosophy' (2 vols. Cambridge, 1748) vol. I pp. 126–139: Charles Hutton (1737–1823) 'A Philosophical and Mathematical Dictionary' (2 vols. London, 1815) vol. II pp. 247–252; Ernst Mach 'The Science of Mechanics' II i 18–19; H. Weiler 'Mechanics' (London, 1957) ch. ix; D. E. Rutherford 'Classical Mechanics' (Edinburgh, 1964) §§ 35–37.

254, 6

See Alexandre Koyré 'A Documentary History of the Problem of Fall from Kepler to Newton' ('Trans. Amer. Phil. Soc.' new series vol. 45 pt. 4 pp. 329–395: Oct. 1955).

254, 11

See for example Newton's 'Mathematical Principles' bk. I sect. vii, 'The rectilinear ascent and descent of bodies.'

254, 14

Hegel inserts the following foot-note at this juncture, 'It can hardly be denied that this so-called *accelerative* force has been most unfortunately named, since the effect it is supposed to have in each moment of time is *uniform* and constant. It is in fact the *empirical* factor in the magnitude of fall, which is a unit of 15 feet on the surface of the earth. The acceleration consists solely of the *addition* of this empirical unit in each moment of time. But on the other hand, *acceleration* might with equal plausibility be attributed to what is called the force of *inertia*, the action of which is held to account for the *persistence* of the velocity attained at the end of each moment of time, i.e. inertia contributes by *adding* this velocity to the said empirical magnitude: and this velocity is *greater* at the end of each moment of time than at the end of the preceding moment.'

Cf. Newton 'Mathematical Principles' definition vii, 'The accelerative quantity of a centripetal force is the measure of the same, proportional to the velocity which it generates in a given time.' Newton goes on to say that at equal distances the force of gravity, 'is the same everywhere; because . . . it equally accelerates all falling bodies, whether heavy or light, great or small'.

See also op. cit. definition viii, 'I refer the motive force to the body as an endeavour and propensity of the whole towards a centre, arising from the propensities of the several parts taken together; the accelerative force to the place of the body, as a certain power diffused from the centre to all places around to move the bodies that are in them . . . I here design only to give a mathematical notion of those forces, without considering their physical causes and seats. Wherefore the accelerative force will stand in the same relation to the motive as celerity does to motion. For the quantity of motion arises from the celerity multiplied by the quantity of matter; and the motive force arises from the accelerative force multiplied by the same quantity of matter. For the sum of the actions of the accelerative force, upon the several particles of the body, is the motive force of the whole.'

Newton was not of course the *first* to define accelerative force; to the Oxford scholastics of the fifteenth century it was already a commonplace: see Pierre Duhem 'Les origines de la statique' (2 vols. Paris, 1907); 'Le mouvement absolu et le mouvement relatif' (Montligeon, 1907).

254, 22

See the note on p. 323. Ernst Mach (1838–1916) observes, with regard to Newton's definitions, that, 'It is . . . a matter of taste and of form whether we shall embody the explication of the idea of force in one or in several definitions. In point of principle, the Newtonian definitions are open to no objections'—. 'The Science of Mechanics' II vii 2.

254, 25

See Newton op. cit., the scholium to the axioms, 'When a body is falling, the uniform force of its gravity acting equally, impresses, in equal intervals of time, equal forces upon that body, and therefore generates equal velocities; and in the whole time impresses a whole force, and generates a whole velocity proportional to the time.'

Cf. Galileo's 'Discorsi e dimostrazioni matematiche' (Leyden, 1638 Eng. tr. Crew, New York, 1914), in which the basic question asked is not *why* but *how* do heavy bodies fall. His demonstration of uniformly accelerated motion is as follows:—

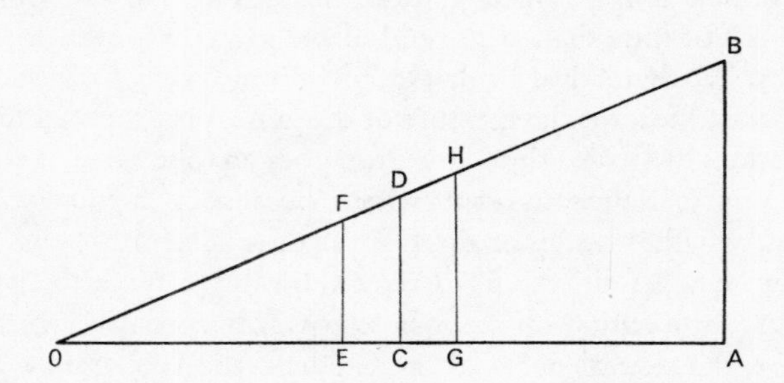

'On the straight line OA let the successive portions represent the times elapsed. Erect perpendiculars (ordinates) at the extremities of these portions to represent the velocities acquired. Any portion of the line OA then denotes the *time* of descent elapsed, and the corresponding perpendicular the *velocity* acquired in such time.'

It will be observed that at instant C, when half the time of descent OA has elapsed, the velocity CD is also half the final velocity AB.

It will also be observed that at the two instants E and G, which are equally distant in opposite directions from the instant C, the velocities EF and GH fall short of and exceed the mean velocity CD by the same amount.

Consequently, whatever loss is suffered in the first half as compared with *uniform* motion, with half the final velocity, is made up in the second half. We may therefore regard the *total* distance as having been *uniformly* traversed with *half the final velocity*. Consequently, if we make the final velocity v proportional to the time of descent t, we shall obtain $v=gt$, where g denotes the final velocity acquired in unit of time—the so-called *acceleration*.

The *space* s descended through is therefore given by the equation $s=(gt/2)$ or $s=gt^2/2$.'

255, 10

At this juncture, Hegel inserts the following foot-note: '*Lagrange*, in his own way, employs the straightforward and perfectly valid procedure in his 'Théorie des fonctions': see pt. III ch. i 'Application de la Théorie à la Mécanique'. He takes the mathematical treatment of functions as given, and in his *application* of the same to mechanics, *discovers* that the ft and bt^2 involved in $s=ft$ occur in nature; $s=ct^3$ does not occur there. At this juncture it is quite right that there should be no attempt to *prove* that $s=bt^2$, but that this relationship should simply be accepted as *occurring* in nature. In the development of the function; t becomes $t=\theta$, and as the series expressing the space traversed in θ time can only make use of the first two terms, the others are omitted. As is usual with Lagrange, this circumstance is dealt with in an analytical manner. It is however only because the first two terms have a determination of a real nature, that they are treated as being of significance to the object, 'on voit que les fonctions primes et secondes se présentent *naturellement*' (Hegel's emphasis) 'dans la mécanique, où elles ont une value et une signification determinées.' (ibid. 4.5). It is true that at this point Lagrange falls into *Newtonian* expressions, abstract or simply uniform velocity derived from the force of inertia, and an accelerative force, and so also introduces the mental fabrications of an infinitely small space of time (θ) having a beginning and an end. This in no way prejudices the legitimacy of his procedure however, in which, instead of these determinations being used to *prove the law*, the relevant aspect of the law is taken up as it is presented in experience, and then submitted to mathematical treatment.'

Cf. A. L. Crelle (1780–1855) 'Lagranges mathematische Werke' (3 vols. Berlin, 1823–1824) vol. I p. 572, where the observation is made that Lagrange is working here, 'merely in relation to observation and experience'. Hegel deals at length with Lagrange's differential calculus, as a sub-category of quantum, in the 'Science of Logic' (tr. Johnston and Struthers, 2 vols. London, 1961) vol. I pp. 276–318: see esp. p. 281.

Joseph Louis Lagrange (1736–1813) was well known in Berlin: he had succeeded Euler as director of the mathematical department of the Berlin Academy in 1766, and remained in the city until 1787; see J. J. Virey 'Précis historique sur la vie et la mort de Joseph-Louis Lagrange' (Paris, 1813). The 'Théorie des fonctions analytiques' (Paris, 1797) was republished in vol. iii of the 'Journal de l'école polytechnique' (Paris, 1813). The main object of the work is to set calculus on a sound basis by relieving the mind of the difficult conception of a limit. In Newton's 'Method of Fluxions' (1671, tr. Colson, London, 1736) there is no way of finding the magnitudes of the limiting ratio, for as the arc and chord are taken to be equal not before or after but only *when* they vanish, they have no being at the very moment when they should be caught and equated. Lagrange comments as follows on this, 'That method has the great inconvenience of considering quantities in the state in which they cease, so to speak, to be quantities; for though we can always well conceive the ratios of two quantities as long as they remain finite, that ratio offers to the mind no clear and precise ideas as soon as both its terms become nothing at the same time.'

He attempts to overcome the difficulty by developing *Taylor's* series for the expansion of variables in powers thereof: see Brook Taylor (1685–1731) 'Methodus incrementorum directa et inversa' (London, 1715); he was in fact the first to show the power of this theorem. By means of it, he proposes to define the differential coefficient of $f(x)$ with respect to x as the coefficient of h in the expansion of $f(x+h)$, and so to avoid all reference to limits. In the algebra of his day however, there was no rigorous theory of *infinite series*. He therefore uses this concept without ascertaining that the series are convergent, and there are serious defects in his proof that $f(x+h)$ can always be expanded in a series of ascending powers of h. See R. Reiff 'Geschichte der Unendlichen Reihen' (Tübingen, 1889); A. L. Cauchy (1789–1857) 'Résumé des leçons . . . sur le calcul infinitésimal' (Paris, 1823); 'Journal de l'École Polytechnique' vol. xii, 1823: R. Taton 'The Beginnings of Modern Science' (tr. Pomerans, London, 1964) p. 413. His 'method of derivatives' as it was called, was at first greatly applauded, but Abel Bürja (1752–1816) of Berlin questioned its rigour as early as 1801, see 'Sur le développement des fonctions en series.' ('Mémoires de l'Academie de Berlin' 1801, cf. the article ibid. 1802), and it has now been generally abandoned.

As Hegel notes, the main importance of this work is that it establishes, though imperfectly, a clear distinction between a purely abstract mode of regarding functions, and their applicability to mechanical problems. It is for this reason that it may be regarded as the starting point of the theory of functions as developed by A. L. Cauchy (1789–1857), G. F. B. Riemann (1826–1866), and K. Weierstrass (1815–1897). It was not entirely original however, for in 'The Residual Analysis' (London, 1764), John Landen (1719–1790) had also attempted to obviate the difficulties of Newton's 'fluxions' by employing algebraic and geometrical principles 'without recourse to some external principle such as the imaginary motion of incomprehensible infinitesimals'. See H. J. J. Winter 'John Landen, F.R.S. . . . Mathematician and Land Agent' (Peterborough, 1944); R. Dugas 'A History of Mechanics' (tr. Maddox, London, 1957) ch. 11; M. Bunge 'Metascientific Queries' (Springfield, 1959) pp. 166–172; M. Behm 'Hegels spekulative Deutung der Infinitesimalrechnung' (Dissertation, Univ. of Cologne, Dec. 16th 1963).

255, 16

See Galileo's 'Discorsi e dimostrazioni matematiche' (Leyden, 1638, Eng. tr. Crew, New York, 1914) Third Day, theorem II prop. ii, 'The spaces described by a body falling from rest with a uniformly accelerated motion are to each other as the squares of the time-intervals employed in traversing these distances.'

256, 7

In order to grasp the significance of this 'deduction', Hegel's preceding treatment of space, time and motion (§§ 254–261) has to be borne in mind, as well as his subsequent use of Galileo's discovery in the exposition of Kepler's laws (§ 270 Remark).

It is evidently meant to be regarded as a refutation of Newton's treatment of the matter in the opening pages of the 'Mathematical Principles'. Newton took

Galileo's discovery to be founded on *two laws*: (i) that every body continues in its state of rest, or of uniform motion in a right line, unless it is compelled to change that state by forces impressed upon it; (ii) that the change of motion is proportional to the motive force impressed; and is made in the direction of the right line in which that force is impressed: and two *corollaries*: (i) that a body, acted on by two forces simultaneously, will describe the diagonal of a parallelogram in the same time as it would describe the sides by those forces separately; (ii) that a direct force may be composed of any two oblique forces, and resolved into the same. See the scholium to the axioms, 'By the first two laws and the first two corollaries, *Galileo* discovered that the descent of bodies varied as the square of the time (*in duplicata ratione temporis*).'

It can obviously be argued that in this 'deduction' Hegel makes excessive use of the determinations he has given space and time in the course of his preceding dialectical *assessments*. Hegel would probably have replied that although this may very well be so, the determinations he is employing are at least more radically and soundly verifiable than Newton's forces.

The non-philosophical importance of this exposition is that it constitutes an attempt to free the treatment of fall from *dogmatic* Newtonianism, and to relate it in a more satisfactory way to both simpler and more complex mechanical phenomena. See the excellent survey of the subject by Ernst Mach (1838–1916), in 'The Science of Mechanics' II viii.

256, 28

Simon Stevinus (1548–1620), the Dutch mathematician, was in fact the first to prove experimentally that bodies differing in weight can have the same rate of fall: see his description of the experiment made at Delft in co-operation with the father of Hugo Grotius: 'De Beghinselen der Weeghconst' (Leyden, 1586) appendix: cf. 'Simon Stevin. The Principal Works' (5 vols. Amsterdam, 1955).

Galileo discovered this about 1590: see his early treatise 'De Motu' in 'Le Opere di Galileo Galilei' (20 vols. Florence, 1929–1939) vol. I pp. 243–419: cf. Salusbury's translation of the 'Dialogue on the Great World Systems' (ed. Santillana, Chicago, 1957) pp. 27–28.

There is of course an extensive literature on Galileo's relations with the church: see K. von Gebler 'Galilei und die römische Curie' (Stuttgart, 1876): Emil Wohlwill 'Galileo and his judges' (London, 1889): Adolf Müller S. J. 'Der Galilei-Prozess' (Freiburg-im-Breisgau, 1909): G. de Santillana 'The Crime of Galileo' (London, 1961). J. J. Fahie 'The Scientific Works of Galileo, with some account of his life and trial' in C. Singer 'Studies in the History and Method of Science' (2 vols. Oxford, 1917–1921) vol. II pp. 205–284.

256, 32

Newton 'Mathematical Principles' bk. III prop. iv theorem 4; bk. III prop. xx problem 4.

257, 5

See John Harris (1667?–1719) 'Lexicon Technicum' (2 vols. London, 1736), article 'Acceleration'.

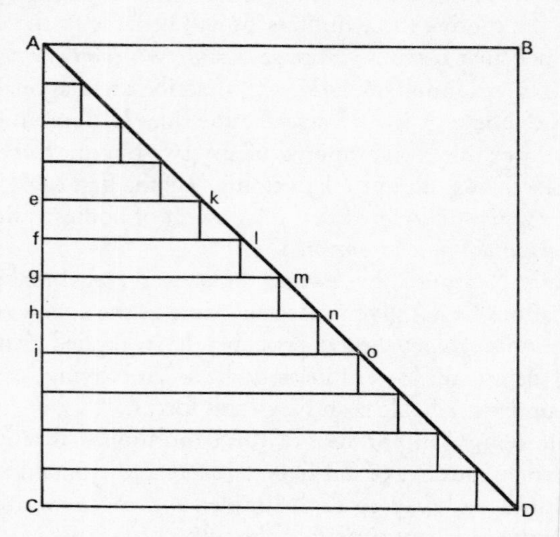

'The consideration of the annexed figure will teach us, that if an heavy body be thus uniformly accelerated in its descent, the space which it describes from the beginning of the time of its motion, shall be just half of that which it would have described, had it gone on for the same time with a velocity equal to what it had acquired in the end of its fall.

Let AC represent the time of its descent, DC the velocity at last acquired; and complete the triangle ACD. Let also the time AC be distinguished into an indefinite number of small parts, as ef . . . etc. and draw the parallels ek . . . etc. to the base CD. Then will ek be as the velocity of the heavy body, in the infinitely small part of time ef, and fl will be the velocity in the small time fg, etc.

But now it is proved in the laws of motion, that the space or length described by any moving body, in any given time, and with a given celerity; is *as the rectangle under the time and the celerity*, wherefore the space described as the rectangle fk; and the space described in the time fg, with the celerity gm, will be as the rectangle gl, etc. wherefore the space run through in the sum of all these times, will be *as the sum of all the triangles*; that is, as the triangle ACD, which contains them all.'

Cf. Thomas Rutherforth (1712–1771) 'A System of Natural Philosophy' (2 vols. Cambridge, 1748) vol. I pp. 94–97.

259, 1

For contrasting interpretations of this famous remark, see J. W. A. Pfaff

(1774–1835), 'Der Mensch und die Sterne' (Nuremberg, 1834), and Orest Danilovic Chwolson (1852–1934) 'Hegel, Haeckel, Kossuth und das 12. Gebot' (Brunswick, 1906) ch. II.

The *logical* foundation of Hegel's argument here is to be found in his treatment of the 'bad infinite': see his 'Science of Logic' (tr. Johnston and Struthers, 2 vols. London, 1961) vol. I pp. 241–253. Cf. W. R. Inge 'God and the Astronomers' (London, 1933).

259, 8

Sir William Herschel (1738–1822): see A. M. Clerke 'The Herschels and Modern Astronomy' (London, 1895); J. B. Sidgwick 'William Herschel, Explorer of the Heavens' (London, 1953). In a paper read to the Royal Society on February 10, 1791, Herschel wrote, 'The milky way itself, as I have shown in some former Papers, consists intirely of stars, and by imperceptible degrees I have been led on from the most evident congeries of stars to other groups in which the lucid points were smaller, but still very plainly to be seen; and from them to such wherein they could but barely be suspected, till I arrived at last to spots in which no trace of a star was to be discerned. But then the gradations to these latter were by such well-connected steps as left no room for doubt but that all these phaenomena were equally occasioned by stars variously dispersed in the immense expanse of the universe': see 'On Nebulous Stars, properly so called' ('Phil. Trans. Roy. Soc.' 1791 pp. 71–88: 'The Scientific Papers of Sir William Herschel' ed. Dreyer, 2 vols. London, 1912 vol. I p. 415).

In his 'Astronomical Observations relating to the Construction of the Heavens' (Phil. Trans. 1811 pp. 269–336, Dreyer op. cit. vol. II pp. 459–497), Herschel attempts to define *thirty two types* of *nebulae*, no. 30 being 'planetary nebulae'. It is probably this paper that Hegel has in mind.

Hegel was of course justified in regarding these definitions as very largely hypothetical. It was probably the wealth and accuracy of Herschel's observations and his admirable reluctance to generalize on the basis of them which laid the foundation of Hegel's cautious attitude towards any kind of theorizing in stellar astronomy.

259, 11

For the state of knowledge with regard to the Milky Way during the 1820's and 1830's, see 'J. S. T. Gehler's Physikalisches Wörterbuch' vol. vi pp. 2281–2288 (Leipzig, 1837). Hegel is referring here to *Kant's* 'Allgemeine Naturgeschichte und Theorie des Himmels' (Königsberg and Leipzig, 1755, 4th ed. 1808): see 'Immanuel Kant. Werke' (ed. W. Weischedel, 6 vols. Wiesbaden, 1960) vol. 1 pp. 265–267. ‚Daß es kleine, etwas mehr als das Finstere des leeren Himmelsraums erleuchtete Plätzchen sein, die alle darin überein kommen, daß sie mehr oder weniger offene Ellipsen vorstellen, aber deren Licht weit schwächer ist, als irgend ein anderes, das man am Himmel gewahr wird

. . In der Tat siehet man, daß die elliptische Figuren diese Arten neblichter Sterne, welche der Herr von Maupertius anführet, eine sehr nahe Beziehung auf den Plan der Milchstraße haben'. Cf. Pierre Louis Morceau Maupertius (1698–1759) 'Discours sur la figure des astres' (Paris, 1742); 'Oeuvres' (4 vols, Lyons, 1756). Kant was also influenced by Thomas Wright (1711–1786) who in his 'Theory of the Universe' (London, 1750) pointed out that the fixed stars are condensed towards the plane of the Milky Way: see H. Dingle 'The Scientific Adventure' (London, 1952) ch. vi.

The paper by Sir William Herschel referred to by Hegel is evidently, 'On the Construction of the Heavens' ('Phil. Trans. Roy. Soc.') vol. 75 p. 213, 1785). Hegel had probably read 'Ueber den Bau des Himmels' (Königsberg, 1791) by G. M. Sommer, which contains translations of three of Herschel's papers and an extract from Kant's work. See 'The Scientific Papers of Sir William Herschel' (ed. Dreyer, 2 vols. London, 1912) vol. 1 p. 251.

259, 16

In thus assessing the accomplishments of the stellar astronomy of his day, Hegel was by no means so unjust as some of his critics have implied. Accurate and substantial knowledge of the stars was at that time extremely scanty.

This 'stellar *geometry*' was evidently to be based on the excellent star-catalogues and atlases then available. The first of these drawn up on modern principles were the 'Historia coelestis britannica' (3 vols. London, 1725) and the 'Atlas coelestis' (London, 1729) by John Flamsteed (1646–1719), which showed the right ascensions and polar distances, as well as the longitudes and latitudes of 2848 stars. James Bradley's 'Astronomical Observations . . . 1750–1762' (ed. Hornsby and Robertson, 2 vols. Oxford, 1798–1805), showed the positions of 3,222 stars. Such was the accuracy of Bradley's observations that this work became the basis of all nineteenth century determinations of the proper motions of the stars, and of successive computations of the precession: see F. W. Bessel (1784–1846) 'Fundamenta Astronomiae' (Regiom., 1818). The precision of work in this field was greatly increased when J. T. Mayer (1723–1762) of the Göttingen Observatory published his famous correction formulae, which made allowances for instrumental deviations: see 'Mayer's Lunar Tables' (ed. Mason, London, 1787), 'Astronomical Observations' (London, 1826), 'Mayer's Catalogue of Stars Corrected' (ed. Baily, London, 1830). Cf. J. E. Bode (1747–1826) 'Vorstellung der Gestirne auf 34 Kupfertafeln' (Berlin, 1782); K. L. Harding (1765–1834) 'Atlas novus coelestis' (7 sects., Göttingen, 1808–1823).

It is just possible however, that Hegel is here confining rational interest in the stars to what were known as the 'figures of stars' (Sternfiguren) i.e. their apparent shapes: see G. S. Klügel (1739–1812) 'Mathematisches Wörterbuch' (7 vols. Leipzig, 1803–1836) vol. iv pp. 546–549.

F. W. Bessel (1784–1846) was the first to determine the *distance* of a star with any accuracy: see 'Bestimmung der Entfernung des 61. Sterns des Schwans'

('Astronomische Nachrichten' 1838 XVI, 1840 XVII): he found its parallax, which is in fact 0·32″, to be 0·37″. For the uncertainty of contemporary work in this field, see the articles by John Pond (1767–1836), published in the 'Phil. Trans. Roy. Soc.' between 1815 and 1825; G. Piazzi (1746–1826) 'Praecipuarum stellarum inerrantium positiones mediae' (Panormi, 1803); G. Calandrelli (1749–1827) 'Risultato di varie osservazioni sopra la parallasse annua di Vega *o α* della Lira' in 'Opuscoli astronomici' (8 vols. Rome, 1803–1824) 1806.

No satisfactory work was done on the *diameter* of stars until 1890.

Edmund Halley (1656–1724) noticed the *movement* of stars: see 'On the change of the latitudes of some of the principal fixed stars' ('Phil. Trans. Roy. Soc.' 1718), as did J. T. Mayer (1723–1762), 'Opera inedita' (ed. Lichtenberg, Göttingen, 1775), and Herschel, 'Account of the changes that have happened during the last 25 years in the relative situation of double stars'. ('Phil. Trans. Roy. Soc.' 1803).

Thirteen *novae* were recorded prior to 1670, but no more were discovered until 1848: Tycho Brahe observed the Nova Cassiopeiae in 1572 and Kepler the Nova Ophiuchi in 1604. Interesting articles on periodic changes in the *brightness* of stars were published by N. Pigott (d. 1804) and John Goodricke (d. 1786) in 'Phil. Trans. Roy. Soc.' 1781–1786.

Developments in spectroscopy, photographic photometry and radiometry would involve a *modern* philosophic treatment of stellar astronomy in assessments of fairly complex *physical* data relating to radiation, luminosity, temperatures and chemical constituency.

See J. E. Bode (1747–1826) 'Kurzgefasste Erläuterung der Sternkunde' (2 vols. Berlin, 1778, 3rd ed. Berlin, 1808); Ernst Zinner 'Die Geschichte der Sternkunde' (Berlin, 1931); G. P. Kuiper 'Stars and Stellar Systems' (9 vols. Chicago, 1965–). Cf. the interesting postulation of 'a hierarchic structure' of star-systems in 'International Encyclopedia of Unified Science' (ed. Neurath, Carnap, Morris, Chicago, 1955) vol. 1 pp. 511–515.

260, 2

'Every particle of matter in the universe attracts every other particle with a force that varies inversely as the squares of the distances between them and directly as the products of their masses.' Newton never states the law in precisely these words; for approximations see 'Mathematical Principles' bk. III general scholium, penultimate paragraph; bk. I prop. lxxvi cor. iii and iv; 'The System of the World' par. 26.

It is the assessments involved in Hegel's presentation of gravitation *at this juncture* which constitute the main originality and importance of his 'Mechanics'. Newton was not primarily concerned with a systematic assessment of his fields of enquiry, although the general lay-out of the 'Mathematical Principles' and his own statements show that he was instinctively aware of the necessity of some such systematization. See the scholium to bk. 1 sec. xi, 'In mathematics we are to investigate the quantities of forces with their proportions consequent upon any conditions supposed; then, when we enter upon physics, we compare those proportions with the phenomena of Nature, that we may know what conditions of those forces answer to the several kinds of attractive bodies. And this preparation being made, we argue more safely concerning the physical species, causes and proportions of the forces'. However, even the definitions and axioms with which he begins his book, admirable and serviceable though they are, contain a certain number of difficulties (see notes pp. 308, 319, 321, 323, 324, 334, 336, 349). Subsequent scientific developments are not strictly relevant to an understanding of *Hegel's* work, but it should perhaps be remembered that when, in 1901, W. Kaufmann showed that the mass of an electron increases rapidly as its speed nears the velocity of light, he disproved Newton's assumption of the invariance of mass, and that Einstein's gravitational theory of 1915 undermined belief in the reality of gravitation as a 'force'.

It cannot be said therefore that Newton's work promotes any satisfactory degree of precision in the interrelating of *qualitatively* distinct fields of physical enquiry. Its merit lies in the clarity and vigour with which certain specific problems are brought within the scope of *mathematical* calculation. The concept of *force* is one of the means he employs to this end. Even if we allow that he distinguished between its heuristic value and its physical reality however (note p. 329), his use of it in the 'Mathematical Principles' in order to relate the *various* phenomena dealt with to the central principle of the law of gravitation, has to be criticized on account of its having led so easily to the assumption that these phenomena could be exhaustively investigated and fully understood by means of a *single* technique. As Alexandre Koyré has remarked, the immediate *result* of his work was that, 'the eighteenth century, with very few exceptions, became reconciled to the ununderstandable'.—'Newtonian Studies' (London, 1965) p. 163.

Hegel recognizes that the law of gravitation embodies the most *comprehensive* generalization the science of his day could make about simply material bodies. He also realizes however, that subordinate to it are several fields of *specific* enquiry in which the law itself is not fully apparent. This leads him to treat geometry, arithmetic, motion, matter, gravity, fall etc. as involving disciplines and studies less complex in subject matter and limited in scope than enquiry into the nature of *universal* gravitation itself. He takes the solar system to involve still more comprehensive generalizations (Kepler's laws) on account of the *particularity* of its component bodies and the *complexity* of their motions (§ 270): see especially the note on Francoeur (p. 332).

In his 'De Orbitis Planetarum' (Jena, 1801), Hegel suggested that *magnetic* theory might provide a more satisfactory explanation of Kepler's laws than Newton's forces (notes pp. 362, 372), but as no facts were forthcoming in his lifetime to confirm this, he failed to develop the idea. The present view that

Keplerian motion involves *both* gravitational *and electrostatic* factors, and that whereas the gravitational force is always attractive, the electrostatic element may be either attractive or repulsive, would certainly have interested him: see H. C. Corben and P. Stehle 'Classical Mechanics' (New York and London, 1960) pp. 93–100; L. Brillouin 'Scientific Uncertainty, and Information' (New York and London, 1964) ch. viii.

At that time, Hegel was not of course alone in realizing that a *physical* explanation of gravitation and related phenomena was needed. Newton (note p. 329) regarded himself as an agnostic in these matters, and Laplace, in his 'Exposition du Système du Monde' ('Oeuvres' vi p. 443, *not* the 2 vol. 1796 ed. quoted by Hegel) not only enquired into the very nature of gravitation, but went so far as to ask whether or not its propagation is instantaneous, 'Le principe de la pesanteur universelle, est-il une loi promordiale de la nature, ou n'est-il qu'un effet général d'une cause inconnue? Ne peut'on pas ramener à ce principe les affinités? Newton, plus circonspect que plusieurs de ses disciples, ne s'est point prononcé sur ces questions auxquelles l'ignorance ou nous sommes, des propriétés intimes de la matière, ne permet pas de répondre d'une manière satisfaisante'.

260, 12

When a tube of very small diameter (like a hair, capillus), open at both ends, is dipped into water, the fluid within it will rise about the level of that without, and its surface become concave. If mercury is used, the fluid in the tube will fall, and its surface become convex. The finer the tube, the greater will be the movement.

This phenomenon attracted attention on account of its appearing to provide an exception to all the laws which regulate the equilibrium of fluids. Robert Hooke (1635–1702) performed experiments with very fine tubes in which the water rose twenty one inches above its surface in the vessel. Newton mentions related phenomena in his 'Opticks' (4th ed. London, 1730) p. 367. James Jurin (1684–1750), in 'On the Suspension of Water in Capillary Tubes' and 'On the Action of Glass Tubes upon Water and Quicksilver' ('Phil. Trans. Roy. Soc.' vol. 30 pp. 739 and 1083): see 'Dissertationes Physico-mathematicae' (London, 1732): put forward the theory that the water which enters the tube *has its gravity taken off* by the attraction of the tube's periphery with which its upper surface is in contact, so that it rises partly because of *attraction* and partly because of the *pressure* of the external water. Thomas Morgan (d. 1743), in his 'Philosophical Principles of Medicine' (London, 1725, 2nd ed. 1730) p. 88, accounted for the phenomenon in a similar manner, as did A. C. Clairaut (1713–1765), in his 'Théorie de la Figure de la Terre' (Paris, 1743) § 59. Clairaut showed that if the law by which the matter of the tube attracts the fluid is the same as that by which the parts of the fluid attract one another, the fluid will rise above the level whenever the intensity of the first of these attractions exceeds half the intensity of the second, and that if it is exactly half, the surface of the column within the tube will be a plane, on a level with the surface without.

In Hegel's day the accepted explanation of capillary attraction was that put forward by Laplace, and Hegel probably mentions the subject here on account of its treatment in the 'Traité de Mécanique Céleste' bk. x supplement ('Oeuvres de Laplace' vol. 4 pp. 389–552); cf. Laplace's articles in the 'Journal de Physique' 1806 pp. 120–128, 246–256; 1819 pp. 292–296: 'Nicholson's Journal' xiv, 1806 pp. 249–258, xvii, 1807 pp. 286–297. Laplace was of the opinion that a narrow ring or zone of glass immediately above the surface of the water, exerts its force on the water, so that the phenomena of capillary tubes may be explained by supposing that the attraction of the glass, combined with the weight of the water and the cohesion of its particles, is the cause of the concave surface, or of the little meniscus of water which terminates the column. Consequently, he regarded this meniscus as a body of water stretched across the tube, and sustained there by the attraction of the glass, while it exerts its own attraction on the particles of the column immediately underneath, by which means the gravity of those particles is diminished, and the water rises in the tube above its level on the outside, to supply their deficiency of weight.

Cf. James Challis (1803–1882) 'Report on the Theory of Capillary Attraction' ('British Association Report' 1834 pp. 253–294).

261, 4

See the note on p. 354.

261, 19

'The Logic of Hegel' (tr. Wallace, Oxford, 1963).

262, 17

It was evidently the 'Theory of the Universe' (London, 1750), by Thomas Wright (1711–1786), which initiated speculations of this kind. Wright pointed out that the fixed stars themselves are not scattered at random, but are condensed towards the plane of the Milky Way. Kant was certainly inspired by Wright's idea. In his 'Allgemeine Naturgeschichte und Theorie des Himmels' (1755) he assumed that matter was originally distributed, in a finely divided condition, throughout the whole of space, and that owing to gravitation, central bodies and nuclei were formed, about which the proximate matter condensed. He assumed that the nuclei gravitated towards the central bodies, and were then diverted under the influence of a repulsive force, so that their fall towards the centre was transformed into a vortical motion about it.

G. L. L. Buffon (1707–1788), who had a great propensity for forming hypotheses, supposed that a comet had collided with the sun, tearing a jet of matter away from its surface, and that this matter had condensed into spheres at various distances from the central body: see his 'Histoire Naturelle' (44 vols. Paris, 1749–1804); Supplement vol. v 'Époques de la Nature'.

The most famous hypothesis of this kind was that put forward by P. S. Laplace (1749–1827) in his 'Exposition du Système du Monde' (2 vols. Paris, 1796). He assumed that the bodies of the solar system originated from an immense incandescent nebula, rotating from west to east, of which the sun is a relic. As this nebula cooled and contracted, its rate of rotation increased, in accordance with the laws of mechanics. A stage was reached at which the centrifugal force at the equator just counterbalanced the gravitational attraction of the nucleus of the nebula, and a ring of matter then detached itself and was left behind. This happened repeatedly; as the rings were unstable however, each broke up into rotating masses, which eventually coalesced to form the separate planets.

This *nebular* hypothesis was generally accepted until Moulton and Chamberlin put forward their *planetesimal* hypothesis at the end of the last century.

Hegel evidently objected to these theories not only because they could not be confirmed, but because they were used in order to account for the centrifugal force held to be involved in the motions of the celestial bodies.

262, 35

See Hegel's 'De Orbitis Planetarum' (Jena, 1801), 'corpora autem coelestia glebae non adscripta et centrum gravitatis perfectius in se gerentia, Deorum more per levem aera incedant'.

The five planets known to antiquity were all given the names of gods: Saturn, Jupiter, Mars, Venus, Mercury. This practice evidently began in Greece in the fourth century B.C., and was influenced by Babylonian and Egyptian astronomy: 'Paulys Real-Encyclopädie der Classischen Altertumswissenschaft' vol. 40 cols. 2017–2185 (ed. Ziegler, Waldsee, 1950). Cf. M. R. Cohen and I. E. Drabkin 'A Source Book in Greek Science' (New York, 1948) pp. 89–134: M. Clagett 'Greek Science in Antiquity' (London, 1957) pp. 83–98.

Cf. A. S. Eddington 'The Nature of the Physical World' (Cambridge, 1929) p. 147, where this remark of Hegel's is misquoted and *defended*, despite its being, 'particularly foolish even for a philosopher'.

262, 37

Cf. Newton 'Mathematical Principles' bk. III prop. vii theorem 7.

263, 1

Michelet omits these quotation marks, and alters the following sentence somewhat: see 'Jenenser Realphilosophie II' p. 23 ‚Auf die himmlische Körperlichkeit müssen daher die Vorstellungen von Stoß, Druck, Ziehen u.dgl. nicht angewendet werden; sie gelten nur von einer andern Existenz der Materie.'

263, 11

‚Die besonderen aber sind, die . . .' Hegel occasionally uses this grammatically shortened form when adding a relative clause, cf. I. 254, 28 ‚die beschleunigte ist, in der die Geschwindigkeit . . .' In the 1817 edition of the 'Encyclopaedia' the passage reads as follows, ‚Die besondern aber sind andere, die . . .,

263, 25

The laws of Kepler are as follows:

(1) The planets move about the sun in ellipses, in one focus of which the sun is situated.

(2) The radius vector joining each planet with the sun describes equal areas in equal times.

(3) The cubes of the mean distances of the planets from the sun are proportional to the squares of their times of revolution.

The first two were discovered between 1602 and 1606, and published in Kepler's 'Astronomia nova' (Prague, 1609): see chapters 40, 58, 59; cf. the German translation by Max Caspar (Munich and Berlin, 1929). The third law was discovered in 1618, and published in the 'Harmonice Mundi' (Linz, 1619, German tr. Caspar, Munich and Berlin, 1939) bk. 5 ch. iii. Cf. G. Holton 'Johannes Kepler's Universe: Its Physics and Metaphysics' ('American Journal of Physics' vol. 24 pp. 340–351, May 1956).

For a recent consideration of them in relation to Newton's theories see T. E. Sterne 'An Introduction to Celestial Mechanics' (New York, 1960).

263, 26

'The Logic of Hegel' (tr. Wallace, Oxford, 1963) pp. 364–366.

In this and the following paragraph Hegel distinguishes between the *analytical* method of cognition, which attempts to understand a complex phenomenon by breaking it down into its simpler constituents, and the *synthetic* method, which starts by accepting a phenomenon in its full complexity and *then* proceeds to indicate simpler aspects of it. He is implying here that Newton followed the first and Kepler the second of these methods: see the notes on pp. 343, and 351 (Francoeur).

Cf. Hegel's 'De Orbitis Planetarum' (Jena, 1801), 'quam physica scientia methodum veram perfecte imitari debebat totum ponendi ex eoque rationes partium deducendi, neutiquam vero ex oppositis viribus, id est, ex partibus totum componendi.'—Lasson's ed. (Leipzig, 1928) p. 364.

263, 28

See Newton's 'Mathematical Principles' bk. I sect. iii: bk. III phen. iv and prop. xiii theorem 13.

264, 5

See Sir J. F. W. Herschel (1792–1871) 'Outlines of Astronomy' (London, 1849) pp. 295, 300, 'The third law of Kepler, which connects the distances and periods of the planets by a general rule, bears with it, as its theoretical interpretation, this important consequence, viz. that it is one and the same force, modified only by distance from the sun, which retains *all* the planets in their orbits about it . . . Of all the laws to which induction from pure observation has ever conducted man, this *third law* (as it is called) of Kepler may justly be regarded as the most remarkable, and the most pregnant with important consequences. When we contemplate the constituents of the planetary system from the point of view which this relation affords us, it is no longer a mere analogy which strikes us . . . The resemblance is now perceived to be a true *family* likeness; they are bound up in one chain . . . subjected to one pervading influence, which extends from the centre to the farthest limits of that great system, of which all of them, the earth included, must henceforth be regarded as members'.

264, 22

Cf. Hegel's reference to Laplace's 'Systeme du Monde' on p. 274.

The calculus, as presented in the 'Mathematical Principles', is certainly lacking in logical rigour. In the opening lemma of bk. I sect. i for example, Newton *supposes* the motion to be calculated as the ultimate criterion of the validity of his exposition (note p. 364). It was probably his awareness of its shortcomings which caused him to delay the publication of his 'Method of Fluxions' (1671, Eng. tr. Colson, London, 1736) for so long. His conception of the basic principles of the calculus had certainly changed by 1704, for in his 'Quadratura curvarum' (London, 1704), he dispenses with the postulate of the infinitely small increment. He writes in the introduction, 'I consider mathematical quantities in this place not as consisting of very small parts, but as described by a continued motion. Lines are described, and thereby generated, not by the apposition of parts, but by the continued motion of points; superficies by the motion of lines; solids by the motion of superficies; angles by the rotation of the sides; portions of time by continual flux: and so on in other quantities. These geneses really take place in the nature of things, and are daily seen in the motion of bodies . . .

Fluxions are, as near as we please, as the increments of fluents generated in times, equal and as small as possible, and to speak accurately, they are in the prime ratio of nascent increments; yet they can be expressed by any times whatever, which are proportional to them.'

In the subsequent exposition it becomes apparent that although Newton has avoided the postulation of infinitely small quantities by introducing motion into his definitions of the point and the line etc., he still requires us to believe that a point may be considered as a triangle, that a triangle may be inscribed in a point, and that three dissimilar triangles become similar and equal when they have reached their ultimate form in one and the same point. For *eighteenth century* criticism of this, see note p. 351.

It is certainly true that bk. I prop. i theorem 1 of the 'Mathematical Principles', which follows immediately after the preliminary sketch of the calculus, gives rise to a conic section in general rather than an ellipse in particular. Newton admits as much in the scholium which concludes bk. I sect. ii, '*In all figures whatsoever*, if the ordinates are augmented or diminished in any given ratio, or their inclination is in any way changed, the periodic time remaining the same, the forces directed to any centre placed in the abscissa are in the several ordinates augmented or diminished in the ratio of the distances from the centre.'

In bk. I sect. iii therefore, where Newton deals with the motion of bodies in eccentric conic sections, the various conic sections, ellipse, hyperbola and parabola are merely assumed. It is quite clear that when he deals with movement in an ellipse he has the planets in mind, but as Hegel notes, the identification is *supposed* rather than *proved*.

Hegel takes this lack of rigour in the Newtonian exposition to be evidence of the fact that Kepler's first law is *essentially more complex* than the law of gravitation as such, and that the attempt to *deduce* it from the latter is therefore futile (note p. 343).

On Newton's treatment of conics see note p. 360. See also H. G. Zeuthen 'Die Lehre von den Kegelschnitten im Alterthum' (Copenhagen, 1886); T. L. Heath 'Apollonius of Perga' (Cambridge, 1961); 'Apollonii Pergaei conicorum libr. VIII' (ed. Halley, 2 vols. Oxford, 1710); J. M. F. Wright 'An Algebraic System of Conic Sections' (London, 1836); J. L. Coolidge 'A History of Conic Sections and Quadric Surfaces' (Oxford, 1945).

264, 25

See pp. 272–3. The reference here is to the famous earth-moon test of the law of gravitation: 'Mathematical Principles' bk. III prop. iv theorem 4, 'The moon gravitates towards the earth, and by the force of gravity is continually drawn off from a rectilinear motion, and retained in its orbit'. Newton told Halley at one time that the theory of lunar motions made his head ache and kept him awake at night so often, that he would think of it no more: see Sir David Brewster 'Memoirs of the Life, Writing, and Discoveries of Sir Isaac Newton' (2 vols. Edinburgh, 1855) vol. II p. 108. He had formulated his theory of gravitation as early as 1665, but it was not until 1685 that he realized the importance of the centre of gravity in the attraction of a sphere (note p. 362).

Newton grapples with the complicated principles involved in the three body problem in bk. III prop. xxii theorem 17: see E. O. Lovett 'The Problem of Three Bodies' ('Science' vol. 29 pp. 81–91, 1909), R. Marcolongo 'Il problema die tre corpi' (Milan, 1919). The moon's motion has not yet been *exactly* explained by gravitational theory. It has been suggested that the cause of the difference between prediction and observation lies in the variation of the *earth's rate of rotation* caused by slight periodic changes in the shape of the earth, or by the varying elevation of the centre of the moon's disc in the course of a month: see for example E. W. Brown's articles in 'Monthly Notices of the Royal Astronomical Society' vols. 73–75, 1913–1915; Z. Kopal 'Physics and Astronomy of the Moon' (London, 1962) p. 24.

264, 37

See the note on p. 332. In both the 1827 and 1830 editions of the 'Encyclopaedia' Hegel referred, incorrectly, to chapter *eleven* of book two.

Francoeur's 'Traité élémentaire de Mécanique' (Paris, 1801) had reached a fifth edition by 1825. Bk. II ch. ii no. 4 is concerned with 'universal gravitation'. Kepler's laws are accepted here as *truths demonstrated by observation*, slight inaccuracies due to perturbation etc. being disregarded. The following propositions are then *deduced* from them:

(i) That the force drawing each planet is directed towards the centre of the sun.

(ii) That the force which moves the planets in ellipses is in inverse proportion to the square of the distance of the centre of these bodies from that of the sun.

(iii) That in their being drawn towards the sun, the planets have weights proportional to their masses.

(iv) That the molecules of matter are mutually attractive in accordance with their masses, and in inverse proportion to the squares of their distances.

Hegel evidently regards these deductions as illustrating the relationship between the universal law of gravitation and the more complex phenomena of the Keplerian laws (note p. 343).

265, 6

See the note on p. 354.

265, 11

In the second edition of the 'Encyclopaedia' (1827), Hegel added the following sentence here, 'I shall not call into evidence the fact that my interest in these matters has occupied me now for twenty-five years.' He evidently had in mind his thesis 'Dissertatio philosophica de Orbitis Planetarum' (Jena, 1801): see 'Hegels Sämtliche Werke' (ed. Lasson, Leipzig, 1928) vol. I pp. 347–401: cf. note p. 372.

265, 23

See the note on p. 336.

265, 26

In Newton's 'Mathematical Principles' the calculations are reduced to *geometric* form. However, in his 'Method of Fluxions' (1671, tr. Colson, London, 1736) Newton helped to lay the foundations of *infinitesimal analysis*.

It is curious that Hegel should not have *attempted* to deny Newton the credit of having been the discoverer of the calculus. The acrimonious priority dispute with Leibniz must have been well known to him. He was evidently content to accept the account of the matter given in the 'Commercium epistolicum' (1712, ed. Keill, London, 1725: ed. Biot and Lefort, Paris, 1856), and by Joseph Raphson (1648–1715) in his 'History of Fluxions' (London, 1715). The truth of the dispute did not come to light until the 1840's and 1850's: see A. De Morgan 'Essays on the Life and Work of Newton' (ed. Jourdain, Chicago and London, 1914).

George Berkeley (1685–1753), in 'The Analyst' (Dublin, 1734), criticized Newton's fluxions as being 'the ghosts of departed quantities', and argued that the fundamental idea of supposing a finite ratio to exist between two absolutely evanescent terms was absurd and unintelligible: see Robert Woodhouse (1773–1827) 'The Principles of Analytical Calculation' (Cambridge, 1803); J. O. Wisdom 'Berkeley's Criticism of the Infinitesimal' ('British Journal for the Philosophy of Science' vol. 4, pp. 22–25, 1953). Berkeley's criticism gave rise to a lively controversy between James Jurin (1684–1750), John Walton of Dublin, Benjamin Robins (1707–1751) and Henry Pemberton (1694–1771), regarding Newton's views on the existence of variables which reach their limits. The constructive outcome of it was Robins' rejection of all infinitely small quantities and presentation of a more logically coherent theory of fluxions in 'A Discourse concerning the Nature and Certainty of Sir Isaac Newton's Methods of Fluxions' (1735, ed. J. Wilson, 2 vols. London, 1761), and 'A Complete System of Fluxions' (2 vols. Edinburgh, 1742) by Colin Maclaurin (1698–1746). In 1813 George Peacock (1791–1868), John Herschel (1792–1871), Charles Babbage (1792–1871) and a few other Cambridge students founded the 'Analytical Society' in order, as they said, to promote the principles of pure 'D-ism' (Leibnizian notation) against those of 'dot-age' (Newton's).

For a *contemporary* treatment of the calculus, see L. N. M. Carnot (1753–1823) 'Réflexions sur la Métaphysique du Calcul Infinitésimal' (Paris, 1813, English tr. 1832).

It was the 'Introductio in analysin infinitorum' (Lausanne, 1748) by Leonhard Euler (1707–1783), which put analytical mathematics on a systematic basis. J. L. Lagrange (1736–1813), see especially his 'Théorie des fonctions analytiques' (Paris, 1797) quoted by Hegel 255, 10, attempted to work out an entirely new basis for the calculus. The culmination of this work with regard to *celestial mechanics* was the 'Mécanique Céleste' (5 vols. Paris, 1798–1827) of P. S. Laplace (1749–1827): Eng. tr. N. Bowditch (4 vols. Boston, Mass., 1829–1839): German tr. J. C. Burckhardt (2 vols. Berlin, 1800–1802), in which Newton's geometric presentation is completely transformed into a fully analytic exposition. Laplace removes all doubt as to the stability of the solar system, so that he was also able to dispense with Newton's postulation of a regulating Deity: see 'Mathematical Principles' bk. III general scholium. When he presented Napoleon with a copy of his book, the Emperor commented, 'M. Laplace, they tell me you have written this large book on the system of the universe, and have never even mentioned its Creator.' The reply was short, 'Je n'avais pas besoin de cette hypothèse-la'. See J. Pelseneer 'La Religion de Laplace' ('Isis' 1945–6 pp. 158–160).

Cf. H. Brougham and E. J. Routh 'Analytical View of Sir Isaac Newton's Principia' (London, 1855); J. Ravetz 'The Representation of Physical Quantities in Eighteenth Century Mathematical Physics' ('Isis' 1961 pp. 7–20).

265, 29

Newton 'Mathematical Principles' bk. I prop. lxv theorem 25; bk. III prop. xiii theorem 13, 'The force of gravity towards Jupiter is towards the sun as 1 to 1067; and therefore in the conjunction of Jupiter and Saturn, because the distance of Saturn from Jupiter will be to the gravity of Saturn towards the sun as 81 to 16·1067: or, as to 1 to about 211. And hence arises a perturbation of the orbit of Saturn in every conjunction of this planet with Jupiter, so sensible, that astronomers are puzzled with it'.

266, 4

Perturbations are the deviations of planets from exact elliptic motion. Newton explained the *long inequality* of Jupiter and Saturn correctly, but he failed to distinguish between the various kinds of perturbation with any degree of comprehensiveness: op. cit. bk. III prop. xiii theorem 13, 'But the actions of the planets one upon another are so very small, that they may be neglected'.

It was P. S. Laplace (1749–1827) who made the first detailed investigations of such variations, and showed clearly that they constitute a class of ordinary and regular periodic perturbations: see 'Sur les inégalités séculaires des planètes et des satellites' (1784); 'Théorie de Jupiter et Saturne' (1785–6); 'Sur les variations séculaires des orbites des planètes' (1787) etc. in 'Mémoires de l'Academie de Paris'. Cf. 'Oeuvres de Laplace' (14 vols. Paris, 1843–1912) vols. 3, 4, 5, 11 12, 13.

Calculations made by J. C. Adams (1819–1892) and U. J. J. Leverrier (1811–1877) on the basis of irregularities in the orbit of Uranus led to the discovery of Neptune by J. G. Galle (1812–1910) in 1846. Cf. Alexis Bouvard (1787–1843) 'Tables astronomiques . . . contenant les tables de Jupiter, de Saturne et d'Uranus' (Paris, 1821), who speaks of, 'une action étrangère et inaperçu qui aurait influencé la marche de la planète' Uranus. The existence of Pluto was also suspected by Bouvard: see G. B. Airy 'Account of some circumstances historically connected with the discovery of the planet exterior to Uranus' ('Monthly Notices of the Royal Astronomical Society' 1846, 7: 124); M. Gosser 'The search for a Planet beyond Neptune' ('Isis' 1964).

267, 2

Newton Mathematical Principles' bk. I sect. ii: see the following note.

267, 30

As Hegel has good reasons for questioning the validity of the hypotheses accounting for the origin of centrifugal force in celestial mechanics (p. 346), the logical rigour of the Newtonian calculus (p. 349), and Newton's use of the principle of the composition of forces (p. 358), and as he points out that Newton never attempted to *prove* that the planets must move about the sun in *ellipses* (p. 350), he is perfectly justified in raising these objections to the traditional explanations of planetary motion. His fundamental reason for doing so has already been indicated (p. 343). Any worthwhile refutation of his argument here must begin by considering these subsidiary points. See Newton on the motions of *projectiles in certain orbits*: 'The System of the World' par. 3 (Cajori's ed. of the 'Mathematical Principles' pp. 551–2). Samuel Vince (1749–1821) 'A Complete System of Astronomy' (3 vols. London, 1814–1823) vol. II pp. 1–28, provides a good *contemporary* example of the sort of exposition Hegel probably has in mind. Cf. N. R. Hanson 'Leverrier: The Zenith and Nadir of Newtonian Mechanics' ('Isis' 1962 pp. 359–378), an account of the ill-starred hidden planet hypothesis, put forward to explain the precession of the perihelion of Mercury on Newtonian principles.

Thomas Rutherforth (1712–1771), 'A System of Natural Philosophy' (2 vols. Cambridge, 1748) vol. I pp. 139–154 provides a good example of the 'old-fashioned' kind of proof mentioned by Hegel on p. 264. Like Newton, he describes the motion of *projectiles*, and then *assumes* that the same principles are at work in the motion of the planets. In fact he calls the centrifugal the 'projectile' force.

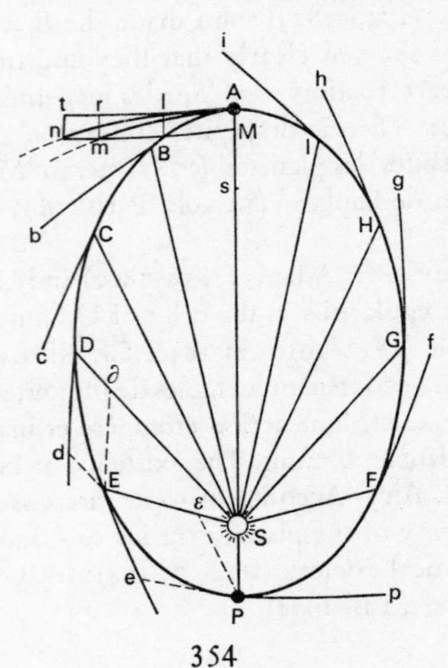

'This may be a little farther explaned, if we go on with considering the angle made by the projectile and centripetal forces. This angle is the least of all when the body is at D, and keeps increasing constantly, till it becomes a right one, when the body arrives at P. The reason of its increasing after the body has passed by D is, because the projectile velocity, or velocity with which the body endeavours to move in the tangent, is greater than what would be requisite to make the body revolve round S in a circle. But the same reason holds when the body is a P: its velocity is still too great to suffer it to move in a circle having PS for its radius or semidiameter. Therefore the angle SPp, as the body moves on, will keep still increasing, and consequently must become greater than a right one. From hence it is evident that after the body is arrived at P, that is, after the angle made by the projectile and centripetal forces is become a right one, it can approach towards S no longer. For if the body was to approach nearer to S, the angle made by the lines Pp and PS must decrease: just as the angle made by the lines Al and AS decreased in the approach of the body towards S, when it set out from A. But the angle at P will increase, as has been proved, whilst the body moves forward from P. Therefore it will not approach nearer to S than when it is at P: but the point P, where this angle is a right one, will be its least distance from *S*.

When the body goes on from P, the velocity being too great for it either to approach nearer to S or to keep at the same distance from S, it will depart from S, and the angle made by the projectile and centripetal forces will increase; so that when the body arrives at F it will be SFf greater than a right one. And because, as the body rises or departs from S, the centripetal force, though it is not sufficient to draw it back again, will retard its motion, the projectile velocity will keep decreasing. Till at last, in the return of the body towards A, this velocity will be such a one as would be just sufficient to make the body revolve in a circle round the point S. Now, whilst the body's velocity was greater than this, the direction, in which it endeavours in every point of its orbit to fly off in a tangent to that point, that is, the direction of the projectile force departed farther from the direction of that force by which it is impelled towards the center, or the angle made by these two forces encreased. Thus when the body was at P, the angle was SPp; when it was at F, the angle was SFf; and when it arrives at G, the angle becomes SGg. But since, as the body goes on from G, it will be still retarded, the tangent, or direction of the projectile force, will approach towards the line, in which the centripetal force acts, that is, this angle will constantly decrease; at H it will be SHh, less than SGg; at I, it will be SIi less than SHh; and at last at A, it will be so far diminished as to be a right one again.'

Hegel suggested, in his 'De Orbitis Planetarum' (Jena, 1801), see note p. 372, that a *magnetic* theory might provide a better explanation of planetary motion. As no facts were forthcoming in his lifetime to confirm this surmisal, he failed to develop it. The involvement of electrostatic principles in Keplerian motion would certainly have interested him: see H. C. Corben and P. Stehle 'Classical Mechanics' (New York and London, 1960) pp. 93–100; L. Brillouin 'Scientific Uncertainty and Information' (New York and London, 1964) ch. vii, 'Weaknesses and limitations of mechanics' pp. 85–105.

267, 36

See the note on p. 363.

268,11

On the problems involved in circular motion, see Ernst Mach (1838–1916) 'The Science of Mechanics' II ii 4, appendix xi; H. Weiler 'Mechanics' (London, 1957) pp. 233–265. Cf. Galileo's 'Dialogue on the Great World Systems' (ed. Santillana, Chicago, 1957) pp. 55, 223 and the note on p. 349. Galileo's neglect of Kepler's laws was certainly due in part to his belief in the *perfection of the circle*. For a recent discussion of the seventeenth century dilemmas Hegel is overcoming in this analysis, see E. Panofsky 'Galileo as a Critic of the Arts' (The Hague, 1954) pp. 24–26, and E. Rosen's review of this book ('Isis' XlVII, 1956, pp. 78–80), A. Koyré 'Attitude esthétique et Pensée scientifique' ('Critique' Oct. 1955 pp. 835–847).

268, 31

The significance of this exposition of Kepler's second law becomes more apparent if it is remembered that the law gave rise to the famous Keplerian problem in the theory of functions: see the statement of it given by Robert Small of Edinburgh in his 'An Account of the Astronomical Discoveries of Kepler' (London, 1804) p. 296, 'Having the area of part of a semi-circle given, and a point in its diameter, to determine an arch of the semi-circle, and an angle at the given point, such that the given area may be comprehended by the lines including the angle, and by the required arch; or, to draw from a given point in the diameter of a semi-circle, a straight line dividing the area of the semi-circle in a given ratio'.

Cf. Newton 'Mathematical Principles' bk. I prop. xxxi prob. 23 and scholium: J. C. Adams 'On Newton's Solution of Kepler's Problem' ('Monthly Notices of the Royal Astronomical Society' vol. 43 pp. 43–49, 1882); F. W. Bessel (1784–1846) 'Analytische Auflösung der Kepler'schen Aufgabe' ('Berlin. Abhand. Acad. Wissen.' 1816–1817 p. 49); 'Bulletin Astronomique' vol. xvii pp. 37–47 (Paris, 1900); J. J. Astrand 'Hülfstafeln zur leichten und genauen Auflösung des Kepler'schen Problems' (Leipzig, 1890); J. P. Møller 'On the Solution of Kepler's Equation' in 'Festschrift für Elis Strömgren' (Copenhagen, 1940) pp. 163–174.

269, 14

See the note on p. 348.

269, 20

Newton 'Mathematical Principles': see bk. III phen. iv and the following propositions. In a scholium here Newton writes, 'The force which retains the celestial bodies in their orbits has been hitherto called centripetal force; but it being now made plain that it can be no other than a gravitating force, we shall hereafter call it gravity.'

269, 36

It was the observations made by Tycho Brahe (1546–1601) at the Stjärneborg observatory on the island of Ven which provided the empirical basis for Kepler's speculations: see J. L. E. Dreyer 'Tycho Brahe' (Edinburgh, 1890), J. von Hasner 'Tycho Brahe und J. Kepler' (Prague, 1872), F. Becket and C. Christensen 'Uraniborg og Stjærneborg' (Copenhagen, 1921), Martin Olsson 'Uraniborg och Stjärneborg' (Stockholm, 1951). Hegel may have read J. T. B. Helfrecht's 'Tycho Brahe, geschildert nach seinem Leben, Meynungen und Schriften' (Hof, 1798); cf. W. Faxe 'Forlämningar af Tycho Brahes Stjerneborg och Uranienborg på ön Hven' (Stockholm, 1824).

When Brahe died unexpectedly near Prague on October 24, 1601, Kepler was given the task of editing his observations, which appeared in the first volume of the 'Astronomiae Instauratae Progymnasmata' (2 vols. Prague, 1602–1603). This work contains a treatment of the motions of the sun and the moon, gives the positions of 777 fixed stars, and was later incorporated into the famous 'Rudolphine Tables' (Ulm, 1627), in which 1005 stars were catalogued, and to which Kepler appended logarithmic and refraction tables. These tables remained the best aid to astronomy, of this kind, until the early eighteenth century. Cf. the note on Jean Picard (1620–1682) and Ole Rømer (1644–1710) II. 235.

See Max Caspar 'Johannes Kepler' (Stuttgart, 1948, tr. C. D. Hellman London and New York, 1959).

269, 39

Nicolaus Copernicus (1473–1543) 'De revolutionibus orbium coelestium' (Nuremberg, 1543), translated by J. F. Dobson as 'On the Revolutions of the Heavenly Spheres' (London, 1955) bk. V ch. 4, "Why the Proper Movements of the Planets Appear Irregular': 'Accordingly as the ancients placed one movement in two eccentric circles, as was shown, we have decreed two regular movements out of which the apparent irregularity is compounded either by a circle eccentric to an eccentric circle, or by the epicycle of an epicycle or by a combination of an eccentric circle carrying an epicycle. For they can all effect the same irregularity, as we demonstrated above in the case of the sun and the moon'.

Cf. L. Prowe 'Nicolaus Coppernicus' (2 vols. Berlin, 1883–4); A. Armitage 'Copernicus, the founder of modern Astronomy' (London, 1938); E. Rosen 'Three Copernican Treatises' (Dover Pubs., 1959), this work contains an excellent bibliography. For a less technical and more autobiographical account see H. Kesten 'Copernicus and his World' (New York, 1945).

270, 6

See the relation between uniform motion in a circle and the regular oscillatory motion of the *pendulum* mentioned by Ernst Mach (1838–1916) 'The Science of Mechanics' II ii 3–10.

270, 21

An oval line consists of any curve shaped like the section of an egg, and is therefore a line which is closed and always concave towards the centre. Hegel probably has in mind the effect of perturbation and precession upon the planetary orbits (notes pp. 353 and 367), and *sinuous* heliocentric orbits such as the moon's.

Kepler evidently grasped the significance of the oval line *before* he formulated the first of his laws: see his 'Astronomia nova' (Prague, 1609) p. 213, 'Itaque plane hoc est: Orbita planetae non est circulus, sed ingrediens ad latera utraque paulatim, iterumque ad circuli amplitudinem in perigaeo exiens, cujusmodi figuram itineris ovalem appellitant'.

Cf. Robert Small of Edinburgh 'An Account of the Astronomical Discoveries of Kepler' (London, 1804) pp. 242–254 and 276–277; E. H. Lockwood 'A book of curves' (Cambridge, 1961).

270, 39

Newton 'Mathematical Principles' (tr. Cajori, Berkeley, 1947), Axioms corollary i, treats the principle of the parallelogram of forces as the corollary to his second law of motion, i.e. that 'the change of motion is proportional to the motive force impressed; and is made in the direction of the right line in which that force is impressed'. As Newton formulates this corollary it is the first distinct enunciation of the principle of the *composition of forces*.

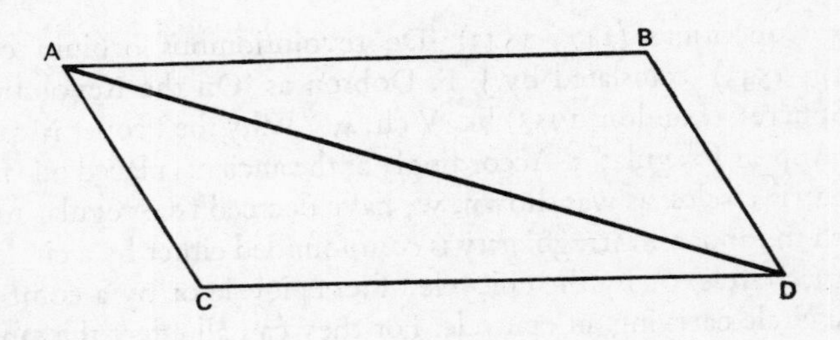

'If a body in any given time, by the force M impressed apart in the place A, should with an uniform motion be carried from A to B, and by the force N impressed apart in the same place, should be carried from A to C, let the parallelogram ABCD be completed, and, by both forces acting together, it will in the same time be carried in the diagonal from A to D.'

By taking this principle of finite mechanics as being *involved* in Kepler's second law, Hegel avoided treating it as necessarily involving distinct and independent forces and motions. Cf. Newton's corresponding use of it in 'the determination of centripetal forces' (op. cit. bk. I sect. ii prop. theorem 1). For subsequent nineteenth century criticisms of the Newtonian concept see Max Jammer 'Concepts of Force' (Cambridge, Mass., 1957) pp. 116–146. Bertrand Russell for example, in 'The Principles of Mathematics' (London, 1956) p. 477 maintains that a force should not be regarded as the sum of its components.

By confining the basic significance of this parallelogram to mathematics, Hegel is therefore more in tune with pre- and post-Newtonian mechanics than with the views of his own day: see P. Duhem 'Les origines de la statique' (2 vols. Paris, 1907); Simon Stevin (1548–1620) 'Wisconstige Gedachtenissen' (Leyden, 1605, tr. Snell 'Hypomnemata Mathematica' 1608); Ernst Mach 'The Science of Mechanics' I iii.

271, 32

See 'Harmonice Mundi' (Linz, 1619 ed. Frisch, 1864) pp. 30–40. Cf. the German tr. of this work by Max Caspar (Munich and Berlin, 1939), and the extract translated by J. H. Walden in 'A Source Book in Astronomy' (ed. H. Shapley and H. E. Howarth, New York, 1929) p. 38. Kepler writes, 'Again, therefore, a part of my "Mysterium Cosmographicum", suspended twenty-two years ago, because I did not then see my way clear, must be completed and introduced here. For, after I had by unceasing toil through a long period of time, using the observations of Brahe, discovered the true distances of the orbits, at last, the true relation of the periodic times to the orbits, and, if you ask for the exact time,

> . . . though late, yet looked upon me idle
> And after long time came;

conceived on the 8th of March of this year, 1618, but unsuccessfully brought to the test and for that reason rejected as false, but, finally returning on the 15th of May, by a new onset it overcame by storm the shadows of my mind, with such a fullness of agreement between my seventeen-years' labour on the observations of Brahe and this present study of mine that I at first believed I was dreaming and was assuming as an accepted principle what was still a subject of enquiry. But the principle is unquestionably true and quite exact: *the periodic times of any two planets are to each other exactly as the cubes of the square roots of their median distances*; this fact should be observed, however, that the arithmetic mean between the two diameters of the elliptical orbit is a little less than the longer diameter'.

271, 34
See § 267.

272, 2
See the notes on pp. 343 and 363. At this juncture Michelet prints a foot-note, evidently by Hegel, 'Laplace, 'Exposition du système du monde' vol. II p. 12 (Paris, an. iv): 'Newton trouva qu'en effet, cette force est réciproque au carré du rayon vecteur'. Newton says ('Phil. nat. princ. math.' I prop. xi et seq.): 'If a body revolves in an ellipse, hyperbola or parabola' the ellipse however passes over into the circle 'then the centripetal force is reciproce in duplicata ratione distantiae.'

For an English translation of Laplace's book see 'The System of the World' (tr. J. Pond, 2 vols. London, 1809). On Newton's contribution to the geometry of conics see op. cit. bk. I lemma xxii et seq.; J. J. Milne 'Newton's contribution to the geometry of conics' in 'Isaac Newton, 1642–1727' (London, 1927) pp. 96–114; Ernst Kötter 'Die Entwicklung der synthetischen Geometrie' (Leipzig, 1901).

Newton meets Hegel's objection in prop. xii prob. viii cor. 2, 'In these Corollaries I consider the circle as an ellipse'.

272, 8
Voltaire gives a competent and very lucid account of the Newtonian theory in 'Élémens de la Philosophie de Newton mis à la portée de tout le monde' (Amsterdam, 1738): see 'Oeuvres Complètes de Voltaire' vol. 41 (Paris, 1828). An English translation of this work was published by J. Hanna (London, 1738). On Voltaire's predecessors, see P. Brunet 'L'introduction des théories de Newton en France au XVIIIe siècle (avant 1738)' (Paris, 1931).

Jean Banières, who, when this work appeared, had just published his 'Traité physique de la lumière' (Paris, 1737), attacked Voltaire's exposition in 'Examen et réfutation des Élémens de la philosophie de Newton par M. de Voltaire' (Paris, 1739), and, of course, elicited a 'Défense du Newtonianisme' (Paris, 1739): see 'Oeuvres' vol. 42 pp. 3–29; cf. H. Guerlac 'Newton in France' ('Isis' 1962 pp. 219–221).

England was by no means as sympathetic to Newtonianism and hostile to Kepler as Hegel seems to have thought. F. Cajori, in his edition of the 'Mathematical Principles' (Berkeley, 1947) pp. 629–632, points out that when Voltaire visited England in 1727, he estimated that there were no more than twenty Newtonians in the whole country, and that even at Cambridge, Newtonianism had not entirely replaced Cartesianism *forty years* after the first publication of the

'Principia'. Curiously enough, Newton's ideas were spread there mainly by means of Samuel Clarke's commentary on a purely *Cartesian* work by Jacques Rohault (1620–1675): see 'Rohault's System of Natural Philosophy' (2 vols. London, 1723). The testy and peevish notes and commentary to be found in the edition of Newton's 'Principia' brought out by William Davis (1771–1807) show the extent to which orthodox English Newtonians felt themselves to be on the defensive in the early years of the last century: see 'The Mathematical Principles of Natural Philosophy by Sir Isaac Newton' (3 vols. London, 1803). Kepler's accomplishments were certainly not unacknowledged this side of the Channel: see S. Vince (1749–1821) 'A Complete System of Astronomy' (3 vols. London, 1814, 1823) vol. I pp. 98–102; Robert Small of Edinburgh 'An Account of the Astronomical Discoveries of Kepler' (London, 1804).

272, 14

Gravity is distinguished from gravitation. *Gravitation* is the universal attraction of every particle of matter for every other, wherever located. Gravity is the resultant effect, at the earth's surface of the earth's gravitation and the centrifugal force caused by its rotation.

Hegel seems to be unaware of the research then being done into the influence of the earth's rotation upon fall: see Thomas Rutherforth (1712–1771) 'A System of Natural Philosophy' (2 vols. Cambridge, 1748) vol. I p. 130, 'Though a heavy body, when it is thrown perpendicularly upwards, appears to ascend and descend in a right line; yet, supposing the earth to turn round its axis, the body does really describe a parabola'. Cf. Johann Friedrich Benzenberg (1777–1846) 'Versuche über die Gesetze des Falles, den Widerstand der Luft und die Umdrehung der Erde' (Dortmund, 1804); Giovanni Battista Guglielmini (d. 1817) 'De diurno terrae motu, experimentis physico-mathematicis confirmato, opusculum' (Bologna, 1792); Ferdinand Reich (1799–1883) 'Fallversuche über die Umdrehung der Erde' (Freiberg, 1832).

272, 20

The mean distance of the moon from the earth is sixty earth-*radii*, or 239,000 miles. Hegel's slip here may be due to Newton's phrasing: see 'Mathematical Principles' bk. III prop. iv theorem 4, 'For if both earth and moon move about the sun, and at the same time about their common centre of gravity, the distance of the centres of the moon and earth from one another will be 60½ semidiameters of the earth'.

272, 28

See note p. 350.

272, 29

See Newton's 'Mathematical Principles' bk. III prop. iv theorem 4, scholium.

272, 34

See J. W. Herivel 'Newton's Discovery of the Law of Centrifugal Force' ('Isis' 1960 pp. 546–553). Unpleasantly enough, this may well be a reference to one of the most memorable of Spence's anecdotes: see Joseph Spence (1699–1768) 'Observations, Anecdotes, and Characters of Books and Men' (ed. Osborn, 2 vols. Oxford, 1966) no. 1259, 'Sir Isaac Newton, a little before he died, said, "I don't know what I may seem to the world, but as to myself, I seem to have been only like a boy playing on the sea-shore and diverting myself in now and then finding a smoother pebble or a prettier shell than ordinary, whilst the great ocean of truth lay all undiscovered before me".' Cf. 'Paradise Regained' bk. iv lines 313–330.

The difficulty physicists encountered in *reproducing* elliptical motion undoubtedly encouraged Hegel to take this attitude: see Sir J. F. W. Herschel (1792–1871) 'Outlines of Astronomy' (London, 1849) p. 300, 'We know of no artificial mode of imitating this species of elliptic motion; though a rude approximation to it . . . may be had by suspending a small steel bead to a fine and very long silk fibre, and setting it to revolve in a small orbit round the pole of a powerful cylindrical magnet, held upright, and vertically under the point of suspension.'

272, 40

Newton's three greatest discoveries, the calculus, the theory of gravitation and the spectrum, were all made about 1665–1666. Hegel probably knew of this event from Voltaire's 'Élémens de la Philosophie de Newton' (Amsterdam, 1738) pt. III ch. iii, 'Un jour, en l'année 1666, Newton retiré à la campagne, et voyant tomber des fruits d'un arbre, à ce que m'a conté sa nièce (Madame Conduitt), se laissa aller à une méditation profonde sur la cause qui entraîne ainsi tous les corps vers une ligne qui, si elle était prolongée, passerait à peu près par le centre de la terre'.

Newton's favourite niece Catherine Barton married John Conduitt in 1717, and for the last ten years of his life the couple lived with him. In 1727 John Conduitt wrote to B. L. B. de Fontenelle (1657–1757) correcting certain errors in the latter's eloge of Newton written for the French Academy, 'In the year *1665*, when he retired to his own estate, on account of the plague, he first thought of his system of gravity, which he hit upon by observing an apple fall from a tree . . . The apple tree is now remaining, and is shewed to strangers'. In 1732 the manor and estate of Woolsthorpe in Lincolnshire, where this event took place, was bought from the Newtons by the Turnor family, and it was Edmund Turnor (1755?–1829), the Lincolnshire antiquary and fellow of the Royal Society, who published Conduitt's letter in his 'Collections, for the History of the Town and Soke of Grantham' (London, 1806) pp. 158–167. The original is in the Portsmouth collection of papers: see L. T. More 'Isaac Newton' (London, 1934).

The original apple tree was blown down by a storm in 1820, but a grafted scion was propagated at the Royal Botanic Gardens at Kew. It is an old variety of cooking apple called the 'Flower of Kent': the apples are flavourless, red streaked with yellow and green, and shaped much like a pear: see H. P. Macomber 'Catalogue of the Babson Newton Collection' (2 vols. New York, 1950–1955) vol. II p. 85.

Newton did not announce the law of universal gravitation until 1686, because until 1685 he was not aware of the importance of the centre of gravity in the attraction of a sphere: see H. H. Turner's letter to 'The Times' March 19, 1927: F. Cajori 'Newton's twenty years' delay in announcing the law of gravitation' in 'Sir Isaac Newton 1727–1927'—'The History of Science Society' (London, 1928) pp. 127–188. Cf. The Portsmouth Collection, Cambridge University Library, Additional Manuscripts 3968, no. 41, bundle 2.

See the reference to the apple story in Hegel's 'De Orbitis Planetarum' (Jena, 1801, ed. Lasson, Leipzig, 1928) p. 378, 'The general public was reconciled to the concept of gravitation less by the way in which the force which is common to the whole universe gives meaning to the expositions of Kepler and other thinkers, than by the teaching that the everyday force which causes a stone to fall to the ground, also moves the celestial bodies in their orbits. The story of Newton's having seen the apple fall has so captured the popular imagination, that it has been quite forgotten that the fall of the whole human race, as well as the subsequent fall of Troy, also began with an apple—a bad omen for the philosophic sciences'. Cf. Sir Thomas Browne (1605–1682) 'Pseudodoxia Epidemica' (London, 1646, German tr. C. Rautner, Frankfurt and Leipzig, 1689) bk. 7 ch. i.

273, 36

See the note on p. 354.

273, 39

See the notes III. 302, 379.

274, 13

See the notes on pp. 331, and II. 323. Cf. K. F. Gauss (1777–1855) 'Fundamentalgleichungen für die Bewegung schwerer Körper auf der rotirenden Erde' ('Werke' V p. 495, 1867). Huyghens was the first to undertake the exact determination of the acceleration of gravity g by means of pendulum observations: see Ernst Mach (1838–1916) 'The Science of Mechanics' II ii 14–15.

274, 18

Copernicus preceded Kepler in this: see 'De revolutionibus orbium coelestium' (Nuremberg, 1543, tr. Dobson, London, 1955), 'I am at least of opinion that gravity is nothing more than a natural tendency implanted in particles by the divine providence of the Master of the Universe, by virtue of which, they, collecting together in the shape of a sphere, do form their own proper unity and integrity. And it is to be assumed that this propensity is inherent also in the sun, the moon, and the other planets'.

Newton was therefore most certainly anticipated in regarding the planets as 'standing in immanent relation to the sun'; see Colin Maclaurin (1698–1746) 'An Account of Sir Isaac Newton's Philosophical Discoveries' (3rd ed. London, 1775) bk. III ch. i; E. Goldbeck 'Kepler's Lehre von der Gravitation' (Halle, 1896), 'Die Gravitation bei Galileo und Borelli' (Berlin, 1897); F. Rosenberger 'Newton und seine physicalischen Principien' (Leipzig, 1895); A. Koyré 'La gravitation universelle de Kepler à Newton' (Paris, 1951); L. D. Patterson 'Hooke's Gravitation Theory and its influence on Newton' ('Isis' 1949 pp. 327–341). The point usually made is however that Newton was the first to formulate the *law of gravitation* (note p. 322). Cf. I. Todhunter 'History of the Mathematical Theories of Attraction' (2 vols. London, 1873).

274, 26

See the note on p. 349. Pierre-Simon Laplace (1749–1827) 'Exposition du Système du Monde' (2 vols. Paris, 1796), 'The System of the World' (tr. J. Pond, 2 vols. London, 1809). Hegel translated this extract from a chapter 'On the principle of universal gravitation'. The original is as follows, 'L'analyse qui dans ses généralités, embrasse toute ce qui peut résulter d'une loi donnée, nous montre que non-seulement l'ellipse, mais toute section conique, peut être décrite en vertu de la force qui retient les planètes dans leurs orbes'.

Cf. Laplace's paper 'Sur le principe de la gravitation universelle et sur les inégalités séculaires des planètes qui en dependent' ('Mémoires de l'Academie' 1773, vol. vii, pub. 1776).

274, 37

Newton 'Mathematical Principles' bk. I lemma i–ix. Hegel is referring in particular to lemma vii, 'I say, that the ultimate form of these evanescent triangles is that of similitude, and their ultimate ratio that of equality . . . And hence in all reasonings about ultimate ratios, we may use any one of these triangles for any other'.

This is of course the famous difficulty of Newton's calculus. George Berkeley (1685–1753) first called public attention to it in 'The Analyst' (Dublin, 1734) when he dubbed the fluxions 'the ghosts of departed quantities' (see note p. 351).

Newton first dealt with the subject in a tract which he sent to Barrow in 1669 'De Analysi per Aequationes Numero Terminorum Infinitas'. His fullest treatment of it is to be found in the 'Method of Fluxions' (written 1671, tr. Colson, London, 1736). It is hardly true to say that there is *no end* to what can be proved if Newton's reasoning is accepted, since the motion calculated is the fundamental determining factor. See op. cit. bk. I lemma i, 'Quantities, and the ratios of quantities, which in any finite time converge continually to equality, and before the end of that time approach nearer to each other than by any given difference, become ultimately equal. If you deny it, suppose them to be ultimately unequal, and let D be their ultimate difference. Therefore they cannot approach nearer to equality than by that given difference D; which is contrary to the supposition.'

Newton himself was however unsatisfied with his early treatment of the infinitely small quantity, and in the 'Quadratura curvarum' (London, 1704) it is abandoned with the remark that, 'errores quam minimi in rebus mathematicis non sunt contemnendi.' Cf. the differences between bk. II lemma ii in the first (1687) and the seond (1713) editions of the 'Mathematical Principles'.

A. De Morgan (1806–1871) 'On the Early History of Infinitesimals' ('Philosophical Magazine' November, 1852); F. Cajori 'A History of the Conceptions of Limits and Fluxions in Great Britain' (Chicago, 1931).

275, 2

See the note on p. 349.

275, 12

See the note on p. 313.

276, 20

Tycho Brahe (1546–1601) attempted to combine certain features of the Ptolemaic and Copernican systems. His 'De Mundi Aetherei recentioribus Phaenomenis' (Uraniborg, 1588) was mainly concerned with the comet of 1577, but it also included a theory of the cosmos according to which the earth retained its *immobility*, the five planets revolved around the sun, and the sun circuited the earth once a year with its entire cortège, while the sphere of the fixed stars continued to perform its all-inclusive diurnal rotation.

This work was privately printed. It became known to the general public when it appeared as volume two of Brahe's 'Astronomiae Instauratae Progymnasmata', edited by Kepler (Prague, 1602–3).

See Kepler's 'The Harmonies of the World' bk. v ch. iii (tr. C. G. Wallis, Chicago, 1952), 'In the case of Tycho Brahe the whole planetary system (wherein among the rest the circles of Mars and Venus are found) revolves like a tablet on a lathe, the midspace between the circles of Mars and Venus; and it comes about from this movement of the system that the Earth within it, although remaining motionless, marks out the same circle around the sun and midway between Mars and Venus, which in Copernicus it marks out by the real movement of its body while the system is at rest'.

276, 23

Nicolaus Copernicus (1473–1543) 'De revolutionibus orbium coelestium'

Nuremberg, 1543, tr. Dobson, London, 1955). In book one of this work Copernicus himself calls the sun the 'spirit, ruler and visible god of the universe' and takes it to be placed at the centre of the universe on account of its perfection, 'Who, in this universal temple, would place this splendid light in another or better place than whence it can shine on all at once?'

277, 9

‚Der Unterſchied der Ruhe an dem, was hier Bewegung iſt, iſt kein realer Unterſchied, kein Unterſchied der Maſſe‘: 'Jenenser Realphilosophie II' p. 25. Michelet changed the meaning of this sentence somewhat by substituting ‚von‘ for ‚an‘; his interpretation is captured if 'its' is removed from the English translation.

277, 14

Newton's formulation of the law of universal gravitation, and failure to explain the *physical* nature of it gave rise to the concept of *action at a distance*, which was challenged in eighteenth and early nineteenth century mechanics by that of the *forces of contact*. This controversy was resolved to some extent by the work of Faraday and Maxwell: see Ernst Mach 'The Science of Mechanics' appendix xv. Cf. A. E. Woodruff 'Action at a distance in nineteenth century electrodynamics' ('Isis' 1962 pp. 439–459); note p. 37.

277, 15

See the note II. 243.

277, 32

Michelet emphasizes this word.

278, 5

Hegel entered the following note in the margin at this juncture ('Jenenser Realphilosophie II' p. 27 n. 3), ‚Vorher, entſtehen, was es iſt, immer ſein Begriff, keine Geſchichte; dieſes iſt gemeint;‘

278, 6

‚ob die Kometen aus der Sonne ausgeworfen werden.‘ Hegel wrote ‚worden‘ (ſind) i.e. 'have been': 'Jenenser Realphilosophie II' p. 27.

278, 9

Aristotle regarded comets as transient combustible bodies consisting of exhalations raised to the upper regions of the air and there set on fire, far below the course of the moon: see 'Meteorologica' 42b25–45a10. J. Hevelius (1611–1687) took them to be formed from the exhalations of the sun: see 'Cometographia' (Danzig, 1668); 'Phil. Trans. Roy. Soc.' 1665 p. 104. Newton was the first to determine their composition and the nature of their orbits with any success: see 'Mathematical Principles' bk. III lemma iv et seq. Fanciful theories regarding their nature were however common during the eighteenth century. Hugh Hamilton (1729–1805) for example, expressed the view that they have the function of bringing back the electric fluid which the planets are continually discharging into the higher regions of their atmospheres; see 'Philosophical Essays' (London, 1766), 'Conjectures on the Nature of the Aurora Borealis, and on the Tails of Comets'.

Cf. H. Williamson 'An Essay on Comets, and an account of their luminous appearance' ('Trans. American Phil. Soc.' I app. 27, 1771); J. A. Deluc 'Gedanken über die Natur der Kometen' ('Berliner astronomisches Jahrbuch' 1803 p. 92); H. Flaugergues (1755–1835) 'Examen critique des différentes hypothèses imaginées pour expliquer . . . des comètes' ('Journal de Physique' 1817 pp. 173, 245: 1818 p. 101).

278, 19

Hegel made the subject of this sentence plural (,Sphären'), but the rest of it singular ('Jenenser Realphilosophie II' p. 28). Hoffmeister's and not Michelet's version has been followed in the translation.

278, 31

Hegel entered the following note in the margin at this juncture ('Jenenser Realphilosophie II' p. 29 n. 2): '*Centre*, generating the whirling motion'.

278, 38

See the note II. 243

279, 15

Precession was discovered by Hipparchus about 125 B.C. by comparing the length of the year determined by the dates of the heliacal risings of certain stars with its length determined by the dates when the shadow of a vertical post was at its average length.

As Hegel notes, this motion is caused by the earth's axis gyrating in a cone while keeping its inclination to the ecliptic practically unchanged. One complete circuit occupies 25,800 years.

See Newton's 'Mathematical Principles' bk. III prop. xxxix, prob. 20; Laplace 'Mémoire sur la Précession des Équinoxes' (read August 19, 1779: 'Memoires de l'Academie' 1777–1780).

279, 16

See 'Jenenser Realphilosophie II' p. 31. Michelet puts this sentence in brackets, and reads ,Rotation, for ,Nutation,. Nutation is the oscillation of the earth's pole of rotation superposed upon its precessional motion through the regression of the moon's nodes.

For articles on the subject available to Hegel see: James Bradley (1672–1762) 'A letter to the Earl of Macclesfield concerning an apparent motion observed in some fixed stars' ('Phil. Trans. Roy. Soc.' 1748 p. 1); J. H. Lambert (1728–1777) 'Ueber die Nutation oder Schwankung bey Voraussetzung der elliptischen-Bewegung des Weltpols um seinen wahren Mittelpunkt' ('Berlin. astron. Jahrbuch' 1776 p. 108); B. A. von Lindenau (1780–1854) 'Eine neue Methode zu einer zuverlässigern Bestimmung der Aberration- und Nutation Constante' ('Berlin. astron. Jahrbuch' 1818 p. 244); John Brinkley (1763–1835) 'The quantity of solar nutation' ('Trans. of the Irish Acad.' vol. xiv pp. 5–38, 1825); F. W. Bessel (1784–1846) 'Nutationsformel', see 'Quarterly Journal of Science' (vol. xx p. 321, 1826).

279, 31

See G. C. Lewis 'An Historical Survey of the Astronomy of the Ancients' (London, 1862); F. E. Manuel 'The Eighteenth Century Confronts the Gods' (Cambridge, Mass., 1959). For an account of Chaldean, Egyptian, Greek and Roman sun-worship, see F. Cumont 'Astrology and Religion among the Greeks and Romans' (New York and London, 1912).

279, 37

This translation has been made from Michelet's version of the sentence, Hegel wrote as follows ('Jenenser Realphilosophie II' p. 32), ‚Alles ist die Totalität der Bewegung, hat seine Zeit und seinem Kreislauf an ihm, aber zurückgetreten unter (ein) Höheres in sich, oder was dasselbe ist, zu höherem Insichsein realisiert'.

280, 10

‚das Organische seine Kraft, also sein Negatives hat': see Hoffmeister's version of this sentence in 'Jenenser Realphilosophie II' p. 32.

280, 14

‚der Mensch teils dadurch daß er': see Hoffmeister's version of this sentence in 'Jenenser Realphilosophie II' p. 32. Cf. the notes II. 311–322

280, 16

Antoine François Fourcroy (1755–1809), see the note III. 347 This is evidently a reference to Fourcroy's analysis of *digestion*: see 'Système des Connaissances Chimiques' (10 vols. Paris, 1800). The work was immensely popular, and was translated into German by F. Wolff (4 vols. Königsberg, 1805–1803) and D. Veith and Wiedemann (5 vols. Brunswick, 1805). William Nicholson brought out an English translation 'A General System of Chemical Knowledge' (11 vols. London, 1804): see vol. ix pp. 22–24 (sect. 8 art. 2 par. 7), 'Digestion . . . is very much varied . . . We may, however, distinguish in it four periods: the first, the preparatory, comprehends the bruising, mastication and deglutition; the alimentary bolus is formed and conducted into the stomach in this first period; the second, which comprehends the digestion in the stomach, or the change of the alimentary matter into chyle, or homogeneous pulp; the third, which belongs to a second change produced in the intestine, and which separates the chylous matter from the excremental; finally, the fourth, which comprehends the absorption of the chyle that has been formed, by the lacteal vessels, and the expulsion of the excrement.

These four periods are very distinct in man, in the mammalia, the birds, the reptiles, the fishes and the insects'.

See Fourcroy's 'La Médecine éclairée par les Sciences Physiques' (4 bks. Paris, 1791–1792), in which many topics related to this are touched upon. Cf. W. A. Smeaton 'Fourcroy, chemist and revolutionary' (Cambridge, 1962) ch. ix.

280, 34

See Samuel Vince (1749–1821) 'A Complete System of Astronomy' (3 vols. London, 1814–1823) vol. I pp. 151–160; 'From observing the course of the planets for one revolution, their orbits are found to be inclined to the ecliptic, for they appear only twice in a revolution to be in the ecliptic; and as it is frequently requisite to reduce their places in the ecliptic, ascertained from observation, to corresponding places in their orbits, it is necessary to know the inclinations of their orbits to the ecliptic, and the points of the ecliptic where their orbits intersect it, called the *Nodes* . . . The motion of the nodes is found, by comparing their places at two different times . . . This motion of the nodes is in respect to the equinox; if therefore we subtract from each 50″,25 the precession of the equinoxes, it will give the motion in respect to the fixed stars, or the real motion. The motion in the following Table is in respect to the equinoxes.

Motion of the nodes in one hundred years.

Planets	M. Cassini	Dr. Halley	M. de la Lande
Mercury	1° . 24′ . 40″	1° . 23′ . 20″	1° . 12′ . 10″
Venus	0 . 56 . 40	0 . 51 . 40	0 . 51 . 40
Mars	0 . 56 . 40	1 . 3 . 20	0 . 46 . 40
Jupiter	0 . 40 . 9	1 . 23 . 20	0 . 59 . 30
Saturn	1 . 35 . 11	0 . 30 . 0	0 . 55 . 30

The *Georgian* Planet has not yet been discovered long enough to determine the motion of its nodes from observation'.

281, 2

See 'The Timaeus of Plato' 36 (ed. R. D. Archer-Hind, London, 1888) pp. 113–115, which contains a useful commentary on the subject. Cf. the detailed analysis in A. E. Taylor's 'Commentary on Plato's Timaeus' (Oxford, 1928) pp. 160–166; F. M. Cornford 'Plato's Cosmology' (London, 1937).

Timaeus took the 'circle of the Other' to be broken up into seven concentric circles, corresponding to the seven 'planets'. These he evidently assumed to be ranged from the Earth at the following *comparative* distances: Moon 1, Sun 2, Venus 3, Mercury 4, Mars 8, Jupiter 9, Saturn 27.

In the preface to his 'Prodromus Dissertationum Cosmographicarum continens Mysterium Cosmographicum' (Tübingen, 1596, German tr. Caspar, Augsburg, 1923), Kepler gives an account of the theory which dawned upon him on July 9–19, 1595, 'If, for the sizes and relations of the six heavenly paths assumed by Copernicus, five figures possessing certain distinguishing characteristics could be discovered among the remaining infinitely many, then everything would go as desired . . . The earth is the measure for all other orbits. Circumscribe a twelve-sided regular solid (dodecahedron) about it; the sphere stretched around this will be that of Mars. Let the orbit of Mars be circumscribed by a four-sided solid (tetrahedron). The sphere which is described about this will be that of Jupiter. Let Jupiter's orbit be circumscribed by a cube. The sphere described about this will be that of Saturn. Now, place a twenty-sided figure (icosahedron) in the orbit of the earth. The sphere inscribed in this will be that of Venus. In Venus's orbit place an octahedron. The spheres inscribed in this will be that of Mercury. There you have the basis for the number of the planets'.

See M. Caspar 'Kepler' (tr. Hellman, London and New York, 1959) II 4; J. L. E. Dreyer 'A History of Astronomy from Thales to Kepler' (ed. Stahl, Dover Pubs., 1953) ch. xv; D. C. Knight 'Johannes Kepler' (London, 1965) pp. 28–37; J. P. Phillips 'Kepler's Echinus' ('Isis' 1965 pp. 196–200).

281, 17

The sequence 0, 3, 6, 12, 48, 96, 192 in Bode's Law (note II. 250) had led astronomers to look for a planet to fill the gap between Mars and Jupiter. Hegel belittled their efforts in the inaugural dissertation (note p. 372) which he defended at Jena on August 27, 1801, but by that time the surmisals had already been confirmed.

On January 1, 1801 Guiseppe Piazzi (1746–1826) of Palermo noticed an eighth magnitude star in Taurus, which had changed its position by the following evening. He watched it until February 11th, when it came too close to the sun for further observation, and on January 23rd communicated his discovery to Barnaba Oriani (1752–1832), the director of the Milan observatory: see 'Corrispondenza astronomica fra Guiseppe Piazzi e Barnaba Oriani' ('Pubbl. del Osserv. di Brera' no. vi pp. 48–49): the letter did not arrive until April 5th. On

January 24th he wrote to J. E. Bode (1747–1826) at Berlin, and this letter was only received on March 20th. Bode suspected that this 'star' was the *planet* he was seeking, and K. F. Gauss (1777–1855), who had just developed an improved method of computing elliptical orbits from three observations: see his 'Theoria motus corporum coelestium' (Hamburg, 1809), confirmed his surmisal. *Ceres*, the largest of the asteroids had been discovered. Cf. Piazzi's letter to Bode of August 1st, published in 'Risultati delle osservazioni della nuova stella scoperta il primo gennajo 1801' (Palermo, 1801), and 'Della scoperta del nuovo pianeta Cerere Ferdinandea' (Palermo, 1802).

On March 28, 1802 H. W. M. Olbers (1758–1840) discovered *Pallas*. The existence of two planets where only one was expected led Olbers to formulate his celebrated hypothesis, according to which these bodies were fragments of a larger planet which had been shattered by an internal convulsion. This theory seemed to be confirmed by the discovery of Juno and Vesta in 1804 and 1807, in the precise regions of Cetus and Virgo where the nodes of such supposed planetary fragments should be situated. His argument was fallacious however: mutual perturbations would quickly have effaced all traces of a common disruptive origin, and the catastrophe, to be perceptible in its effects, would have had to have been fairly recent. No more asteroids were discovered until 1845.

See H. W. M. Olbers 'Entdeckung eines beweglichen Sterns (Pallas)' ('Bode, Astron. Jahrbuch' 1805, pp. 102–112); 'Beobachtung eines von Herrn Harding zu Lilienthal am 1 Septbr. 1804 entdeckten Wandelsterns' (op. cit. 1807, pp. 245–247); 'Beobachtungen der Juno und Pallas' (op. cit. 1808, pp. 179–184); 'Entdeckung und Beobachtung eines vierten neuen Planeten (Vesta) zwischen Mars und Jupiter am 29 März 1807' (op. cit. 1810, pp. 194–201).

281, 18

For a contemporary English account of Jupiter and its satellites see Samuel Vince (1748–1821) 'A Complete System of Astronomy' (3 vols. London, 1814–1823) vol. I pp. 231–262.

281, 22

For a detailed account of knowledge of Saturn at this time, see A. F. O. Alexander 'The Planet Saturn' (London, 1962). Between 1789 and 1808 Sir William Herschel published eight papers on the planet in the 'Phil. Trans. of the Royal Society'.

281, 23

While watching the stars at Bath on the evening of March 13, 1781, Sir Frederick William Herschel (1738–1822) noticed a round, slowly moving, nebulous disk which he took at first to be a comet. He announced it as such to the Royal Society: see 'Account of a Comet' ('Transactions', 1781 p. 492), but a few weeks of observation showed it to be moving in a nearly circular orbit at a distance from the sun about nineteen times that of the earth. Its planetary character was thus established, and Herschel named it the *Georgium Sidus* in honour of his royal patron: see 'On the name of the new planet' ('Phil. Trans. Roy. Soc.' 1783 p. 1). It was Johann Ehlert Bode (1747–1826) who proposed that it should be known as *Uranus* ('Astronomisches Jahrbuch' 1785 p. 191), and this name was generally accepted on the continent, although in England the body was known as the Georgian planet until about 1850.

Bode ('Astronomisches Jahrbuch' 1784 p. 219, 1785 p. 189) attempted to show that Tycho Brahe had observed Uranus as early as 1587, that Flamsteed had seen it on Dec. 23, 1690 ('Historia Coelestis Britannica' 1725 vol. II p. 86), and that it had been sighted on various occasions during the *middle* of the eighteenth century. Not all his assertions have been substantiated, and there can at least be no doubt that Herschel was the first to recognize that the body is not a star or a comet.

On January 11 1787, Herschel detected Titania and Oberon: see 'An account of the discovery of the two satellites revolving round the Georgian planet' ('Phil. Trans. Roy. Soc.' 1787 p. 125). He later claimed to have discovered four further satellites: see 'On the discovery of four additional satellites to the Georgium Sidus' ('Phil. Trans. Roy. Soc.' 1798 pp. 1, 47), but careful investigation of his observations has shown that the supposed objects could not have been of this character. Ariel and Umbriel were not discovered until 1851–2. See Herschel's 'A series of observations of the satellites of the Georgian Planet' ('Phil. Trans. Roy. Soc.' 1815 pp. 293–362).

J. H. Schröter (1745–1816) also saw Titania and Oberon: see 'Observations on the satellites of the Georgium Planet' ('Tilloch's Philosophical Magazine' II 1798 pp. 282–290), as did Sir John Herschel (1792–1871) in 1828. In his 'Treatise on Astronomy' (London, 1831) p. 298 however, the younger Herschel says of these bodies that, 'they have never been discerned but with the most powerful telescopes which human art has yet constructed, and this only under peculiar circumstances'.

Cf. G. N. Fischer (1748–1800) 'Ueber das Monden-System des Uranus' ('Berliner astronomisches Jahrbuch' 1790 p. 213); 'The Scientific Papers of Sir William Herschel' (ed. Dreyer, 2 vols. London, 1912); A. F. O. Alexander 'The Planet Uranus' (London, 1965).

281, 26

Hegel's inaugural dissertation 'De Orbitis Planetarum' (Jena, 1801) should perhaps be mentioned here, as it is usually cited in connection with this topic. On the last page of this work, Hegel criticizes the *a priori* theorizing of his day, which used the arithmetical series of Bode's law (note p. 370) as a reason for searching for a planet to fill the gap between Mars and Jupiter, and suggests, evidently not without some irony, that the sequence attributed to the demiurge in the 'Timaeus' (note p. 370) might provide a better guide, as it not only accounts for the *known* planetary sequence, but also simplifies consideration of the satellites of Jupiter and Saturn. On this occasion the *a priori* intuitive approach was however confirmed by the discovery of Ceres in January 1801 (note p. 370). It is perhaps worth remembering that no theoretical justification for Bode's Law has yet been found, and that the discovery of Neptune in 1846 disproved it to some extent.

The *main* importance of Hegel's dissertation lies in the first two sections. In the first, the astronomy of the day is submitted to a radical analysis which, with regard to the topics discussed, closely resembles the mature expositions of the 'Encyclopaedia'. The distinction between 'pure' and applied mathematics is drawn, universal gravitation is shown to be *implicit* in Kepler's laws, the rigour of Newton's calculus is questioned, the use of forces to explain planetary motions and the pendulum is criticized, the *Newtonian* God is banished from rational mechanics etc.

In the second section Hegel makes an interesting attempt to explain the structure of the solar system in the light of the *magnetic* theories of his day, bringing out the possible importance of light, lines of cohesion, poles, culmination points etc., and emphasizing the 'purity' of Kepler's laws. This section is clearly hypothetical; it is interesting however, not only as an anticipation of later ideas (note p. 343), but as an example of *a priori* theorizing which, as Hegel did not live to see it borne out by facts, he failed to develop. Cf. the note on J. F. W. Herschel's experiment (p. 362).

The bad press which this dissertation has been given in general articles and text-books is remarkable, not only on account of the learning, acumen and distinction of the writers who have contributed to it, but because, unlike many of their kind, almost all these pundits seem to have taken the trouble to read right through to the *end* of what is, after all, a rather obscure, difficult, and unobtainable Latin treatise.

See Georg Lasson 'Hegels Erste Druckschriften' (Leipzig, 1928) pp. 347–405; T. L. Haering 'Hegel, sein Wollen und sein Werk' (2 vols. Leipzig and Berlin, 1929–1938) vol. I pp. 699–762; Rudolf Wolf 'Geschichte der Astronomie (Munich, 1877) pp. 684–5; 'Mémoires de l'Academie de Berlin' 1786–7 p. 341; 'Berliner astronomisches Jahrbuch' 1791 p. 235; 1806 p. 224; 1809 p. 113; 'Zachs monatliche Correspondenz' 1803 p. 74; 1808 p. 545; 1813 p. 389 'Transactions of the Cambridge Philosophical Society' I 1822 p. 179. Otto Class 'Kepler und Newton und das Problem der Gravitation in der Kantischen, Schellingschen und Hegelschen Naturphilosophie' (Heidelberg, 1908).

282, 19

In his 'Lectures on the History of Philosophy' (tr. Haldane and Simson, 3 vols. London, 1963) vol. III p. 247, Hegel gives as the origin of this remark

Descartes' 'Principles of Philosophy' pt. III sects. 46, 47: see 'Descartes. Philosophical Writings' (tr. and ed. Anscombe and Geach, Nelson, 1954) pp. 225–226 and J. G. Buhle (1763–1821) 'Geschichte der neuern Philosophie' (6 vols. Göttingen, 1800–1804; French tr. by Jourdan, 6 vols. Paris, 1816). He is not quoting Descartes' actual words.

Cf. 'Principles of Philosophy' pt. II, arts. 4, 10; VIII, 45; IX, 68: 'Le Monde' in Descartes' 'Oeuvres' (ed. Adam and Tannery, Paris, 1897–1913) vol. ix p. 35: 'Discours de la Méthode' ibid., vi p. 42 et seq.: Alexandre Koyré 'Newtonian Studies' (London, 1965) app. D.

INDEX TO TEXT VOL. 1

INDEX TO FOREWORD AND NOTES VOL. 1